Lesson Masters B

THE UNIVERSITY OF CHICAGO SCHOOL MATHEMATICS PROJECT

ALGEBRA

INTEGRATED MATHEMATICS

Further practice on
SPUR objectives

Scott Foresman
Addison Wesley

Editorial Offices: Glenview, Illinois • Menlo Park, California
Sales Offices: Reading, Massachusetts • Atlanta, Georgia • Glenview, Illinois
Carrollton, Texas • Menlo Park, California

http://www.sf.aw.com

Contents

ISBN: 0-673-45769-9

http://www.scottforesman.com

3 4 5 6 - BI - 0 0 9 9 9 8 9 7

Name ____

LESSON MASTER 1-1 B

Questions on SPUR Objectives

Vocabulary

1. Explain what a *variable* is.

____

____

In 2–8, write the correct symbol for each mathematical verb.

2. is less than ________

3. is approximately equal to ________

4. is greater than or equal to ________

5. is equal to ________

6. is less than or equal to ________

7. is not equal to ________

8. is greater than ________

9. Tell whether or not the given sentence is an open sentence. Write *yes* or *no*.

a. $2.5g$ ______ **b.** $6\frac{1}{2} < 6\frac{5}{8}$ ______ **c.** $m^2 = 81$ ______

d. $24 < 8A$ ______ **e.** $y \geq 14$ ______ **f.** $0.1855 - w$ ______

10. Write an inequality comparing $\frac{6}{11}$ and $\frac{1}{2}$

a. using the symbol "$>$." ________

b. using the symbol "$<$." ________

11. Write an inequality comparing $\frac{3}{4}$ and $\frac{5}{6}$

a. using the symbol "$\geq$." ________

b. using the symbol "$\leq$." ________

Name

In 12–14, let r = Ruth's math test score. Write a sentence in words for each algebraic sentence.

12. $r \geq 84$ __________

13. $r \neq 84$ __________

14. $r < 100$ __________

15. Give a number that is a solution to the sentence in Question 14. __________

16. Let A = the land area of Rhode Island in square miles. Write in inequality to describe the following statement:

    The land area of Rhode Island is less than 2,000 square miles. __________

Skills Objective A: Find solutions to open sentences using trial and error.

17. Which of the numbers 3, 6, and 10 are solutions of $4 + n = 10$? __________

18. Which of the numbers 4, 5, and 8 are solutions of $9 - b = 4 \cdot b - 11$? __________

19. Which of the numbers 1, 4, and 7 are solutions of $2 \cdot m \geq 8$? __________

20. Which of the numbers 8, 15, and 20 are solutions of $\frac{h}{4} < 8$? __________

In 21 and 22, give three solutions to each open sentence.

21. $u > 4.8$ __________ __________ __________

22. $v \leq 13.5$ __________ __________ __________

In 23 and 24, give both solutions to the equation.

23. $a^2 = 64$ __________ __________

24. $d^2 = 1$ __________ __________

25. Give an example of an inequality for which 6 is a solution. __________

Name ______________________________

LESSON MASTER 1-2 B **Questions on SPUR Objectives**

Vocabulary

1. A *set* is a collection of objects called members or ____________.

In 2–7, write *W* if the number is a whole number, *I* if the number is an integer, and *R* if the number is a real number. List all terms that apply.

2. -4 __________ **3.** 17.3 __________ **4.** $\sqrt{15}$ __________

5. $\frac{2}{3}$ __________ **6.** 266 __________ **7.** -7.886 __________

8. Suppose you are asked to find the whole numbers that are in the solution set of the inequality $x < 7.6$.

a. What is the domain of x? __________

b. What is the solution set for the inequality? __________

In 9–14, tell if the interval is open, closed, or neither.

9. -10 -2 0 __________

10. $9 > s > -7$ __________

11. 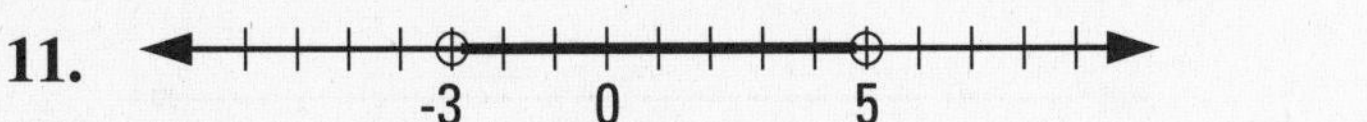

____

12. $4 \leq d \leq 14.6$ __________

13. -1 0 6 __________

14. $3 \geq u > -3$ __________

Properties Objective E: Read and interpret set language and notation.

In 15–18, name two elements in each set.

15. set of planets __________ **16.** set of integers __________

17. {-4, 10, 13, -8.9} __________ **18.** {cat, rat, sat} __________

19. Which of the following sets are equal?

A = {6, 9.4} B = {9.4, 6, 7}

C = {6, 9.4, 7, 5} D = {7, 6, 9.4} __________

Name ____________________

Uses Objective I: In real situations, choose a reasonable domain for a variable.

In 20–23, *multiple choice*. Which is the most reasonable domain for the variable?

(a) set of whole numbers **(b) set of integers**

(c) set of positive real numbers **(d) set of real numbers**

20. v = the number of registered voters in an election ____________

21. t = the temperature at noon in Toronto ____________

22. g = the amount of gas in a car's gas tank ____________

23. a = altitude with respect to sea level ____________

Representations Objective L: Draw and interpret graphs of solution sets to inequalities.

24. Explain how the graph of $n < 3$ differs from the graph of $n \leq 3$.

____

____

In 25–27, graph the solution set on a number line.

25. $y > -4$ when y is an integer.

26. $-2 < j < 5$ when j is an integer.

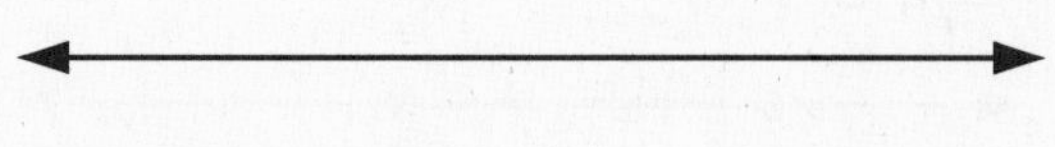

27. $1.6 \geq k > 1.1$ when k is a real number.

In 28–31, *multiple choice*. Select from the four choices in 20–23 above. Which domain was used in each graph of $y \geq -4$?

28. 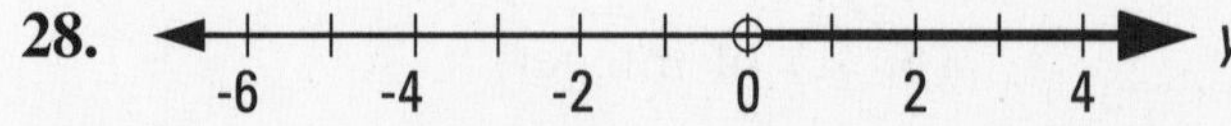

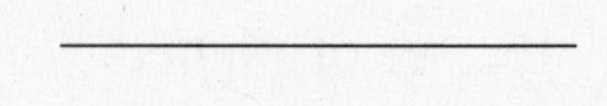

29. 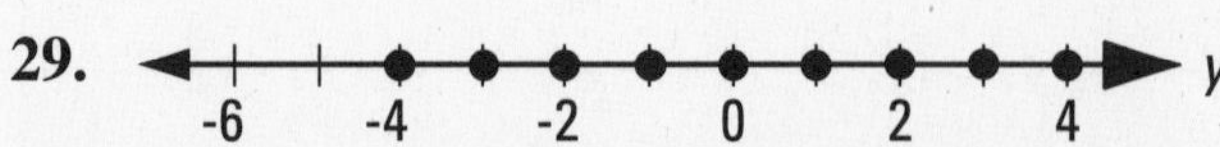

30. 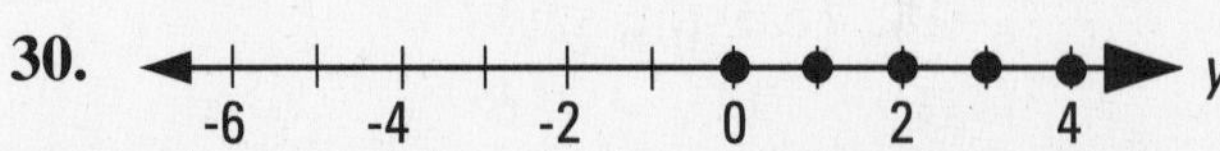

31. 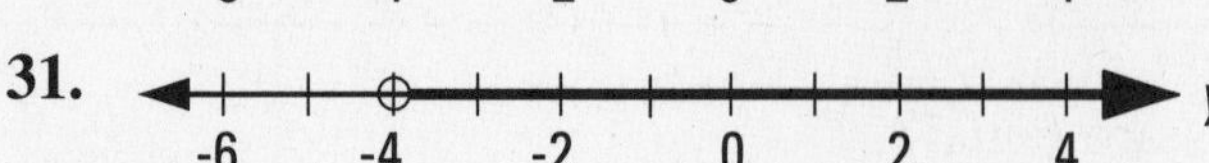

Name

LESSON MASTER 1-3 B

Questions on SPUR Objectives

Skills Objective B: Find unions and intersections.

1.

For the Venn diagram at the left, list the elements of

a. V ∪ W. __________

b. V ∩ W. __________

2. Let R = {0, -2, -4, -6} and S = {-2, -1, 0, 1, 2}. Draw a Venn diagram to illustrate

a. R ∩ S.

b. R ∪ S.

3. Let A = {1, 4, 9, 16, 25} and B = {2, 4, 8, 16}.

a. Give the union of A and B. __________

b. Give the intersection of A and B. __________

4. Let G = the set of divisors of 18 and H = the set of divisors of 27. List the elements of G ∩ H.

____

Properties Objective E: Read and interpret set language and notation.

5. When is the intersection of two sets equal to the null set?

____

6. Suppose M ∩ N = {0, 8} and M ∪ N = {0, 2, 4, 6, 8}. Draw a Venn diagram to show sets M and N that fit this description. There are several possible answers.

Name ____

▶ **LESSON MASTER 1-3 B** *page 2*

Representations Objective L: Draw and interpret graphs of solution sets to inequalities.

7. Graph the solution sets. Let the domain be the set of real numbers.

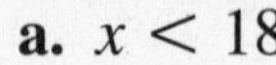
a. $x < 18$

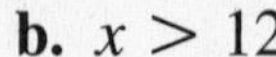
b. $x > 12$

c. $x > 12$ and $x < 18$

d. $x > 12$ or $x < 18$

8. The heights, in inches, of the members of the drill team satisfy the inequality $64 \le h < 72$.

a. Graph this interval.

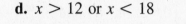

b. Describe the interval with two inequalities linked by the word "and."

____

9. A meteorologist graphed the temperatures for Monday, Tuesday, and Wednesday.

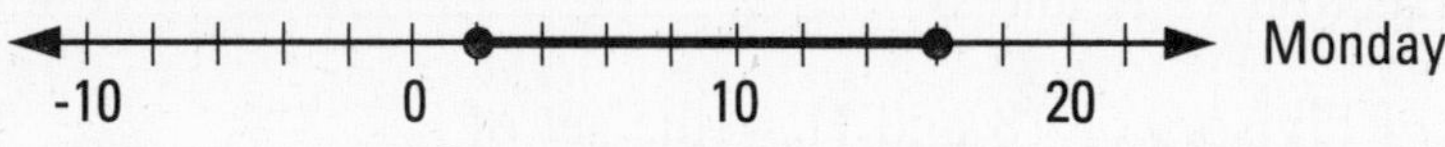

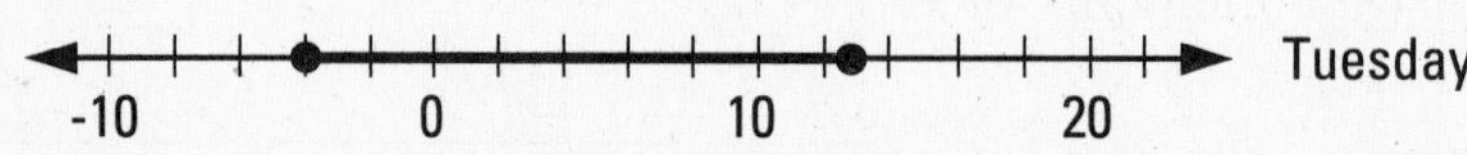

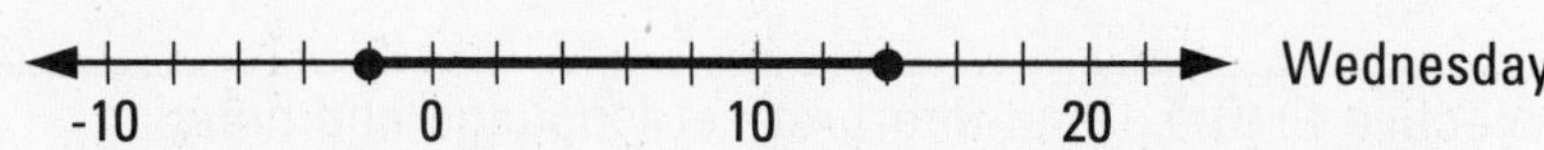

a. Graph the temperatures during the three-day period.

b. Is your answer to Part a the union or the intersection of the three graphs? ____________

c. To describe the interval from Part a, fill in the blanks:

_______ $\le x \le$ _______

Name ______________________________

LESSON MASTER 1-4 B

Questions on SPUR Objectives

Vocabulary

In 1–9, tell if each is a numerical expression, an algebraic expression, or neither.

1. $42ab$ ______________

2. $7x = 21$ ______________

3. $3^2 + 9(7 - 1)$ ______________

4. $\frac{4m}{20}$ ______________

5. g ______________

6. $24.7 + 6(y^2 + 31)$ ______________

7. $22 \geq u$ ______________

8. $16 = 4^2$ ______________

9. Finding the numerical value of an expression is called ______________ the expression.

Skills Objective C: Evaluate numerical and algebraic expressions.

In 10–21, evaluate each expression when e = 5, f = 3.2, and g = 0.

10. $4e$ ______________

11. $e + f$ ______________

12. $7^2 + 22$ ______________

13. $3(33 - 3^3)$ ______________

14. $\frac{8e}{2}$ ______________

15. $e - fg$ ______________

16. $9 + \frac{5}{3}$ ______________

17. $\frac{2e + f}{1.1} - 3eg$ ______________

18. $e^2 + f^2 + g^2$ ______________

19. $(8 + 7)(8 - 7)$ ______________

20. $2(3 + 7)^2 - 6 \cdot 9$ ______________

21. $6.1e + 2.9g$ ______________

22. 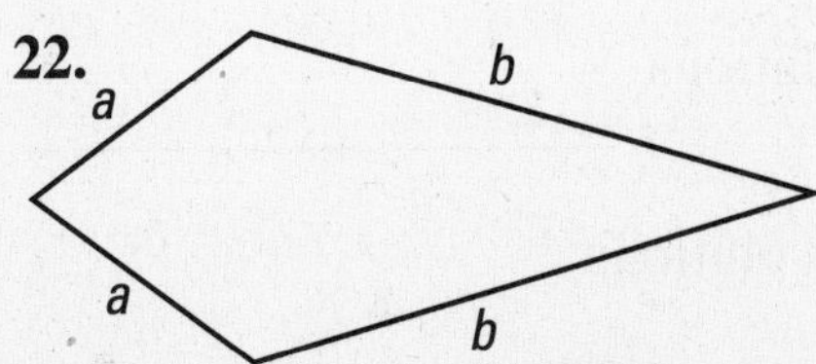

The perimeter of the quadrilateral at the left is $2a + 2b$. Find the perimeter when $a = 6.75$ and $b = 14.4$.

____

Name ______________________________

23. What is the value of the BASIC expression (4 * 3 + 9)/(40 − 38)? ____________

In 24 and 25, write each expression in BASIC.

24. $7(2.2 + 9)$ ____________

25. $(5 \cdot 6 - 3.07)^5$ ____________

In 26 and 27, tell what you would input on a computer to evaluate each expression when u = 7 and v = 5.5.

26. $\frac{3u + 9}{v - 4}$ ____________

27. $5(u + v)^2$ ____________

28. Which expression, A or B, has the greater value? Explain your answer.

A = 50 − 25 − 10 − 5 B = 50 − (25 − (10 − 5))

____

____

29. **a.** Evaluate $4m^2$ when $m = 3$. ____________

b. Evaluate $(4m)^2$ when $m = 3$. ____________

c. Find a value of m so that the value of $4m^2$ is the same as the value of $(4m)^2$. ____________

Review Objective A, Lesson 1-1

30. Which of the numbers 1, 2, and 7 are solutions of $11 + n = 18$? ____________

31. Which of the numbers 3, 6, and 9 are solutions of $6 \cdot u - 11 = 19 + u$? ____________

32. Which of the numbers 5, 9, and 18 are solutions of $7 \cdot e \leq 80$? ____________

33. Which of the numbers 12, 17, and 24 are solutions of $\frac{h}{3} > 7$? ____________

Name ______________________________

LESSON MASTER

Questions on SPUR Objectives

Vocabulary

1. a. *Multiple Choice.* Which of the equations below is a formula for y in terms of other variables? ____________

(a) $b = y - mx$ (b) $y = mx + b$ (c) $x = \frac{y - b}{m}$

b. What are the other variables? ____________

Uses Objective J: Evaluate formulas in real situations

2. A sports concession sells T-shirts and caps. The price P of a purchase, including sales tax, is given by the formula

$$P = 1.07(9.75C + 12T)$$

where C = the number of caps purchased and T = the number of T-shirts purchased. Find the cost of each order. If rounding is necessary, round up to the next cent.

a. 3 caps and 2 T-shirts ____________

b. 4 T-shirts ____________

c. 1 cap ____________

3. Use the formula $S = 4\pi r^2$ for the surface area of a sphere. Find the surface area of a basketball with radius 4.8 inches. ____________

4. The formula $M = 0.38E$ gives the weight on Mars M of a person who weighs E pounds on Earth. If a person weighs 120 pounds on Earth, how much does that person weigh on Mars? ____________

5. The formula $t = 0.15b$ can be used to find the amount of a tip t on a restaurant bill of b dollars. What would the tip be on a restaurant bill of $18.49? ____________

6. Mrs. Day wants to invest in stocks that are expected to pay 6.5% interest and bonds that should pay 5%. For an investment of S dollars in stocks and B dollars in bonds, the amount of yearly income I is given by this formula: $I = 0.065S + 0.05B$

How much money will Mrs. Day earn each year if

a. she invests $1,000 in stocks and $2,000 in bonds? ____________

b. she invests $1,500 in stocks and $1,500 in bonds? ____________

7. Carpet often comes in rolls 12 feet wide. The number of square yards Y in a piece of carpet L feet long is given by the formula

$$Y = \frac{4}{3}L.$$

Find the number of square yards in a piece of carpet that is

a. 15 feet long. ___

b. 22 feet long. ___

8. When Jeff calls his uncle, the cost C of a call for m minutes is given by the formula

$$C = 0.55 + 0.15m.$$

Find the cost of a 7-minute call. ___

9. The formula $C = \frac{5}{9}(F - 32)$ converts the temperature from degrees Fahrenheit to degrees Celsius.
Find the Celsius temperature to the nearest degree for

a. 77°F. ___

b. 54°F. ___

c. 98.6°F. ___

d. 32°F. ___

10. a. Recall the formula $d = rt$. Fill in the blank to complete this BASIC program which computes distances traveled.

```
10 PRINT "DISTANCE TRAVELED"
20 INPUT "RATE"; R
30 INPUT "TIME"; T
40 LET D = ________
50 PRINT "DISTANCE"
60 PRINT D
70 END
```

b. What will the computer find for the distance when R = 55 and T = 4.5? ___

Name ______________________________

LESSON MASTER

Questions on SPUR Objectives

Vocabulary

1. Since $4^2 = 16$, we say that 4 is the ______________ of 16.

2. Write the radical symbol. ______________

3. For each number below write *perfect square* or *not perfect square.*

a. 21 ______________

b. 36 ______________

c. 8000 ______________

d. 810 ______________

Skills Objective C: Evaluate numerical and algebraic expressions.

In 4–9, evaluate each expression when $a = 25$, $b = 7$, and $c = 9$.

4. $\sqrt{a}$ ______________

5. $\sqrt{b + c}$ ______________

6. $b\sqrt{a}$ ______________

7. $\sqrt{ac}$ ______________

8. $-\sqrt{a}$ ______________

9. $-\sqrt{a - c}$ ______________

Skills Objective D: Evaluate square roots with and without a calculator.

In 10–13, give a. the exact square roots of the given number and b. the approximate square roots, rounded to the nearest hundredth.

10. 37 **a.** ______________ **b.** ______________

11. 418 **a.** ______________ **b.** ______________

12. 5 **a.** ______________ **b.** ______________

13. 60 **a.** ______________ **b.** ______________

In 14 and 15, the area of a square is given.
a. Give the exact length of a side of the square.
b. Give the length of a side rounded to the nearest hundredth.

14. 876 sq ft **a.** ______________ **b.** ______________

15. 10 sq mi **a.** ______________ **b.** ______________

Name ______________________________

▶ LESSON MASTER 1-6 B *page 2*

In 16–25, evaluate without a calculator.

16. $\sqrt{81}$ ________ **17.** $-\sqrt{16}$ ________

18. $3\sqrt{49}$ ________ **19.** $10\sqrt{64}$ ________

20. $\sqrt{9} + \sqrt{16}$ ________ **21.** $\sqrt{9 + 16}$ ________

22. $\sqrt{7^2}$ ________ **23.** $(\sqrt{7})^2$ ________

24. $\sqrt{9} \cdot \sqrt{9}$ ________ **25.** $8 \cdot \sqrt{9} \cdot \sqrt{9}$ ________

In 26–29, evaluate and give the answer to the nearest thousandth.

26. $\sqrt{5} + \sqrt{2}$ ________ **27.** $\sqrt{7} + \sqrt{0}$ ________

28. $\sqrt{0.8} \cdot \sqrt{0.9}$ ________ **29.** $5 \cdot \sqrt{4.1} \cdot \sqrt{3.8}$ ________

In 30 and 31, an equation is given.
a. Describe each solution using the radical symbol.
b. Write each solution as a decimal rounded to the nearest hundredth.

30. $x^2 = 144$

a. ____________________ **b.** ____________________

31. $211 = h^2$

a. ____________________ **b.** ____________________

32. If an object is dropped, it falls *d* feet in *t* seconds. Then $t = \sqrt{\frac{d}{16}}$.

If an object were dropped from the top of the Sears Tower, which is 1454 feet tall, how long would it take the object to hit the ground? Round your answer to the nearest tenth of a second. ________

Properties Objective F: Use the Square of the Square Root Property.

33. According to the Square of the Square Root Property, if *a* is not negative, $\sqrt{a} \cdot \sqrt{a} =$ ________.

34. *Multiple choice.* Which of the following is equal to $\sqrt{x^2} \cdot \sqrt{x^2}$? ________

(a) x (b) x^2 (c) x^4

Name ______________________________

Questions on SPUR Objectives

Vocabulary

1. An example of a pattern is called a(n) ____________________.

2. What is a *counterexample* to a pattern?

____

____

Properties Objective G: Give instances or counterexamples of patterns.

In 3–7, give two instances of the pattern.

3. $m + m + m + m = 4m$

______________________ ______________________

4. $\frac{xy}{x} = y$

______________________ ______________________

5. $a(4 + 6) = 4a + 6a$

______________________ ______________________

6. $w \cdot w^2 = w^3$

______________________ ______________________

7. d dimes is equal to $0.1d$ dollars

______________________ ______________________

In 8–11, give a counterexample to the pattern.

8. $\frac{a + b}{a} = b$ ______________________

9. $v + v + v = v \cdot v \cdot v$ ______________________

10. $b < bc$ ______________________

11. $n^2 > n$ ______________________

Name ______________________________

▶ LESSON MASTER 1-7 B *page 2*

Properties Objective H: Use variables to describe patterns in instances.

12.

A panel of cedar fencing has 2 posts. Describe the following pattern using one variable.

1 panel has $1 + 1$ posts.

2 panels have $2 + 1$ posts.

3 panels have $3 + 1$ posts.

____

13. a. Describe this pattern with one variable.

$3 + 12 > 3$

$3 + 2\frac{1}{2} > 3$

$3 + 44.2 > 3$ ______________________________

b. Find a number other than 3 that is an instance of this pattern. ______________________________

c. Find a number that is a counterexample to the pattern. ______________________________

14. a. Describe this pattern with one variable.

$4^3 > 4^2$

$\left(\frac{5}{2}\right)^3 > \left(\frac{5}{2}\right)^2$

$8.3^3 > 8.3^2$ ______________________________

b. Find another integer that is an instance of this pattern. ______________________________

c. Find an integer that is a counterexample to the pattern. ______________________________

d. Find a non-integer that is a counterexample to the pattern. ______________________________

15. Describe this pattern with two variables.

$6 + 6 + 6 + 5 + 5 = 3 \cdot 6 + 2 \cdot 5$

$41 + 41 + 41 + 9 + 9 = 3 \cdot 41 + 2 \cdot 9$

$2.8 + 2.8 + 2.8 + .31 + .31 = 3 \cdot 2.8 + 2 \cdot .31$

____

Name

LESSON MASTER 1-8 B

Questions on SPUR Objectives

Vocabulary

In 1–3, name a. the hypotenuse and b. the legs.

1.

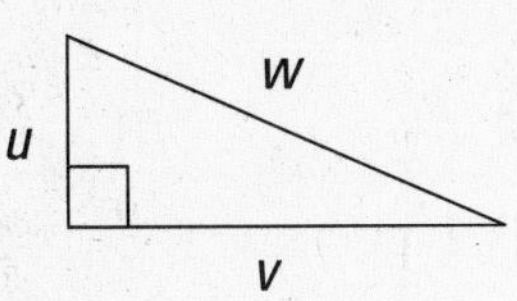

a. ____________

b. ____________

2.

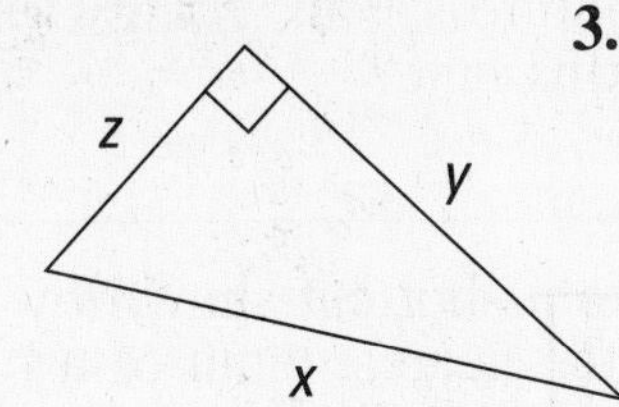

a. ____________

b. ____________

3.

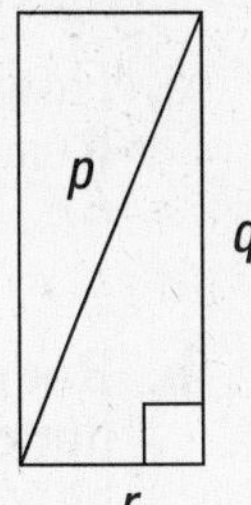

a. ____________

b. ____________

4. What is *theorem*?

____

____

Uses

Objective K: Apply the Pythagorean Theorem to solve problems in real situations.

5. The diagram at the right shows three square offices built around a lobby. Square tiles cover the floors of the two smaller offices.

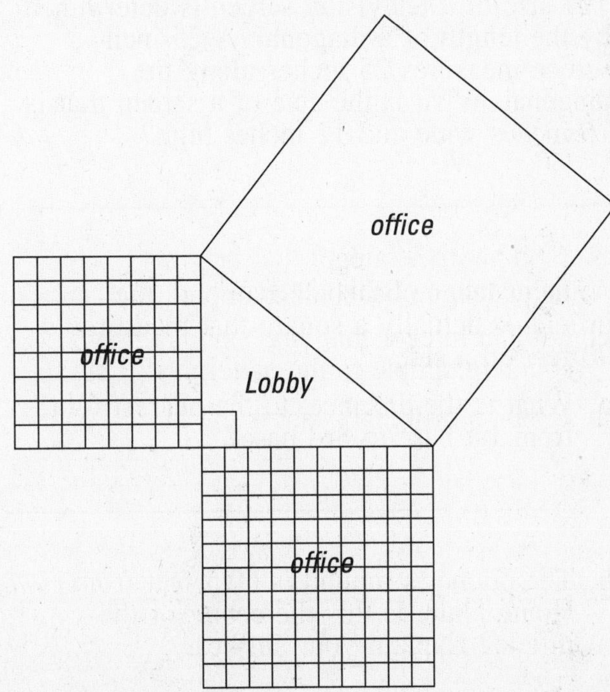

a. How many tiles would be needed for the floor of the largest office?

____

b. If each tile measures 1 foot on a side, what is the length of a wall of the largest office to the nearest tenth?

____

▶ **LESSON MASTER 1-8 B** *page 2*

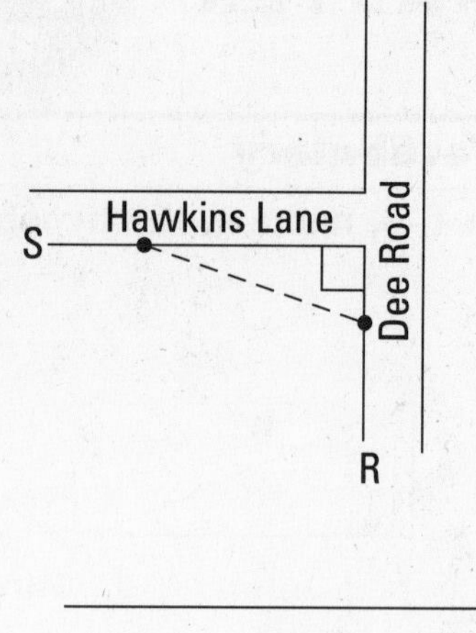

6. Rodolfo lives at point R and Steve lives at S. When Rodolfo walks to Steve's house, he can walk 2 blocks along Dee Road and 6 blocks along Hawkins Lane.

a. How long is Rodolfo's walk along Dee Road and Hawkins lane?

____

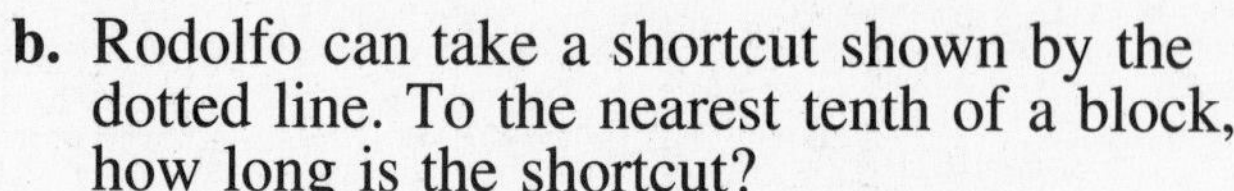

b. Rodolfo can take a shortcut shown by the dotted line. To the nearest tenth of a block, how long is the shortcut? ______________

c. How much shorter is it for Rodolfo to take the shortcut than to walk along the roads? ______________

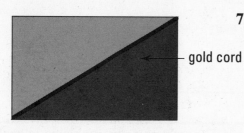

7. The student council is designing a new school flag which will measure 3 feet by 5 feet. A piece of gold cord will be sewn along one diagonal. To the nearest inch, how much cord is needed?

____

8. The size of a television screen is determined by the length of a diagonal. A 25-inch screen measures 25 inches along the diagonal. What is the size of a screen that is 16 inches wide and 12 inches high?

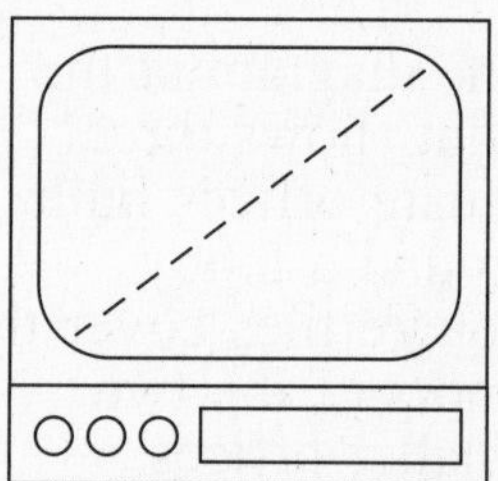

____

9. A major league baseball diamond, the infield, is actually a square that measures 90 feet on a side.

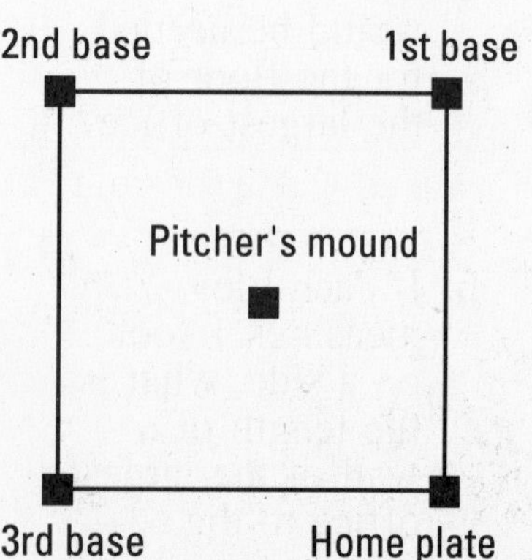

a. What is the distance, to the nearest foot, from 1st base to 3rd base?

____

b. The pitcher's mound is 60.5 feet from Home plate. Is this the center of the infield? Explain your answer.

____

____

Name

LESSON MASTER **1-9 B**

Questions on SPUR Objectives

Properties Objective G: Give instances or counterexamples of patterns.

1.

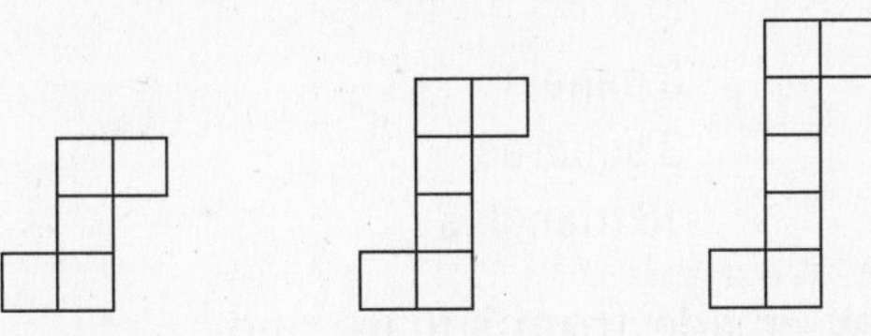

a. In the space above, sketch the next two instances in the pattern.

b. Fill in the chart below.

Number of Squares	5	6	7	8	9	...	n
Perimeter							

2. Shown below is a pattern made with square and triangular blocks.

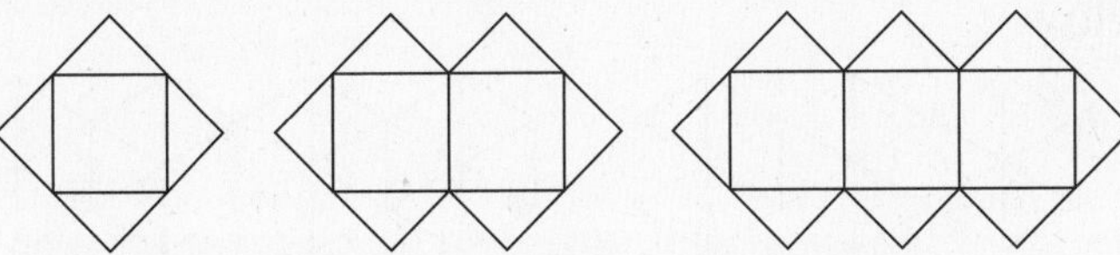

a. Draw the fourth instance in the pattern.

b. How many blocks will be needed to make the 20th instance? How many of these blocks will be triangular? Explain how you got your answers.

Properties Objective H: Use variables to describe patterns in tables.

For 3 and 4, use the chart at the right.

e	f
1	3
2	6
3	9
4	12

3. Does the equation $f = e + 2$ describe the numbers in the table? Explain why or why not.

4. Does the equation $f = 3e$ describe the numbers in the table? Explain why or why not.

Name

5. 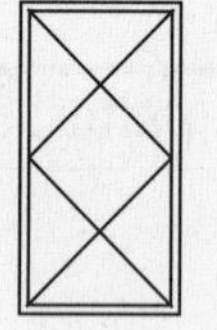  

1 panel	2 panels	3 panels
1 square	2 squares	3 squares
6 triangles	12 triangles	18 triangles

The diagram above shows windows made from square and triangular pieces of glass. Let p = the number of panels, s = the number of square pieces, and t = the number of triangular pieces.

a. Write a formula that describes the relationship between p and s. ______________

b. Write a formula that describes the relationship between p and t. ______________

In 6–8, use the pattern below.

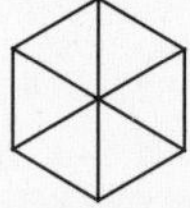 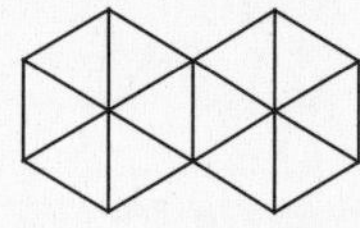 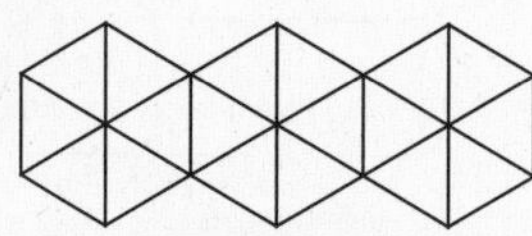 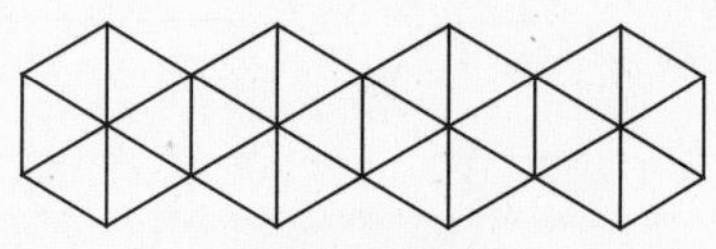

1 hexagon	2 hexagons	3 hexagons	4 hexagons
6 triangles	12 triangles	18 triangles	24 triangles
perimeter = 6	perimeter = 10	perimeter = 14	perimeter = 18

6. Let h = the number of hexagons and t = the number of triangles. Describe the relationship between h and t. ______________

7. Explain why the formula $p = h + 10$ does not relate the perimeter p of the figure to the number of hexagons.

____

____

8. A correct formula giving the perimeter in terms of the number of hexagons is $p = 4h + 2$. Show that the formula works for a figure with 6 hexagons by drawing the figure and finding the perimeter.

____

Name

LESSON MASTER 2-1 B

Questions on SPUR Objectives

Skills Objective F: Identify and apply the Commutative and Associative Properties of Multiplication.

In 1–5, tell whether the statement illustrates the Commutative Property of Multiplication or the Associative Property of Multiplication.

1. $4m = m \cdot 4$ __________
2. $7(x^3y) = 7(yx^3)$ __________
3. $5\left(\frac{1}{3}r\right) = \left(5 \cdot \frac{1}{3}\right)r$ __________
4. Five 2-foot-long boards have the same total length as two 5-foot-long boards. __________
5. The amount of discount on two 40-dollar speakers at 10% off is the same as twice the discount on one 40-dollar speaker at 10% off. __________

In 6–13, simplify.

6. $3t \cdot 10u$ __________
7. $6g^3 \cdot 2 \cdot 25$ __________
8. $\frac{1}{8}d \cdot 16e$ __________
9. $\frac{2}{5} \cdot 18 \cdot 5$ __________
10. $10a \cdot 5a \cdot 12a$ __________
11. $15y^2 \cdot 5y$ __________
12. $100w \cdot 23 \cdot 0.5$ __________
13. $20ab \cdot 4a \cdot 2bc$ __________

Uses Objective G: Apply the Area Model for Multiplication in real situations.

In 14-16, find the area of the shaded region.

14.

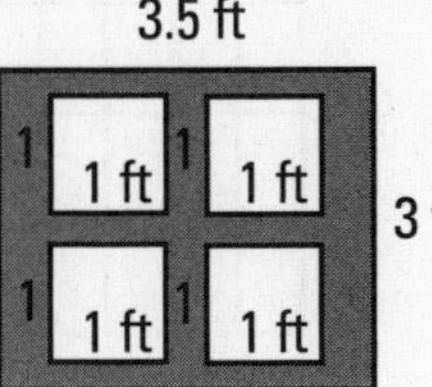

____

15.

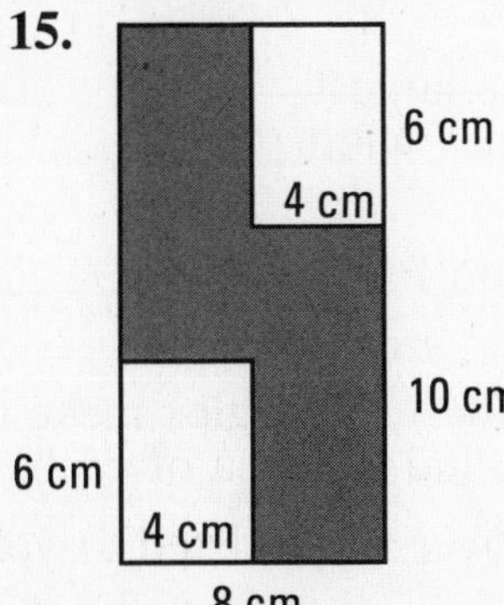

____

16.

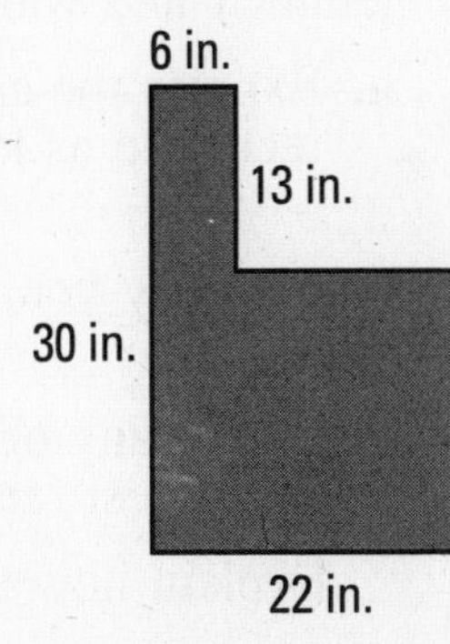

____

Name

17. A building code requires that a garage have a floor area no greater than 8% of the area of the lot. Mr. Koo is planning to build a 21-ft-by-24-ft garage on a 50-ft-by-130-ft rectangular lot. Is the garage within the code requirements? Why or why not?

18. Find the volume of a storage crate that measures 2 m by 2.5 m by 4 m.

19. How many boxes 2″ × 2″ × 1″ can be packed in a carton 2 ft by 2 ft × 1 ft?

Representations Objective J: Use rectangles, rectangular solids, or rectangular arrays to picture multiplication.

21. A box has the dimensions shown. What is its volume?

.5 m

1.2 m

2 m

22. Write a multiplication sentence suggested by the array at the left.

♠♠♠♠♠♠♠♠♠♠♠♠♠♠♠♠♠♠
♠♠♠♠♠♠♠♠♠♠♠♠♠♠♠♠♠♠
♠♠♠♠♠♠♠♠♠♠♠♠♠♠♠♠♠♠
♠♠♠♠♠♠♠♠♠♠♠♠♠♠♠♠♠♠
♠♠♠♠♠♠♠♠♠♠♠♠♠♠♠♠♠♠
♠♠♠♠♠♠♠♠♠♠♠♠♠♠♠♠♠♠

23. At the right, each of the smallest rectangles has length y and width x.

x

y

a. Express the area of the largest rectangle as length times width.

b. Simplify your answer to Part a.

c. How many of the smallest rectangles make up the largest rectangle? Find the area of each.

Explain how these answers are related to your answer in Part b.

Name ______

LESSON MASTER  **2-2 B** Questions on SPUR Objectives

Vocabulary

1. What number is called the *multiplicative identity*? ______

2. What is another name for *reciprocal*? ______

Properties Objective F: Identify and apply the following properties: Multiplication Property of 1; Property of Reciprocals; Multiplication Property of Zero.

In 3–11, give the reciprocal.

3. $\frac{4}{5}$ ______ **4.** $3\frac{1}{4}$ ______ **5.** $-\frac{9}{7}$ ______

6. $\frac{1}{8}$ ______ **7.** $\frac{e}{f}$ ______ **8.** $\frac{w}{-2}$ ______

9. 0.4 ______ **10.** -1.6 ______ **11.** $\frac{a}{m + n}$ ______

12. Write a key sequence to find the reciprocal of .385 on a calculator that has no reciprocal key.

______

13. *Multiple choice.* Which equation shows that p and q are reciprocals? ______

(a) $p + q = 1$ (b) $\frac{p}{q} = 1$ (c) $pq = 1$ (d) $1p = q$ (e) $\frac{p}{q} = \frac{q}{p}$

In 14–19, a. tell whether the two numbers are reciprocals, and b. briefly explain why or why not.

14. $\frac{3}{4}$ and .75 **a.** ______ **b.** ______

15. 6 and $\frac{1}{6}$ **a.** ______ **b.** ______

16. $\frac{1}{8}$ and -8 **a.** ______ **b.** ______

17. 7 and -7 **a.** ______ **b.** ______

18. $-\frac{5}{3}$ and $-\frac{3}{5}$ **a.** ______ **b.** ______

19. 10,000 and 0.00001 **a.** ______ **b.** ______

Name ______________________

▶ **LESSON MASTER 2-2 B** *page 2*

In 20–23, compute mentally.

20. $5{,}766(100 - 99)$ ______ **21.** $(94.7)(3.81)(0)(.711)$ ______

22. $\frac{204}{17} \cdot \frac{17}{204} \cdot \frac{13}{15}$ ______ **23.** $13.085 \cdot \frac{13}{3} \cdot \frac{3}{13}$ ______

In 24–29, simplify. Name the property used to simplify.

24. $\frac{1}{g - h} \cdot (g - h)$ ______

______

25. $25(4r - 4r)$ ______

______

26. $\frac{8y^3}{8y^3} \cdot 12$ ______

______

27. $(4a + 7)(3a + 90)(2a + 11)(0)$ ______

______

28. $(35ab)(57 - 56)$ ______

______

29. $\frac{uv}{x} \cdot \frac{x}{uv}$ ______

______

Review Objective L, Lesson 1-2

In 30–32, graph the solution set to the inequality on the number line.

30. $y < -2$ when y is an integer

31. $-3 \leq j \leq 2$ when j is a real number

32. $2.5 > k \geq 1.9$ when k is a real number

Name

LESSON MASTER 2-3 B

Questions on SPUR Objectives

Skills Objective A: Multiply and simplify algebraic fractions.

In 1–12, use the Equal Fractions Property to simplify.

1. $\frac{50}{75}$ ____________

2. $\frac{3t}{7t}$ ____________

3. $\frac{10u}{25u}$ ____________

4. $\frac{rs}{3r}$ ____________

5. $\frac{220}{1100c}$ ____________

6. $\frac{45mn}{15m}$ ____________

7. $\frac{4gh}{12gj}$ ____________

8. $\frac{1700}{400}$ ____________

9. $\frac{28d}{14d}$ ____________

10. $\frac{16xy^2}{8x}$ ____________

11. $\frac{19w^2}{12w}$ ____________

12. $\frac{fg}{g^2}$ ____________

13. *Multiple choice.* Choose the fraction which is *not* equal to the others. ____________

(a) $\frac{7m}{10m}$ (b) $\frac{14}{20y}$ (c) $\frac{35}{50}$ (d) $\frac{70ab}{100ab}$

In 14–27, multiply. Simplify the product where possible.

14. $\frac{2}{5} \cdot \frac{7}{8}$ ____________

15. $\frac{11}{2} \cdot \frac{3}{4}$ ____________

16. $\frac{u}{v} \cdot \frac{a}{b}$ ____________

17. $\frac{m}{f} \cdot \frac{f}{y}$ ____________

18. $20 \cdot \frac{2r}{7}$ ____________

19. $\frac{4w}{5} \cdot \frac{5}{4w}$ ____________

20. $\frac{3a}{2a} \cdot \frac{1}{6}$ ____________

21. $\frac{1}{b} \cdot b$ ____________

22. $62k \cdot \frac{1}{62}$ ____________

23. $\frac{st}{9} \cdot \frac{2}{su}$ ____________

24. $\frac{110b}{9c} \cdot \frac{3c^2}{44b^2}$ ____________

25. $\frac{2.5e}{f^2} \cdot \frac{f^2}{e^2}$ ____________

26. $\frac{2}{3d} \cdot \frac{h}{8} \cdot \frac{6d}{a}$ ____________

27. $\frac{85}{100} \cdot \frac{30}{7s} \cdot \frac{10s}{3r}$ ____________

Name

28. Janine's math classroom is $\frac{2}{3}$ as long and $\frac{3}{4}$ as wide as the computer lab. How do the areas of these two rooms compare?

____

____

29. A box is $\frac{1}{2}$ as long, $\frac{1}{2}$ as wide, and $\frac{1}{2}$ as high as a crate. How many of these boxes will fit in the crate? Explain how you got your answer.

____

____

Representations Objective J: Use rectangles to picture multiplication.

30. What multiplication sentence is pictured at the right?

____

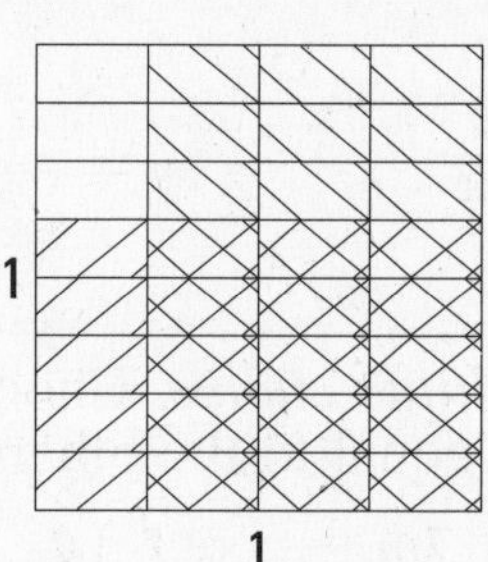

31. Draw a picture at the right to represent the product $\frac{1}{3} \cdot \frac{2}{5}$.

32. The largest rectangle at the right has width x and length y.

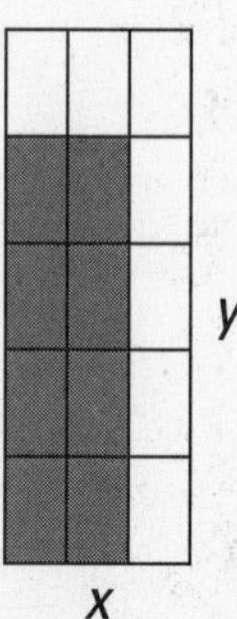

a. If each of the smallest rectangles has the same dimensions, what are these dimensions? What is the area of each of the smallest rectangles?

__________ __________

b. What is the area of the shaded region? __________

c. What product of algebraic fractions is represented by the product of the length and width of the shaded region? __________

Name

LESSON MASTER 2-4 B

Questions on SPUR Objectives

Uses Objective H: Apply the Rate Factor Model for Multiplication in real situations.

1. Mr. Kremers drove at an average speed of 50 miles per hour. How far did he travel in $6\frac{1}{2}$ hours?

2. Ms. Grabinski drove 450 miles on 15.4 gallons of gas. Compute the mpg (miles per gallon) for her car.

3. If a box of cereal contains 24 servings, how many boxes are needed to serve breakfast to 130 campers?

4. A box of tile contains 40 pieces. Five boxes will cover 25 square feet. What area can be covered by 400 tiles?

5. Over a quarter-mile distance, an elephant can run at a speed of 25 miles per hour. How many miles per *minute* is this?

6. A 120-gram serving of pudding contains 170 calories in food energy.

a. What is the number of calories per gram?

b. A person burns about 5 calories per minute of walking. How long will it take to burn off the calories from a serving of this pudding?

7. A cookbook says to cook a beef roast 35 minutes per pound. How many *hours* will it take to cook a $6\frac{1}{2}$-pound roast?

8. It takes about 1.4 columns to print 100 entries in the North-Metro phone book.

a. If there are four columns per page, how many entries are on a page?

b. About how many entries are there in the 340-page North-Metro phone book?

c. About how many pages would it take to list a quarter million entries?

Review Objective C, Lessons 1-4 and 1-6

In 9–24, evaluate each expression when $x = 4$, $y = 5.1$, and $z = 2.8$.

9. $8x$

10. $x + y$

11. $\frac{21x}{7}$

12. $xy - z$

13. $y^2 - 2x$

14. $6.1x + 2.9z$

15. $(x + y)^2$

16. $\sqrt{x}$

17. $x^2 + y^2 + z^2$

18. $\frac{7y + 2z}{14}$

19. $10(3y - 4z)$

20. $-\sqrt{16x}$

21. $-x^2 - y^2$

22. $xyz - zxy$

23. $\frac{y + z}{y - z}$

24. $\frac{3x^2}{4} \cdot \frac{4}{3x}$

Name

LESSON MASTER 2-5 B

Questions on SPUR Objectives

Skills Objective B: Multiply positive and negative numbers.

In 1 and 2, write a product as a negative rate, and give the answer.

1. Mr. Ladd is hoping to lose 3 pounds per month on a special diet. What does he expect his change in weight to be after 6 months? ______

2. Over the past 8 years, the population of Riverside has dropped about 1,200 people per year. What was the total change for this time period? ______

3. Show that $-\frac{5}{8}$ is the reciprocal of $-\frac{8}{5}$. ______

4. Show that -1 is the reciprocal of -1. ______

In 5–24, multiply. Simplify where possible.

5. $-8 \cdot -4$ ______
6. $-5 \cdot 9$ ______
7. $6 \cdot 7 \cdot -1$ ______
8. $-3 \cdot -5 \cdot -1 \cdot 8$ ______
9. $10 \cdot 16 \cdot 0 \cdot -4$ ______
10. $-26 \cdot -16$ ______
11. $-1 \cdot 1 \cdot 1 \cdot -1$ ______
12. $-1.18 \cdot -22$ ______
13. $-c \cdot -d$ ______
14. $-4m \cdot 3$ ______
15. $-11g \cdot -7h$ ______
16. $5a \cdot 2a \cdot -6a$ ______
17. $(-9)^2$ ______
18. $(-4)^3$ ______
19. $-(3y)^2$ ______
20. $(-2p)^3$ ______
21. $-\frac{2}{9} \cdot \frac{3}{4}$ ______
22. $-\frac{u}{5} \cdot -\frac{5}{u}$ ______
23. $-\frac{5h}{6} \cdot \frac{-h}{3}$ ______
24. $\frac{9x}{4y} \cdot -\frac{y^2}{3x}$ ______

In 25 and 26, two expressions are given. Evaluate a and use your answer to help with b.

25. **a.** $8.5 \cdot 46.2$ ______ **b.** $-8.5 \cdot -46.2$ ______

26. **a.** $\frac{2h}{3} \cdot \frac{4}{9}$ ______ **b.** $\frac{3}{2h} \cdot \frac{9}{4}$ ______

Name

27. Evaluate $3m + 18$ when $m = -4$. ____________

28. Evaluate $\frac{-6d}{3}$ when $d = -10$. ____________

29. Evaluate $\frac{5r}{12} \cdot r$ when $r = -6$. ____________

30. Evaluate $(-2f)^2$ when $f = 5$. ____________

31. Evaluate $-2x^2 + 7x - 1$ when $x = -3$. ____________

Properties Objective F: Identify and apply the Multiplication Property of -1.

In 32–41, tell whether the expression is positive or negative.

32. $(-9)^3$ ____________

33. $(-1)^{15}$ ____________

34. $(-8)^2$ ____________

35. $(-13)^4$ ____________

36. $(-6)^6$ ____________

37. -6^6 ____________

38. $(-5)(-2)(-1)(-8)$ ____________

39. $(-1)(-8)(6.4)(-1)$ ____________

40. $5 \cdot 9 \cdot -3 \cdot 8 \cdot 2$ ____________

41. $-(-18)$ ____________

42. *Multiple choice.* Which of the following is equivalent to the opposite of the opposite of n? ____________

(a) $\frac{1}{n}$ (b) $-1n$ (c) $1n$ (d) $1 - n$

Review Objective J, Lesson 1-5

43. Use the formula $V = e^3$ to find the volume V of a box that measures 80 cm along each edge e. ____________

44. The formula $F = \frac{9}{5}C + 32$ converts the temperature from degrees Celsius to degrees Fahrenheit. Find the Fahrenheit temperature to the nearest degree for

a. 55°C. ____________

b. 25°C. ____________

c. 0°C. ____________

d. -10°C. ____________

Name

LESSON MASTER 

Questions on SPUR Objectives

Skills Objective C: Solve and check equations of the form $ax = b$.

In 1–11, solve the equation and check your answer.

1. $\frac{2}{5}y = -44$

2. $44c = 99$

3. $-7p = -154$

4. $\frac{1}{3}d = \frac{7}{6}$

5. $59 = -\frac{1}{8}x$

6. $3.8s = 475$

7. $\frac{h}{12} = 16$

8. $-\frac{7}{12} = -\frac{11}{4}k$

9. $\frac{y}{5} = -\frac{7}{10}$

10. $15\left(\frac{1}{3}\right)n = 350$

11. $-7(1.6)n = 39.2$

Properties Objective F: Identify and apply the Multiplication Property of Equality.

12. Large orders of certain items are sometimes sold by the *gross*. A gross is a dozen dozen, or 144. An equation for this relationship is 1 gross = 144 units.

Tell how you would apply the Multiplicative Property of Equality to this equation to find the number of units in 72 gross.

Name

13. For the solution to the equation $60e = 210$, tell which of the properties at the right justifies each step.

Associative Property of Multiplication
Multiplicative Identity Property of 1
Property of Reciprocals
Multiplication Property of Equality

$$60e = 210$$

$$\frac{1}{60} \cdot 60e = \frac{1}{60} \cdot 210$$ ____________

$$\left(\frac{1}{60} \cdot 60\right)e = \frac{210}{60}$$ ____________

$$1e = 3.5$$ ____________

$$e = 3.5$$ ____________

Uses Objective H: Apply the Rate Factor Model for Multiplication in real situations.

---

14. All the sides of a regular polygon have the same length. The formula $p = ns$ gives the perimeter of a regular polygon with n sides of length s.

a. Use this formula to write an equation that can be used to find the number of sides of a regular polygon with sides of length 8 and a perimeter of 144. ____________

b. Solve the equation from Part a for n. ____________

c. Solve $p = ns$ for n. ____________

15. A plane flies from Chicago to Dallas, a distance of 800 miles, in 1.8 hours.

a. Write a multiplication equation based on the formula $d = rt$.

____

b. Solve the equation from Part a for r and check.

____

check: ____________

16. Jean types 68 words per minute. At this rate, how many words can she type in a half hour?

____

17. A marathon is a footrace of 42.2 kilometers. One mile is about 1.6 kilometers. What is the distance of a marathon in miles?

____

Name

LESSON MASTER 2-7 B

Questions on SPUR Objectives

Skills Objective C: Solve and check equations of the form $ax = b$, when a or b is zero or -1.

In 1–15, solve the equation.

1. $18m = 0$

2. $0w = 12$

3. $-d = 67$

4. $0 = 0p$

5. $-5.2 = -u$

6. $17.5 = 0s$

7. $0 = -5h$

8. $(-f) = -81$

9. $-m = 0$

10. $-n = \frac{5}{9}$

11. $-3.94y = 0$

12. $0 = (22 - 22)k$

13. $0.49 = -(-(-x))$

14. $0 = (16 - 11)h$

15. $(9 - 10)c = 31$

In 16–22, tell if the equation has no solution, one solution, or an infinite number of solutions. Do not solve.

16. $44g = 210$ ______________________

17. $783 = 0t$ ______________________

18. $-u = 54$ ______________________

19. $0q = 0$ ______________________

20. $\frac{2}{3} = 0a$ ______________________

21. $\frac{9}{8} = -3d$ ______________________

22. $0 = 0v$ ______________________

Name ____________________

▶ **LESSON MASTER 2-7 B** *page 2*

In 23–27, write an equation of the form $ax = b$ that has the given solution.

23. Solution: 3 ____________________

24. Solution: 0 ____________________

25. Solution: All real numbers ____________________

26. No solution ____________________

27. Solution: -5 ____________________

Properties Objective F: Identify and apply the following properties: Multiplication Property of -1; Multiplication Property of Zero; Multiplication Property of Equality.

In 28–30, find all solutions and use properties of multiplication to explain why the answer makes sense.

28. $0c = 0$

____

____

29. $0c = 27$

____

____

30. $-a = 0.459$

____

____

Review Objective L, Lesson 1-3

In 31–34, graph the solution set. Consider the domain as the set of real numbers.

31. $x < 13$

32. $y \geq -4$

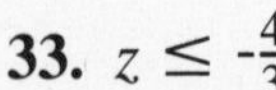

33. $z \leq -\frac{4}{3}$

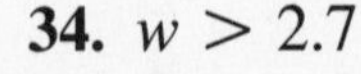

34. $w > 2.7$

Name

LESSON MASTER 2-8 B

Questions on SPUR Objectives

Skills Objective D: Solve and check inequalities of the form $ax < b$.

In 1–12, solve and check the inequality.

1. $7y < 56$

2. $99 \geq 11e$

3. $-5p > 30$

4. $27 \leq -3m$

5. $-\frac{7}{8}k > 63$

6. $-1.9s \geq -0.95$

7. $\frac{u}{15} > -7$

8. $-\frac{1}{3} \leq -\frac{3}{10}k$

9. $-396 < 55f$

10. $-r > 77$

11. $\frac{1}{5} \geq -2x$

12. $\frac{5}{6}d \leq 75$

Properties Objective F: Identify and apply the Multiplication Property of Inequality.

13. What inequality results if both sides of $-6 < 10$ are multiplied by -1? __________

14. What inequality results if both sides of $-\frac{3}{5}x < -24$ are multiplied by $-\frac{5}{3}$? __________

Name ______________________________

15. *Multiple choice.* If $r < s$, then which sentence is true? __________

(a) $s < r$ (b) $-r > -s$ (c) $-r < s$

16. If a number is greater than 1,000, why must its opposite be less than -1,000?

____

____

Uses Objective G: Apply the Area Model for Multiplication in real situations.

17. The park board is planning a new rectangular playground. The width will be 75 feet, and its area may not exceed 10,000 square feet. What is the maximum length?

a. Write an inequality involving the length. __________

b. Solve the inequality. __________

c. Answer the question. __________

Uses Objective H: Apply the Rate Factor for Multiplication in real situations.

18. Mr. Sanchez has a 22-pound turkey in the freezer. If he allows $\frac{3}{4}$ pound per person, how many people can he serve?

a. Write an inequality describing the number of people he can serve. __________

b. Solve the inequality. __________

c. Answer the question. __________

19. The gas tank of Dorothy's car holds 12.6 gallons of gas. If she get 18 miles to the gallon, how far can she drive on a full tank?

a. Write an inequality describing the distance she can drive on a full tank. __________

b. Solve the inequality. __________

c. Answer the question. __________

Name ______________________________

LESSON MASTER 2-9 B

Questions on SPUR Objectives

Uses Objective I: Apply the Multiplication Counting Principle.

1. An earring shop offers a certain style of earrings in gold or silver, with garnets, jade, onyx, or pearls, and for pierced or unpierced ears. Use a list or a tree diagram to show all the possibilities for this style.

2. A bakery offers rye bread in 1-pound or $1\frac{1}{2}$-pound loaves, with seeds or without, and sliced or unsliced. How many choices of rye bread are there? ____________

3. Freshmen at Louis Academy must take one course from each of the following:

English (Literature or Creative Writing)
Mathematics (Algebra, Geometry, or Advanced Algebra)
Social Studies (World Cultures or American History)
Science (Lab Survey, Biology, or Physics)
Fine Arts (Choir, Band, Orchestra, Freshman Art, Speech, or Drama)
Foreign Language (French, Spanish, Italian, German, or Russian)
Gym (Swimming, Wrestling, or Aerobics)

How many different freshman programs are possible? ____________

4. Write a problem involving the Multiplication Counting Principle that has as its answer $2 \cdot 4 \cdot 3$.

____

____

____

5. Write a problem involving the Multiplication Counting Principle that has as its answer 4^3.

____

____

____

Name ___

6. A customer calling Cavalier Savings and Loan on a touch-tone phone is instructed to press 1 for the Savings Department, 2 for the Checking Department, 3 for the Home Loan Department, or 4 for the Commercial Loan Department. After making that selection, the customer is told to press 1 followed by the account number to hear the current balance, 2 followed by the account number to hear information about the last transaction, or 3 to talk to an employee from that department. How many different selections are possible?

___

7. Some license plates contain two letters followed by 4 numbers such as GY 1884.

a. How many such plates are possible? ___

b. How many are possible if you cannot use the letters I or O? ___

c. Why do you think the letters I and O might be excluded?

___

8. A science test has six multiple-choice questions each with five options, A, B, C, D, and E. The test also has eight true-false questions.

a. How many different ways are there for a student to answer the questions on the test? ___

b. How many different ways are there for a student to answer the questions on the test if there are p multiple-choice questions and q true-false questions? ___

9. a. In how many ways can 12 children line up at the drinking fountain? ___

b. How many ways are there if this week's "front captain" is first? ___

10. A bicycle lock uses a combination of 4 digits, each ranging from 1 to 6.

a. How many different combinations are possible? ___

b. Frannie forgot her combination but does remember that the middle two digits are 5 and 5. What is the greatest number of possible combinations she would have to try until she finds the right one? ___

Name

LESSON MASTER  2-10 B

Questions on SPUR Objectives

Vocabulary

1. An arrangement of letters, names, or objects is called a ______.

2. Explain how to read 18! and tell what it means.

______

______

Skills Objective E: Evaluate expressions containing a factorial symbol.

In 3–5, evaluate.

3. 4! ______ **4.** 7! ______ **5.** 10! ______

6. Are 9! and $9 \cdot 8!$ equal? Explain.

______

______

7. Are $3! \cdot 4!$ and $(3 \cdot 4)!$ equal? Explain.

______

______

8. Tell if the following statement is *true* or *false* and justify your answer. If $n > 1$, n! is even.

______

______

9. Explain how to evaluate $\frac{100!}{98!}$ without a calculator.

______

______

______

In 10–12, find *n*.

10. $n! = 24$ ______ **11.** $n! = 1$ ______ **12.** $n! = 362{,}880$ ______

Uses Objective I: Apply the Permutation Theorem.

In 13–18, tell if the Permutation Theorem can be used to solve the problem. Write *yes* or *no*.

13. In how many ways can 14 books be lined up on a shelf? __________

14. How many different sets of 2-letter initials are there? __________

15. How many different ways are there to arrange a trip to 20 cities? __________

16. In how many ways can you choose a sandwich from a choice of 4 breads, 2 fillings, and 2 spreads? __________

17. In how many different orders can 11 people get off an elevator one at a time? __________

18. How many different outfits can be made from 3 skirts and 5 blouses? __________

19. In the movie *Close Encounters of the Third Kind*, aliens transmit a message that consists of five different tones of music played one at a time.

a. In how many orders can five different tones be played with none repeated? __________

b. In how many orders can six different tones be played with none repeated? __________

c. In how many orders can seven different tones such as DO-RE-MI-FA-SOL-LA-TI, be played with none repeated? __________

d. In how many different orders can the 12 black and white keys indicated below be played if no key is played twice? __________

12 keys

e. Write an expression for the number of different orders there are for playing the 88 black and white keys of a piano if no key is played twice. __________

Name ______________________________

LESSON MASTER 3-1 B

Questions on SPUR Objectives

Skills Objective A: Use properties of addition to simplify expressions.

In 1–9, simplify the expression.

1. (10 + -2) + -6 ______________

2. (-4 + 9) + (-9 + 4) ______________

3. 19.99 + 4.95 + 0.05 + 0.01 ______________

4. 38 + (3p + 9) ______________

5. -17 + (x + -13) ______________

6. (b + 22) + -18 ______________

7. (m + 11) + (n + 44) ______________

8. (e + -26) + (24 + 2f) ______________

9. 9 + (h + -6.5) + 2.4 ______________

10. In a magic square, each row, column, and diagonal has the same sum. Fill in the boxes at the right so each of these sums is -3.

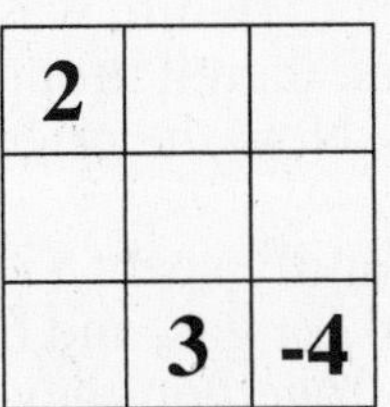

2		
	3	-4

Properties Objective E: Identify the Commutative and Associative Properties of Addition.

In 11–14, tell which property of addition is illustrated.

11. (5 + 7v) + -16 = 5 + (7v + -16)

____

12. (9 + -4w) + (8r + 33) = (8r + 33) + (9 + -4w)

____

13. (11 + 2g) + 80 = (2g + 11) + 80

____

14. (-7 + 8a) + (9a + 14) = -7 + (8a + 9a) + 14

____

Name ________________

15. Give three instances of the Commutative Property of Addition.

____

16. Give three instances of the Associative Property of Addition.

____

Uses Objective G: Apply the Putting-Together and Slide Models of Addition to write linear expressions and equations involving addition.

In 17–19, write an addition expression or equation suggested by each situation.

17. Doreen is Y years old.

a. 7 years from now, Doreen's age will be ________.

b. 2 years ago, Doreen's age was ________.

18. The price of a yard of denim was \$4.66. The price rose d dollars, then it dropped 49¢, and then rose 18¢. Now the price of denim is ________.

19. On a vacation, a family spent \$750 for hotels, \$622 for food, \$94 for gas, and E dollars for other expenses. Altogether, they spent \$1700. ________

20. Refer to the graphs below.

a. In Week 1, the total number of books checked out is expressed by the sum ________.

b. In Week 4, the total number of books, checked out is expressed by the sum ________.

c. In Week 5, if f fiction books and n nonfiction books were checked out, then the total number of books checked out is expressed by the sum ________.

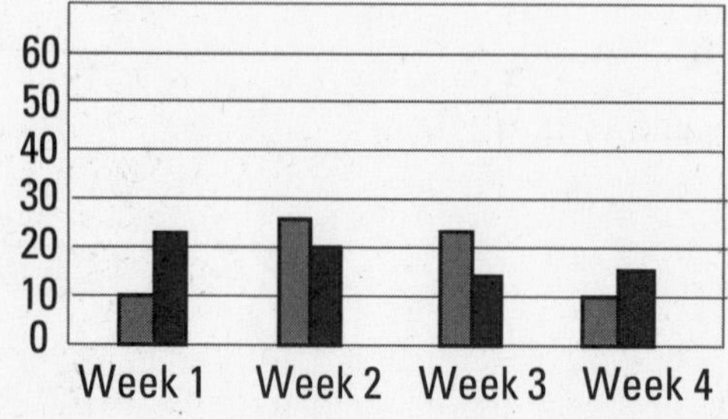

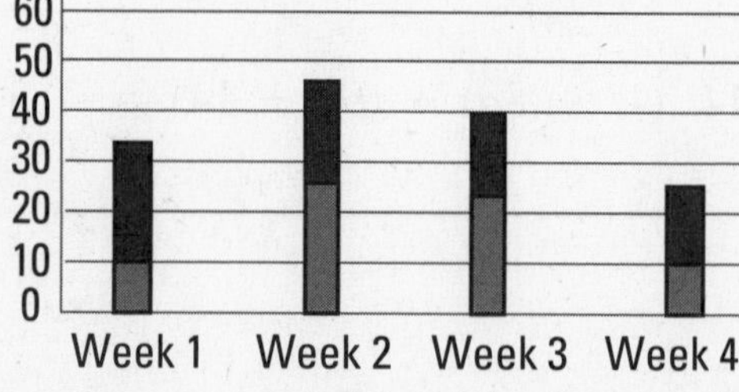

Name ______________________________

LESSON MASTER 3-2 B

Questions on SPUR Objectives

Skills Objective A: Use properties of addition to simplify expressions.

In 1–8, simplify the expression.

1. -(-94) ____

2. -8.66 + 8.66 ____

3. $-\frac{6}{5} + \frac{6}{5}$ ____

4. $-4g + 0$ ____

5. -(-704) + -704 ____

6. $(e + -232) + 232$ ____

7. (-44 + 99) + (-99 + 44) ____

8. $(9v + -16) + 16$ ____

Skills Objective B: Solve and check equations of the form $x + a = b$.

9. a. Check whether $x = 6.1$ is the correct solution to the equation $-14.2 + x = 8.1$.

____

b. Use another method to check whether $x = 6.1$ is the correct solution.

____

In 10–18, solve and check the equation.

10. $u + -13 = 7$

11. $2e = 852$

12. $66 = f + 88$

13. $-21 + r = -37$

14. $45 = -\frac{5}{8}x$

15. $2.8 + w = 7.4$

16. $\frac{7}{12} + d = -\frac{5}{12}$

17. $-5.09 = -5.09 + h$

18. $-6.15 = -.03k$

Name ______________________________

Properties Objective E: Identify and apply the Additive Identity Property, the Property of Opposites, the Opposite of Opposites Property, and the Addition Property of Equality.

In 19–21, a. give another instance of the property illustrated and b. name the property.

19. $\frac{5}{9} + -\frac{5}{9} = 0$ **a.** ______________ **b.** ______________

20. $0 + \pi = \pi$ **a.** ______________ **b.** ______________

21. $-(-19) = 19$ **a.** ______________ **b.** ______________

In 22 and 23, give the number that should be added to both sides to solve the equation quickly.

22. $x + -18 = 94$ __________ **23.** $5.11 = y + 4.9$ __________

24. a. If 37 is added to both sides of the equation $m + 22 = -4$, what is the result? __________

b. Does the equation you wrote for part a have the same solution as the equation $m + 22 = -4$? __________

Uses Objective G: Apply models for addition to write and solve equations of the form $x + a = b$.

In 25 and 26, write and solve an equation to answer the question.

25. After receiving orders from the captain, a submarine rose 120 feet to 40 feet below sea level. At what level was the submarine before the captain gave the orders?

______________ equation ______________ answer

26. Mr. Craig received notice that his checking account was overdrawn by $55. After making a deposit, his new balance was $480. How much did he deposit?

______________ equation ______________ answer

Name

LESSON MASTER 3-3 B

Questions on SPUR Objectives

Representations Objective I: Draw and interpret two-dimensional graphs.

1. The chart below compares different schools, showing the number of computers at the school and the number of minutes students averaged at a school computer per week.

School Computers

School	Computers per 100 Students	Minutes Used per Student per Week
Douglas	21	75
Young	14	55
Lincoln	13	64
West Lloyd	11	40
Fernandez	10	85
Carlisle	8	44
East Lloyd	8	35
Hadley	7	32
Powell	7	27
Thayer	5	18

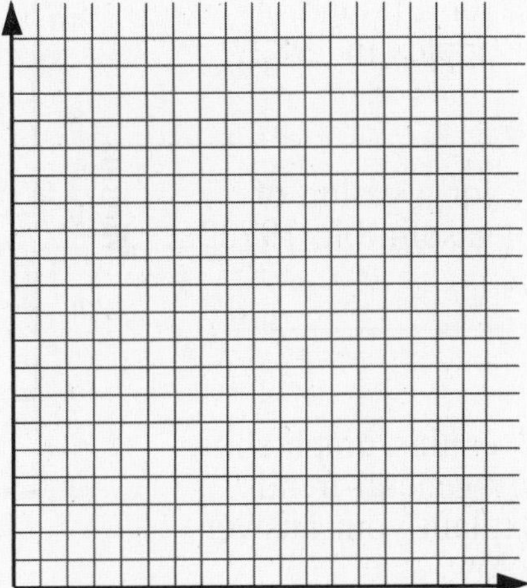

a. Draw a graph of the data on the grid, showing computers per 100 students on the horizontal axis and minutes used per student per week on the vertical axis.

b. Describe any trends you see. Are there any schools that do not follow this trend?

____

____

____

____

c. If a school has 12 computers per 100 students, give a reasonable prediction for the average number of minutes per week each students uses the computer.

____

▶ LESSON MASTER 3-3 B *page 2*

In 2 and 3, use the graph below, which shows how long the average American had to work, before taxes, to purchase the goods and services shown.

2. On the average, about how long did a worker have to work

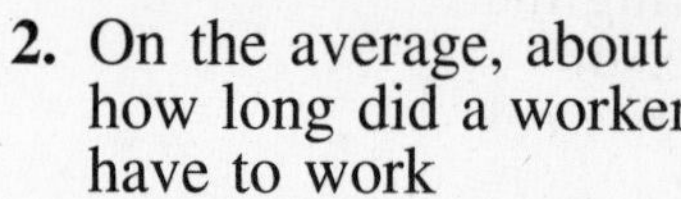

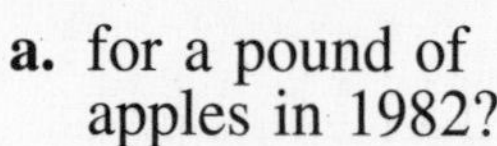

   a. for a pound of apples in 1982? ______________

   b. for a gallon of gasoline in 1972? ______________

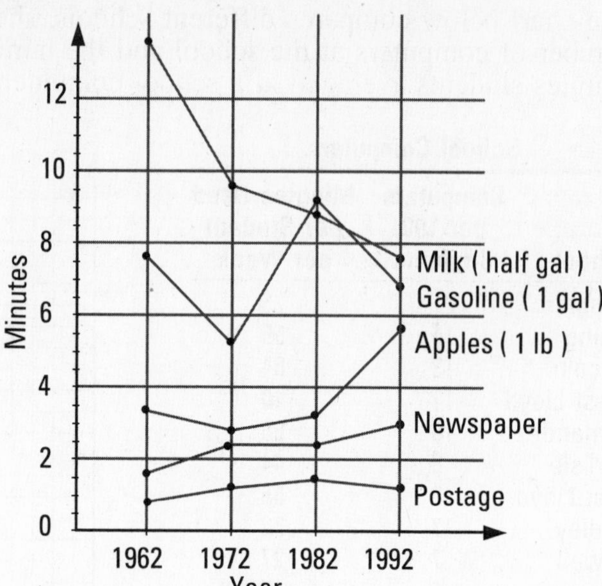

3. Does this graph show any general trends? Explain your answer below.

____

____

4. Use the graph at the right. It has two different vertical scales. To plot a point on this graph, use the student's ACT exam score along the horizontal axis and the student's grade-point and class rank on the two vertical axes. If the point plotted is *on or above* the line graphed, the student is considered for admission to the university. Would a student be considered for admission if the student

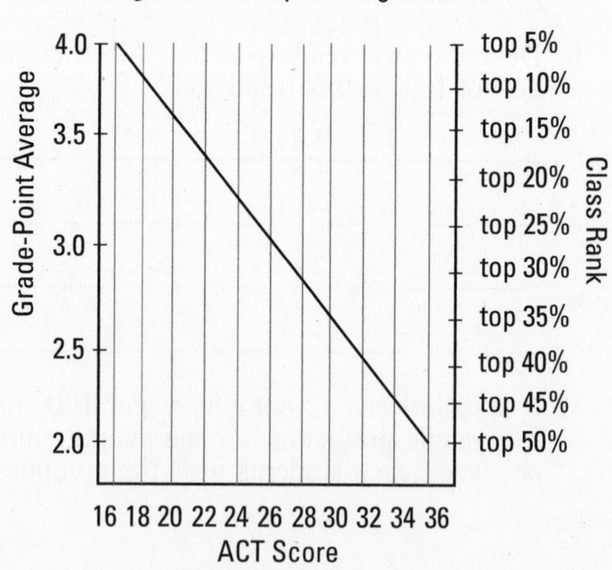

   a. scored 26 on the ACT and has a 3.29 grade-point average? ________

   b. scored 20 on the ACT and is in the top 25% of the class? ________

Name ____________________

LESSON MASTER 3-4 B

Questions on SPUR Objectives

Representations Objective J: Draw and interpret two-dimensional slides on a coordinate graph.

For 1–5, use the grid at the right. *P′A′R′T′Y′* is the image of sliding pentagon *PARTY* 4 units right and 3 units up. *P″A″R″T″Y″* is the image of *P′A′R′T′Y′* under the slide 6 units left and 3 units up.

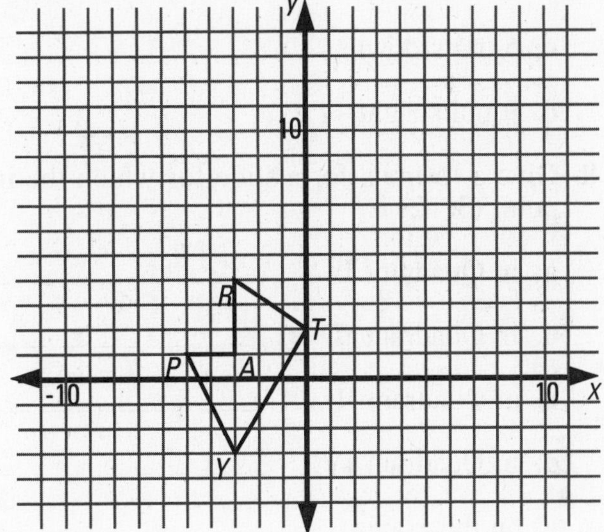

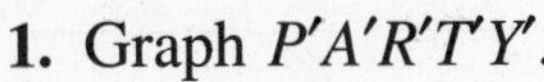

1. Graph *P′A′R′T′Y′*.

2. Graph *P″A″R″T″Y″*.

3. Give the coordinates of *Y″*.

____

4. The coordinates of *P* are (-5, 1). Explain how to find the coordinates of *P′* without graphing.

____

____

5. The coordinates of *A* are (-3, 1). Explain how to find the coordinates of *A″* without graphing.

____

____

6. Give the coordinates of the point *N* = (-5, 9) under a slide

   a. 1 unit right and 3 units down. ____________

   b. 6 units left and 10 units down. ____________

   c. 5 units right and 4 units up. ____________

   d. 7 units up. ____________

   e. 2 units left. ____________

   f. *h* units right and *k* units up. ____________

Name

7. Give the coordinates of the point $Q = (x, y)$ under a slide

a. 4 units left and 8 units up. ________

b. 5 units right and 4 units up. ________

c. 5 units down. ________

d. 9 units right. ________

8. Give a formula for a slide for which the image of the point (3, -2) is

a. in Quadrant I. ________

b. in Quadrant II. ________

c. in Quadrant III. ________

d. in Quadrant IV. ________

e. on the x-axis. ________

f. on the y-axis. ________

In 9–12, use the graph at the right which shows M and its image, M', after a slide.

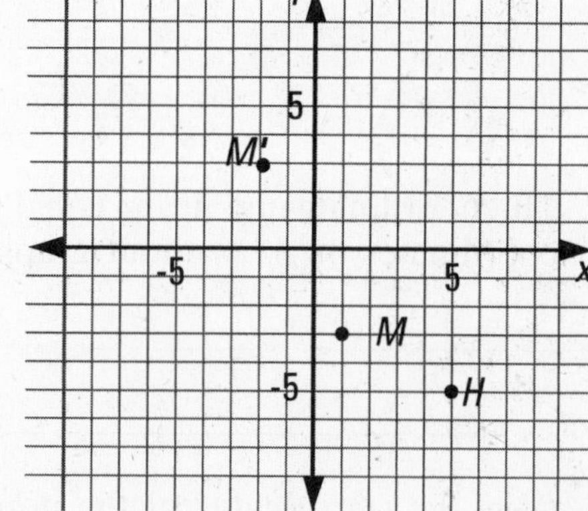

9. Describe the slide.

____

10. Point H is shown on the graph. Plot H', its image under the same slide that was used to go from M to M'.

11. Fill in the blanks to describe the slide algebraically:

The image of (x, y) is $(x +$ ______, $y +$ ______.)

12. a. Give a formula for the slide that would move M' onto M. ________

b. Compare your answer in Part a to your answer to Question 9 and explain what you notice.

____

____

Name

Questions on SPUR Objectives

Skills Objective B: Solve and check equations of the form $ax + b = c$.

1. Write a check to determine if $m = -18$ is the correct solution of $21 + -3m = 75$.

In 2–13, solve and check the equation.

2. $3d + 81 = 117$

3. $-2g + -16 = 4$

4. $-7 = 9f + 20$

5. $-75 = 4y$

6. $\frac{2}{3}t + 16 = 62$

7. $-33 = f + -14$

8. $20 = 30 + -\frac{x}{4}$

9. $8.22 = 1.6h + .22$

10. $-\frac{7}{9}a = 77$

11. $2.7 + 6s + 1.8 = 6.5$

12. $2\frac{1}{2} + 2n = 2\frac{3}{4}$

13. $9 + -7k = 2 + -77$

14. If -6 is added to each side of $6x - 8 = 40$, what is the resulting equation?

15. Does your answer to Question 14 have the same solution as $6x - 8 = 40$? Explain why or why not.

Name

Uses Objective G: Apply models for addition to write and solve equations of the form $ax + b = c$.

In 16–19, write an equation to describe the situation, solve the equation, and answer the question.

16. Ellen bought buttons and $2\frac{1}{2}$ yd of fabric. The buttons cost $1.95, and the total bill without tax was $19.40. What was the cost per yard of the fabric?

equation ______ solution ______ answer ______

17. Jake's phone service is $21 per month plus 25¢ for each local call, with long-distance calls extra. Last month, with $6.14 in long-distance charges, his bill was $36.64. How many local calls did he make?

equation ______ solution ______ answer ______

18. Cindy has saved $57 and wants to buy a shirt and two pairs of jeans at $25 a pair. Without tax, how much can she spend on a shirt?

equation ______ solution ______ answer ______

19. The Andersons wish to fence in the back and the two sides of their yard. Their lot is 50 feet wide. If they purchase 140 feet of fencing, how long can the fence be along each side?

equation ______ solution ______ answer ______

Representations Objective K: Use balance scales to represent equations.

20. a. What equation is represented by the diagram at the right?

______

b. What two steps can be done with the objects on the scale to find the weight of a box?

______

______

21. a. Sketch a balance-scale diagram for $3w + 4 = 10$.

b. What is the value of w? ______

Name

LESSON MASTER

Questions on SPUR Objectives

Vocabulary

In 1–6, tell if the terms are *like* or *unlike*.

1. $7v \quad 9v^2$ ______

2. $a \quad 8a$ ______

3. $5c^2 \quad -3c^2$ ______

4. $-y \quad 44y$ ______

5. $88g \quad 88$ ______

6. $-r^2 \quad r^2$ ______

Skills Objective A: Use the Distributive Property to simplify expressions.

In 7–18, simplify the expression.

7. $3u + 11u$ ______

8. $s + 13s$ ______

9. $9m + 3m + -5m$ ______

10. $3d + 17 + -8d$ ______

11. $15 + -7f + -21 + -2f$ ______

12. $h + h + h + h$ ______

13. $12g^2 + 18g^2$ ______

14. $-5y^2 + 7y + 6y^2$ ______

15. $7 - u^2 + 4u + 9u + u^2$ ______

16. $\left(\frac{3}{4}t + 16\right) + \left(-\frac{1}{2}t + 4\right)$ ______

17. $(14x^2 + 7x) + (-x + 19)$ ______

18. $6(4j) + 13 + -23j$ ______

In 19 and 20, simplify. Check your answer by substituting 10 for *x* in both the original expression and your answer.

19. $2x + 7x^2 + -3x + x^2$ ______

______

______

______

20. $9.4x + 3x$ ______

______

______

______

Skills Objective B: Solve and check equations of the form $ax + b = c$.

In 21 and 22, solve and check the equation.

21. $10q + -4q = -72$

22. $21d + 16 + 13d = 67$

Properties Objective E: Identify and apply the Distributive Property.

In 23–25, tell whether or not the Distributive Property is involved. Write *yes* or *no*.

23. $-(-9) = 9$ ________

24. $-9a + 3a = -6a$ ________

25. $\frac{2}{3}b + \frac{1}{3}b = b$ ________

Uses Objective G: Apply models for addition to write and solve equations involving like terms.

In 26 and 27, write an equation to describe the situation, solve the equation, and answer the question.

26. Helen bought a blouse, jeans, and a pair of shoes for $72. The blouse and jeans cost the same amount, and the shoes cost $6 more than the blouse. How much did the jeans cost?

________ equation   ________ solution   ________ answer

27. The area of Ms. Whitecloud's property is 7,800 square feet. Her house occupies one fourth the area of land as the rest of the property. How many square feet of land does the house cover?

________ equation   ________ solution   ________ answer

Representations Objective K: Use area models to represent the Distributive Property.

28. a. What is the area of the top rectangle? ________

b. What is the area of the bottom rectangle? ________

c. What is the area of the largest rectangle? Give your answer in simplified form. ________

x

13

5

Name

LESSON MASTER **3-7 B**

Questions on SPUR Objectives

Skills Objective A: Use the Distributive Property to simplify expressions.

In 1–12, simplify the expression.

1. $6(8m + 7)$

2. $-9(y + 5)$

3. $u(7u + 10)$

4. $w(w - 12)$

5. $12(3 - 2y)$

6. $h + 5(h + 8)$

7. $4g(g + 3) + 2g^2 + -g$

8. $-4(r + 8) + 9(r + 8)$

9. $15a + 7 + -25a$

10. $2.5(5f - 3)$

11. $\frac{1}{2}(s + 17)$

12. $4k + -3(j + k + 8) + 2(3j + -8k)$

Skills Objective B: Solve and check equations of the form $ax + b = c$.

In 13–16, solve and check the equation.

13. $2(3x + 18) = 102$

14. $7(j + -4) + j = 4$

15. $24 = 20(6 + -5y) + 4$

16. $3.1d(2d + 7) + -6.2d^2 = 19.53$

Properties Objective E: Identify and apply the Distributive Property.

In 17–20, tell if the equation involves the Distributive Property.

17. $6a + (7 + 3a) = 6a + (3a + 7)$ ____________

18. $5n + 13n + -16 = 18n + -16$ ____________

19. $7(2a + 6b + c) = 14a + 42b + 7c$ ____________

20. $15t + (7u + -v) = (15t + 7u) + -v$ ____________

Properties Objective F: Use the Distributive Property to perform calculations mentally.

21. If a recipe makes 60 cookies, how many does a recipe and a half make? Explain how you can mentally compute your answer.

____

22. There are 19 students in Room 216. Mentally compute the cost if the entire class buys

a. juice at $.75 each. ________ **b.** caps at $12 each. ________

Representations Objective K: Use area models to represent the Distributive Property.

In 23 and 24 express the area of each largest rectangle as a. length times width and b. the sum of the areas of the smaller rectangles.

23.

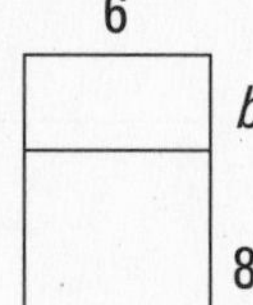

a. ____________

b. ____________

24.

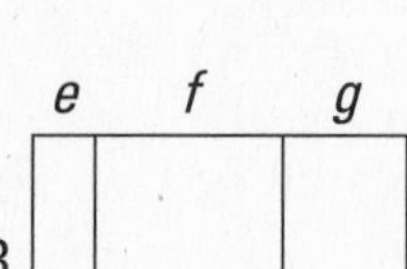

a. ____________

b. ____________

Name

LESSON MASTER 3-8 B

Questions on SPUR Objectives

Uses Objective H: Write expressions and solve problems involving linear patterns with two variables.

In 1–9, use the sequence of designs shown below.

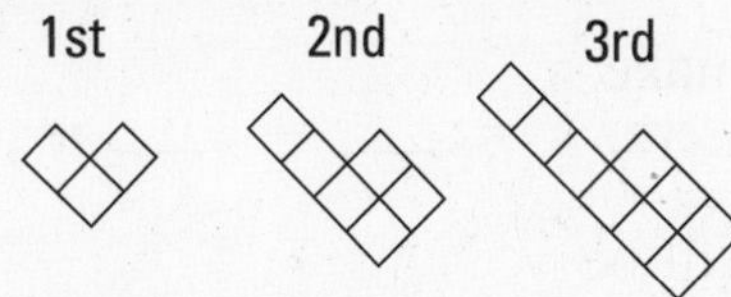

1. Draw the next design in the sequence.

2. Complete the chart below to show the perimeters of the first through fifth designs.

Design Number	Perimeter
1	8
2	
3	
4	
5	

3. If the perimeter of a design is 40, what would the perimeter of the next design be? __________

4. If n = the design number and p = the perimeter, then the relationship between them is described by $p = 4n + 4$.

a. Find the perimeter of the 18th design. __________

b. Which design has perimeter 128? __________

Name ____________________

5. Complete the chart at the right.

n = Design Number	s = Number of Squares
1	
2	
3	
4	
5	

6. If one design has 45 squares, how many squares will the next design have? ________

7. Fill in the blanks to make a formula for this pattern. s = ___ + ___ n

8. How many squares will be in the 25th design? ________

9. Which design is made up of 66 squares? ________

In 10–12, use the chart at the right. It shows a price list for wallet-size pictures.

Number of Prints	Price
1 dozen	$24
2 dozen	$32
3 dozen	$40
4 dozen	$48
5 dozen	$56

10. How much would 120 prints cost? ________

11. Describe how the price changes as the number of prints increases.

____

____

12. Write an equation for the cost c of p dozen prints. ________________

13. The Central Valley Gas Company charges customers $16.50 per month for up to 150 therms used and $.06 for each therm after that.

    a. At the right make a table showing the cost of 100, 150, 200, 250, and 300 therms used during the month.

    b. Write a formula for the cost c in terms of the number t of therms used when $t \geq 150$.

    ____

    c. What is the cost of 680 therms used in a month?

    ____

Name ______________________________

LESSON MASTER

Questions on SPUR Objectives

Skills Objective C: Add algebraic fractions.

In 1–14, find the sum.

1. $\frac{x}{z} + \frac{y}{z}$ ________

2. $\frac{m}{5} + \frac{n}{5}$ ________

3. $\frac{a}{9} + \frac{a}{9}$ ________

4. $\frac{1}{c} + \frac{2}{c} + \frac{3}{c}$ ________

5. $\frac{3}{10} + \frac{9}{10}$ ________

6. $-\frac{2}{5} + \frac{7}{5}$ ________

7. $-\frac{4}{9} + -\frac{7}{9}$ ________

8. $5\frac{7}{8} + \frac{5}{8}$ ________

9. $\frac{3}{r} + -\frac{12}{r}$ ________

10. $\frac{2m}{7} + \frac{6m}{7} + -\frac{m}{7}$ ________

11. $-\frac{7}{8k} + \frac{15}{8k}$ ________

12. $\frac{4}{3y} + -\frac{2}{3y} + \frac{10}{3y}$ ________

13. $\frac{x + 7}{5u} + \frac{3x + 2}{5u}$ ________

14. $\frac{7p + -3}{2ab} + \frac{9p + 5}{2ab}$ ________

In 15 and 16, tell what common denominator you could use to add the fractions.

15. $\frac{x}{9}$ and $\frac{3x}{12}$ ________

16. $\frac{2v}{5}$ and $-\frac{7v}{6}$ ________

In 17-22, write as a single fraction.

17. $\frac{3x}{8} + \frac{5x}{4}$ ________

18. $-\frac{4a}{7} + \frac{12a}{3}$ ________

19. $-\frac{5m}{3} + -\frac{3m}{8}$ ________

20. $h + \frac{h}{3}$ ________

21. $\frac{2y}{5} + \frac{3y}{2} + \frac{y}{15}$ ________

22. $9j + \frac{5j}{6}$ ________

In 23 and 24, simplify each expression.

23. $-\frac{4}{5}s + \frac{2}{3}s$ ________

24. $\frac{2e + 7}{e} + \frac{-7}{e}$ ________

Name

25. On Monday, AFZ's stock dropped $2\frac{1}{4}$ points. On Tuesday it rose $\frac{7}{8}$ of a point. What was the net change? ______________

26. On Friday, the river rose $2\frac{1}{2}$ feet. On Saturday it rose another $2\frac{1}{4}$ feet. On Sunday it receded $1\frac{3}{4}$ feet. What was the net change in the level of the river? ______________

Properties Objective E: Identify and apply the Distributive Property.

In 27–30, tell if the equation involves the Distributive Property.

27. $\frac{5}{9} + \frac{1}{2} = \frac{10}{18} + \frac{9}{18}$ ______________

28. $a\left(\frac{1}{9}\right) + b\left(\frac{1}{9}\right) = (a + b)\frac{1}{9}$ ______________

29. $\frac{e}{k} + \frac{2}{k} = \frac{e + 2}{k}$ ______________

30. $\frac{9m}{m} = 9$ ______________

Review Objective C, Lesson 2-8

In 31–36, solve and check the inequality.

31. $9n > 36$

32. $84 \leq 12c$

33. $-5p < 5$

34. $58 \geq -2v$

35. $-\frac{3}{4}j < 27$

36. $-0.8u \leq -0.64$

Name

LESSON MASTER 3-10 B

Questions on SPUR Objectives

Skills Objective D: Solve and check inequalities of the form $ax + b < c$.

1. Scott solved $-4x + 3 > 43$ and got a solution of $x > -10$. He thought it was right because he checked it like this:

Does $-4(-10) + 3 = 43$?

Yes; $-4(-10) + 3 = 40 + 3 = 43$.

Scott's solution is incorrect. Explain why his check did not point this out.

In 2–7, solve and check the inequality.

2. $4k + 8 > 52$

3. $-1 \geq 5e + 9$

4. $-5p + 16 < 11$

5. $-6 \leq -m + 4$

6. $18 + \frac{k}{8} < 21$

7. $3(4.1s + 10) \geq -43.8$

Uses Objective G: Apply models for addition to write and solve inequalities of the form $ax + b < c$.

In 8 and 9, write an inequality to describe the situation and solve the inequality to answer the question.

8. During an eight-hour day, Ms. Swenson earns \$95 plus 12% of the cost of the clothing she sells. What is the cost of the clothing she must sell if she wants to earn at least \$150?

_______________ inequality _______________ answer

9. Student Council has \$55 budgeted for service awards. They plan to buy a plaque for \$19 and spend the rest on service pins. How many service pins can they purchase if each one costs 75¢?

_______________ inequality _______________ answer

Representations Objective K: Use balance scales to represent sentences.

10. a. Write an inequality to describe the diagram at the right.

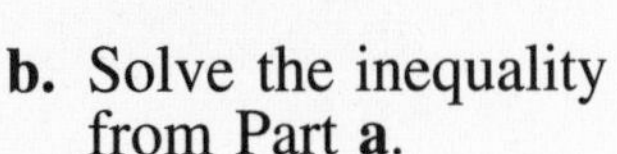

____

b. Solve the inequality from Part **a**.

____

Representations Objective L: Graph solutions to inequalities of the form $ax + b < c$ on a number line.

11. *Multiple choice.* Which of the graphs below shows the solutions of $-4d + 7 \geq -5$? _______________

(a) 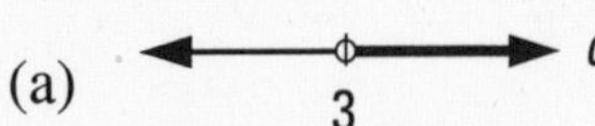

(b) 

(c) 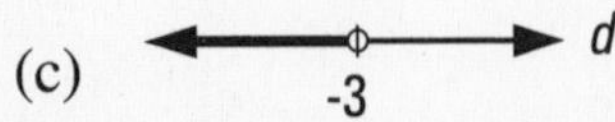

(d) 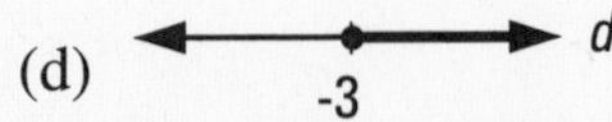

In 12–15, graph the solution to the inequality you solved in

12. Question 2.

13. Question 3.

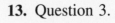

14. Question 6.

15. Question 7.

Name

LESSON MASTER

Questions on SPUR Objectives

Skills Objective A: Simplify expressions involving subtraction.

In 1–13, simplify the expression.

1. $4 - 13$

2. $-6 - 19$

3. $20 - -10$

4. $-7 - -15$

5. $-17 - -17$

6. $\frac{5}{6} - \frac{11}{12}$

7. $-8.3 - -9.44$

8. $10m - 4m + 3m$

9. $13u - u$

10. $p + 5 - 4p$

11. $-4d - 8e + -4 + 6d - -9e - 11$

12. $-\frac{9}{10}a - \frac{3}{5}a - \frac{1}{2}a$

13. $\frac{4r}{s} - \frac{7r}{s}$

14. Evaluate $h^2 - h$, when $h = -3$.

15. Evaluate $18 - g^2$, when $g = 5$.

16. Evaluate $-a - -b$, when $a = -10$ and $b = 6$.

17. Evaluate $100 - 200 + 300 - 400 + \ldots + 900 - 1{,}000$.

Name ______

18. Let E = the height of the Wicked Witch of the East and let W = the height of the Wicked Witch of the West. If $E - W < 0$, which Witch is taller? Explain how you know.

______

______

______

Properties Objective E: Apply the Algebraic Definition of Subtraction.

In 19–22, use the table below. It shows how a financial adviser records the weekly closing prices for shares of KDmetro stock. The numbers in the Change row show how the price compares to the price the previous week. Complete the table.

WEEK	1	2	3	4	5	6
CLOSING PRICE	144.25	142.50	145.375	145.875	143.00	144.375
CHANGE		-1.75	2.875	**19.** ?	**20.** ?	**21.** ?

19. ______ **20.** ______ **21.** ______

22. How could you find the change in price for Week 2

a. using subtraction? ______

b. using addition? ______

23. Write a calculator key sequence to find 44 − -19

a. by subtracting. ______

b. by adding. ______

In 24–29 rewrite each subtraction as an addition. Do not simplify.

24. $-8 + u - 14$ ______

25. $12 - 9y - 4y$ ______

26. $32 - -41$ ______

27. $5e - -e$ ______

28. $1 - 100$ ______

29. $-r - 7r + 2r - -4r^2$ ______

Name

LESSON MASTER

Questions on SPUR Objectives

Uses Objective H: Use the Take-Away and Comparison Models for Subtraction to write expressions and equations involving subtraction.

In 1–6, use the table below. Remember that a negative profit is a loss.

PROFITS FOR SMITH ENTERPRISES (IN MILLIONS OF DOLLARS)			
CLOTHING		**OTHER VENTURES**	
Women's Apparel	4.6	Sunglasses	-0.6
Men's Apparel	3.1	Toiletries	1.9
Children's Apparel	-1.5	Watches	-0.2
Shoes	0.8		

1. Which enterprise was the most profitable? __________

2. Which enterprise was the least profitable? __________

3. How much more did the most profitable enterprise earn than the least profitable did? __________

4. What was the range of earnings for the clothing enterprises? __________

5. What was the range of earnings for the other ventures? __________

6. What was the range of earnings for all seven enterprises? __________

7. Let C = the weight of Gloria's cat and D = the weight of Gloria's dog. The dog weighs more than the cat. Which difference is positive, $C - D$, or $D - C$? __________

8. Let K = Kyoto's age now. Write an expression for Kyoto's age

 a. 9 years ago. __________ b. 5 years from now. __________

In 9 and 10, write a subtraction expression for the length of the segment marked with a question mark (?).

9. 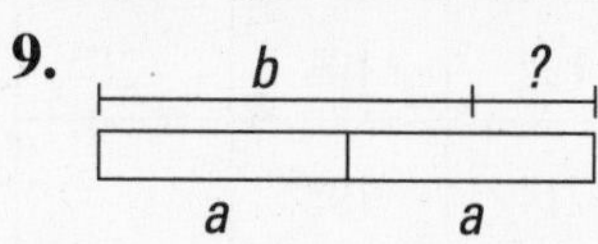

____

10. 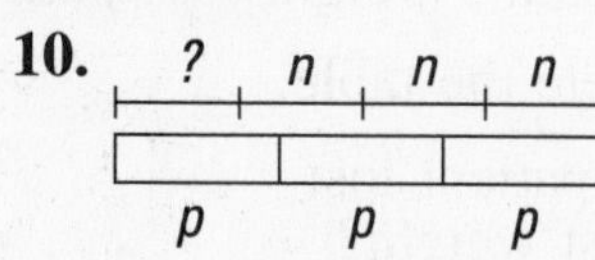

____

Name

▶ **LESSON MASTER 4-2 B** *page 2*

11. At the right are the attendance figures for Crestville's Pioneer Festival.

1991	3,043
1992	2,945
1993	2,760
1994	3,178

a. What was the change from 1992 to 1993?

b. What was the change from 1993 to 1994?

12. Each spring, Lurvelle's discounts all winter merchandise 40%.

a. If a winter coat was originally priced at \$256, what is the amount of discount?

b. What is the sale price of the coat in Part **a**?

c. If a winter jacket was originally priced at J dollars, what is the sale price of the jacket?

13. Let M = Meg's age. Sam's age is $M - 8$, and Lill's age is $M + 2$.

a. Arrange the three ages in order from least to greatest.

b. How much older is the oldest person than the youngest person? Explain how you determined the answer.

14. Point M is x units to the right of -16. N is 8 units to the left of 10.

-16 M N 10

a. Write an expression for the coordinate of M.

b. Find the coordinate of N.

15. At the right are the weights of four of Dr. Norton's weight-loss patients.

a. Complete the table.

b. Which patient lost the most weight?

Patient	Jan.	Oct.	Change
Morgan, S.	192	166	-26
Rojas, F.	214	195	
Ozu, D.	166		-11
Lake, M.		189	6

Name

LESSON MASTER **4-3 B**

Questions on SPUR Objectives

Skills Objective B: Solve and check linear equations involving subtraction.

In 1–9, solve and check each equation.

1. $5m - 12 = 38$

2. $-8g - 13 = 43$

3. $-50 = 6e - 44$

4. $84 - x = 27$

5. $-18.4 = -0.3y - -3.4$

6. $\frac{5}{6}u - -17 = 102$

7. $7(19h - 3) = 112$

8. $-3(a + 20) - 2a = 25$

9. $102 - 7d = 11$

Skills Objective C: Solve and check linear inequalities involving subtraction.

10. *Skill sequence.* Solve.

a. $8x - 40 = 360$ ________

b. $8x - 40 < 360$ ________

c. $8 - 40x = 360$ ________

d. $8 - 40x < 360$ ________

Name ____

▶ **LESSON MASTER 4-3 B** *page 2*

In 11–13, a. solve and b. graph each inequality.

11. $-5t - 37 > -77$ **a.** ________ **b.** ⟵――――――――⟶

12. $23 - p \leq -47$ **a.** ________ **b.** ⟵――――――――⟶

13. $-67 < 7g - 18$ **a.** ________ **b.** ⟵――――――――⟶

Uses Objective H: Use models for subtraction to write sentences involving subtraction.
Objective I: Solve problems using linear sentences involving subtraction.

In 14–18, write a subtraction sentence to describe the situation. Then solve the sentence to answer the question.

14. Mrs. Franco's initial investment of $3620 lost $12 per week. After x weeks, its value was $3464. How many weeks had elapsed?

________________ equation ________________ answer

15. When a certain number is multiplied by 15 and the product is subtracted from 18, the answer is -87. What is the number?

________________ equation ________________ answer

16. In the morning, there were 284 bottles of suntan lotion at Sunny's Beach Shop. By the end of the day, fewer than 3 dozen remained. How many bottles were sold?

________________ equation ________________ answer

17. Farmer's State Bank provides free travelers' checks to customers having at least $1000 in a savings account. Susan Chin wants to withdraw $1750 from her savings account for a trip. How much must be in her account in order for her to get free travelers' checks?

________________ equation ________________ answer

18. The SFM Corporation bought a 12,000-ft^2 piece of property for a new office building. The building is to occupy 4,800 ft^2. How much of the area will be landscaped if the area left for the parking lot is 3,500 ft^2?

________________ equation ________________ answer

Name ______________________________

LESSON MASTER

Questions on SPUR Objectives

Representations Objective K: Use a spreadsheet to show patterns and make tables from formulas.

In 1–4, use the spreadsheet below, which shows the enrollment figures at Eaglecrest High School.

	A	B	C
1	class	girls	boys
2	Freshmen	112	105
3	Sophomores	133	136
4	Juniors	120	124
5	Seniors	118	110
6			
7			

1. What is in cell B4? ______________

2. Which cell contains the number 136? ______________

3. Suppose the formula =B2+B3+B4+B5 is entered in cell B6.

   a. What value will appear in cell B6? ______________

   b. What quantity does this value represent?

   ____

4. What formula should be entered in cell C7 to find the average number of boys per class?

   ____

In 5–8, the Broadstreet Theater sells first-floor tickets for $35.00 each and balcony seats for $22.00. The spreadsheet below shows the ticket sales for last month's concerts.

	A	B	C	D
1	Concert	First-floor	Balcony	Ticket sales
2	Horton Quintet	418	277	20724.00
3	Red Magnets	533	245	24045.00
4	LaGrange Choir	404	183	18166.00
5	Dora Chalmers	351	216	17037.00
6	Sioux Dancers	430	238	
7	TOTAL	2136	1159	

5. What is the formula used in cell C7 to calculate the total number of tickets sold for balcony seats?

   ____

Name ______________________

6. a. What formula could be entered in cell D6 to find the total ticket sales for the Sioux Dancers' concert? ______________

b. What number will appear in cell D6? ______________

7. Give two different formulas that could be entered in cell D7 to give the total ticket sales for all five concerts.

______________ ______________

8. Suppose 200 balcony seats had been sold for the LaGrange Choir concert. Besides cell C4 changing to show 200, what other cells would show a different amount? ______________

In 9 and 10, use the spreadsheet below. Chad, who is treasurer of the Student Council uses the spreadsheet to keep track of the dance committee's funds. He has columns for how much they take in each month through ticket sales, donations, and bake sales, and also for what they spend during the month financing the dances.

	A	B	C	D	E	F	G
1	MONTH	START	TICKETS	DONATIONS	BAKE SALES	EXPENSES	BALANCE
2	J	110.38	214.00	25.00	40.75	181.66	208.47
3	F	208.47	190.00	40.00	22.11	208.16	252.42
4	M	252.47	154.00	0.00	15.16	244.05	177.58

9. What formula could Chad be using in cell G2 for the committee's balance at the end of the month. ______________

10. Chad decides to add a column to show how the end-of-the-month funds change from month to month.

a. If cell H3 has the formula =G3−G2, what number will appear? ______________

b. If cell H4 has the formula =G4−G3, what number will appear? ______________

c. Why do the answers to Parts **a** and **b** have different signs?

____

____

____

11. In a spreadsheet, suppose cell A6 contains the number 18 and cell C6 contains the number 25. If cell F6 contains the formula =(2*C6−A6)^2, what number will appear in cell F6? ______________

Name ____________________

LESSON MASTER  **Questions on SPUR Objectives**

Skills Objective D: Use the Opposite of a Sum or Difference Property to simplify expressions and solve equations.

1. *Multiple choice.* Which expression is *not* equal to $-(12x - 4)$? ______

(a) $-4(3x - 1)$ (b) $-12x - 4$

(c) $-12x + 4$ (d) $-12x - -4$

2. Teresa simplified $-3(9y - 5)$ and got $-27y - 15$.

a. Substitute 10 for y to show that Teresa did the problem incorrectly.

____

b. How do you think Teresa got the wrong answer?

____

In 3–16, simplify the expression.

3. $-(m + n)$ ______

4. $-(m - n)$ ______

5. $-(4e - 13)$ ______

6. $-(-4e + 13)$ ______

7. $-6(-3a + 15)$ ______

8. $-5(x - y + 7)$ ______

9. $13v - (3v + 10)$ ______

10. $(6s + 4) - (7s + 3)$ ______

11. $24 - (6r - 12)$ ______

12. $-(5.3x + 3) - (2y - 8.7)$ ______

13. $5b - (7b + 2) + (3b + 2)$ ______

14. $\frac{2x}{3} - \frac{7x + 1}{3}$ ______

15. $\frac{3m}{4} - \frac{3m - 3}{8}$ ______

16. $\frac{2u + 4}{5} - \frac{u - 9}{4} - \frac{1 - 5u}{2}$ ______

Name

In 17–22, solve the equation.

17. $-(j + 9) = 15$

18. $8 - (6x - 4) = -48$

19. $7h - (6 + 9h) = 8$

20. $-56 = -2(5w + 8) - (3w - 12)$

21. $9x - 6(-2x + 1) = -6$

22. $-3(y - 6) - (2y + 8) = 20$

Review Objective I, Lesson 3-3

23. The table below compares the first 10 days the municipal pool was open, showing the temperature at noon and the number of swimmers.

Day	Noon Temperature	Number of Swimmers
June 11	73	221
June 12	71	163
June 13	74	180
June 14	84	209
June 15	93	311
June 16	90	266
June 17	90	206
June 18	92	271
June 19	85	240
June 20	81	188

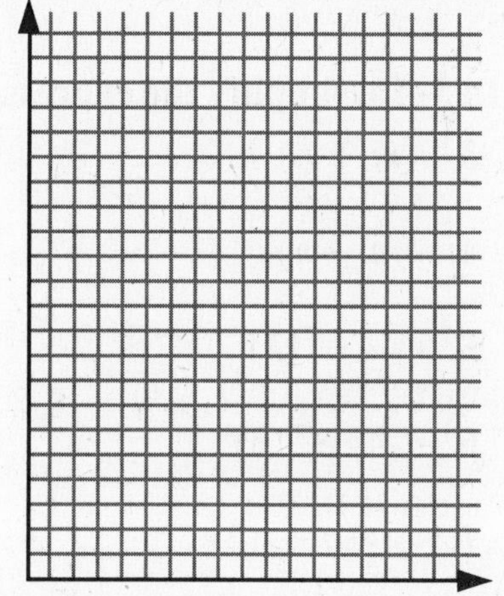

a. Graph the data on the grid, showing noon temperature on the horizontal axis and number of swimmers on the vertical axis.

b. Describe any trends you see. Are there any days that do not follow this trend? What factors might explain this?

Name

LESSON MASTER **4-6 B**

Questions on SPUR Objectives

Representations Objective L: Graph equations of the forms $x + y = k$ and $x - y = k$.

1. *Multiple choice.* Choose the equation that describes all four of the points in the graph at the right.

   (a) $x + y = -1$

   (b) $x + y = 1$

   (c) $x - y = -1$

   (d) $x - y = 1$

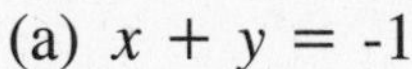

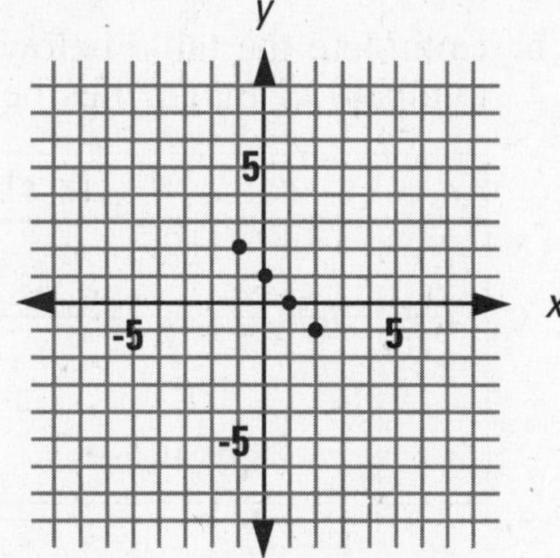

2. There are 3 more people in the Artrip family than in the Barrios family. Let a be the number of people in the Artrip family and let b be the number of people in the Barrios family.

   a. Which equation describes this, $b = a + 3$ or $b = a - 3$? ________

   b. Complete the table below with some possible numbers for sizes of the two families.

Size of Artrip family, *a*	Size of Barrios family, *b*	Ordered pair (*a*, *b*)
7		
8		
9		
10		

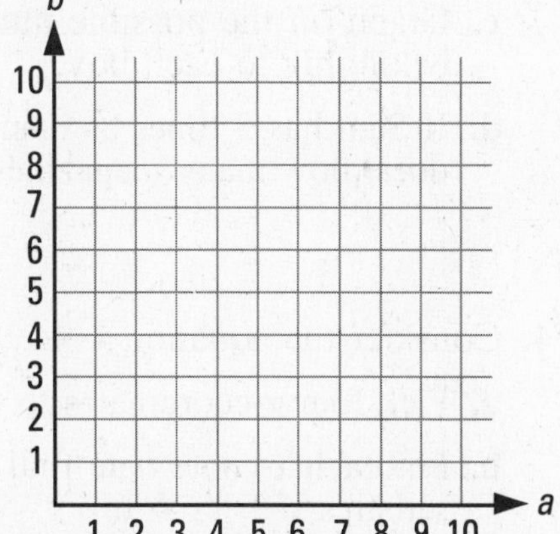

   c. Graph the possible numbers for the sizes of the two families.

   d. If together the two families have 13 members, how many people are in each family? ________

   e. Does the ordered pair (2, -1) satisfy the equation you chose in Part **a**? Can this ordered pair be used in the situation about the two families? Tell why or why not.

____

____

3. There are 12 magazines on a table. Ron owns r of them and Sam owns the rest of them s.

a. Write an equation to describe this situation. ____________

b. Complete the table below to show some of the possible numbers of magazines belonging to the two boys.

r	s	(r, s)
1		
2		
3		
4		
5		

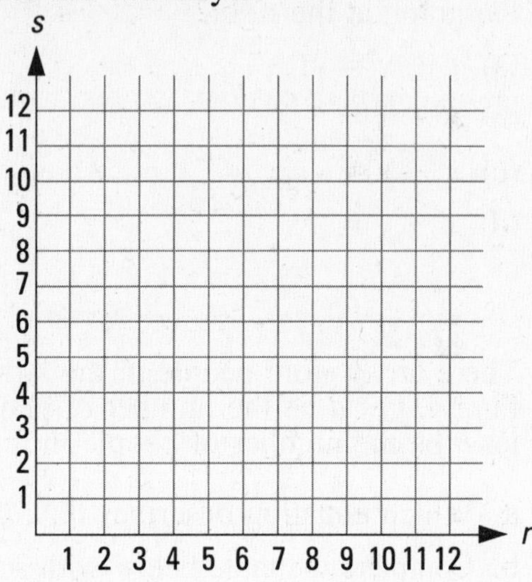

c. Graph *all* the possible numbers of magazines belonging to each boy.

d. If Sam has 3 times as many magazines as Ron does, how many magazines does each boy have?

____

4. Consider the equation $x + y = 6$.

a. Pick four x-coordinates to use in the table below.

b. For each x-coordinate find the y-coordinate that satisfies $x + y = 6$.

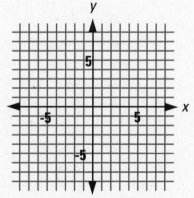

x	y	(x, y)

y
5
-5 5 x
-5

c. Graph *all* ordered pairs that satisfy the equation.

Name ______________________________

LESSON MASTER

Questions on SPUR Objectives

Vocabulary

1. Define *supplementary angles.*

____

____

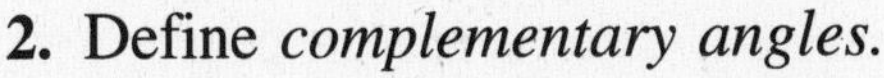

2. Define *complementary angles.*

____

____

Properties Objective F: Use the definitions of supplements and complements and the Triangle Sum Theorem.

3. Use a protractor.

 a. Find the measure of the angle at the right. ______

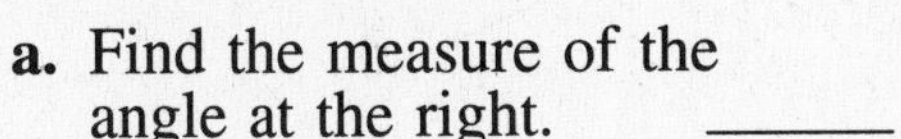

 b. Draw a complement of this angle. c. Draw a supplement of this angle.

In 4–7, the measure of an angle is given. Find the measure of a. a complement b. a supplement.

4. 24° **a.** ________ **b.** ______ 5. 45° **a.** ________ **b.** ________

6. 126° **a.** ________ **b.** ______ 7. $b°$ **a.** ________ **b.** ________

8. **a.** Write an equation relating the measures of the angles shown at the right.

 ____

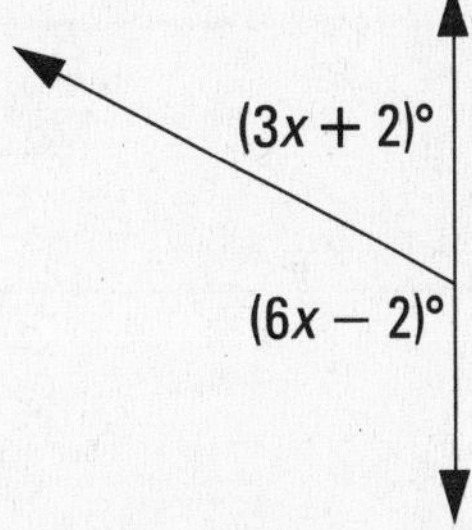

 b. Find the value of x. ________

 c. Find the measure of the smaller angle. ________

9. $\angle A$ and $\angle B$ are supplements. The measure of $\angle A$ is 10 more than 4 times the measure of $\angle B$. Write and solve an equation to find the measure of each angle.

______________________________ $m\angle A =$ ________ $m\angle B =$ ________
equation

Name ______________________________

► **LESSON MASTER 4-7 B** *page 2*

10. Write an expression to represent the measure of $\angle SUN$ in terms of p and q.

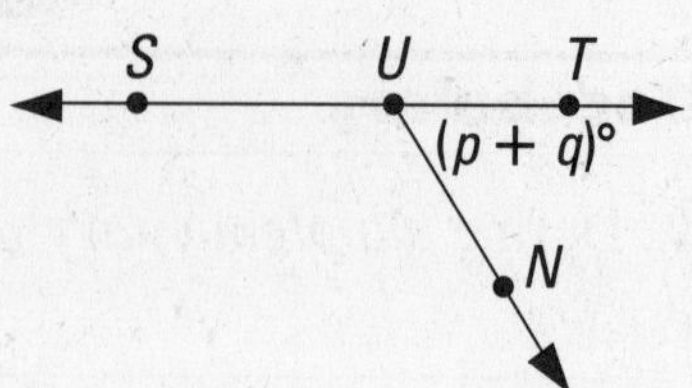

____

11. Use a protractor to draw a triangle with a 100° angle and a 35° angle. What is the measure of the third angle?

____

In 12–14, a. write an equation relating the angle measures.
b. Find the value of the variable.
c. Find the measures of any unknown angles.

12.

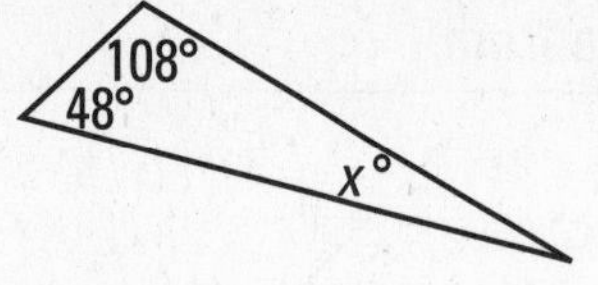

a. ______________________________

b. ______________________________

c. ______________________________

13.

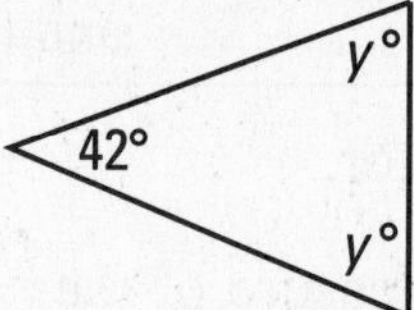

a. ______________________________

b. ______________________________

c. ______________________________

14.

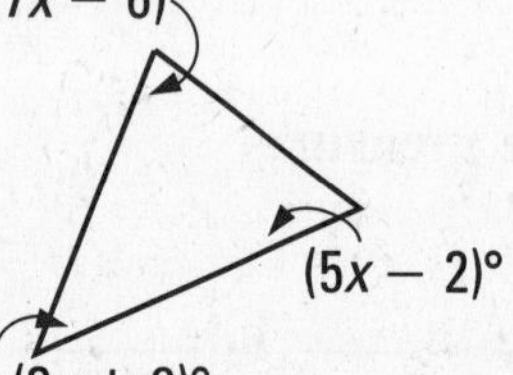

a. ______________________________

b. ______________________________

c. ______________________________

In 15 and 16, find the angle measures.

15.

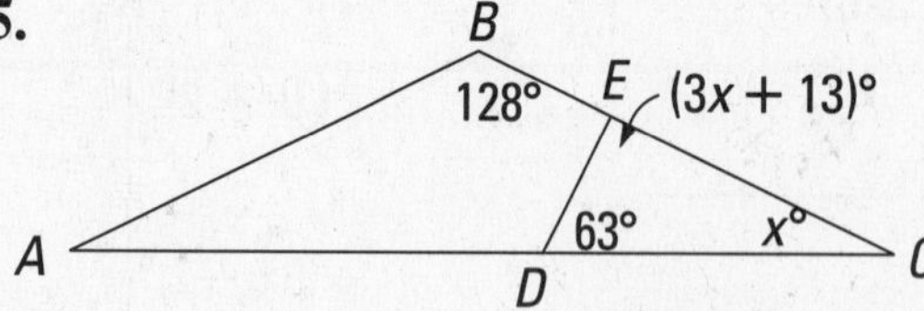

$m\angle CED =$ ______________________________

$m\angle BAC =$ ______________________________

16. *MNOP* is a square.

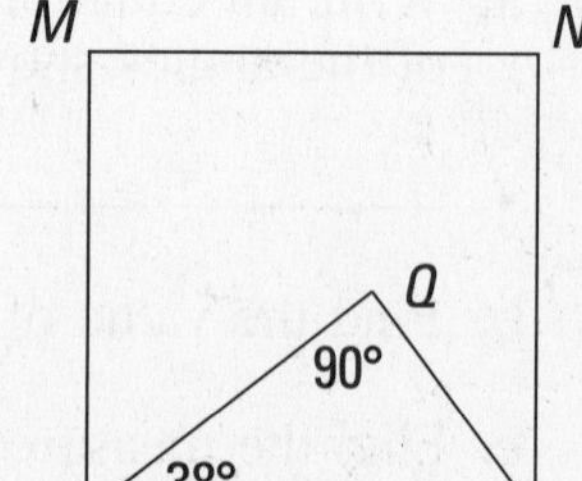

$m\angle POQ =$ ______________________________

$m\angle QON =$ ______________________________

Name ______________________________

LESSON MASTER

Questions on SPUR Objectives

Properties Objective G: Use the Triangle Inequality to determine possible lengths of sides of triangles.

In 1–3, write an expression for the length of $\overline{YZ}$ in terms of *a* and *b*.

1.

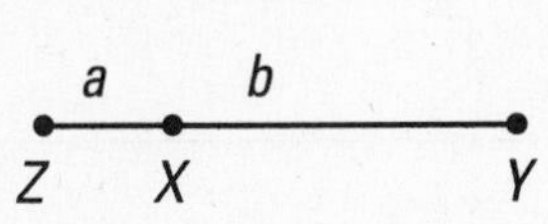

2.

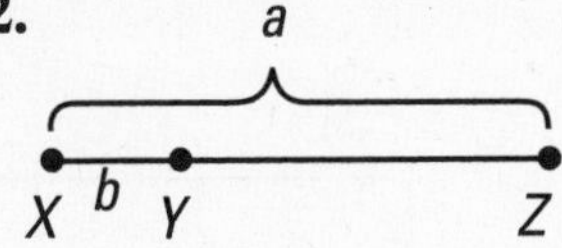

3.

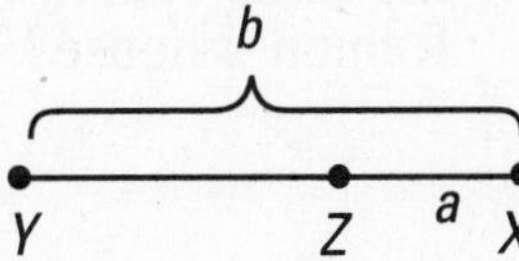

__________ __________ __________

4. Fill in the blanks.

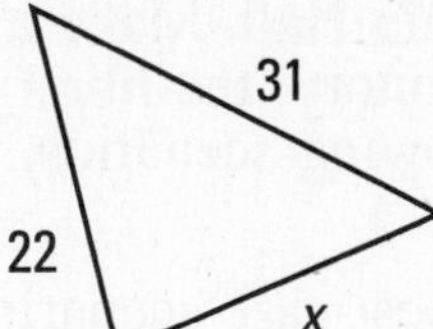

a. $x <$ __________

b. $x >$ __________

c. __________ $< x <$ __________

In 5–10, tell whether the three numbers can be the lengths of sides in a triangle.

5. 3, 7, 9 __________ **6.** 4, 6, 4 __________

7. 2, 10, 14 __________ **8.** 7, 17, 7 __________

9. 12, 1, 13 __________ **10.** 15, 3, 16 __________

11. In ΔBIG, $BG = 13.7$ and $IG = 30.4$. The length of BI must be between what two numbers? __________

12.

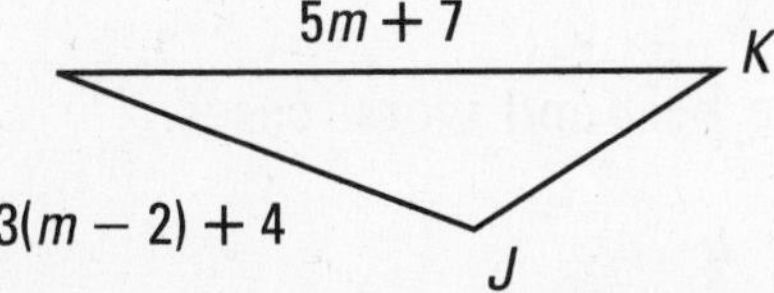

Fill in the blanks with simplified expressions.

__________ $< JK <$ __________

Uses Objective J: Apply the Triangle Inequality in real situations.

13. Southcrest is 25 miles from Franklin and 48 miles from Granville. Is it possible that Franklin is 76 miles from Granville? Explain why or why not.

____

____

____

In 14 and 15, assume there are direct paths between the buildings involved.

14. It takes Kirk 10 minutes to bike to Ramon's house and 22 minutes to bike to Matt's house. Assuming Matt bikes at the same speed, how long would it take for him to bike to Ramon's house?

15. Every morning Kate leaves her dormitory and walks to the library, then to Cragin Hall, and then back to the dormitory. The dormitory is 5 blocks from the library and 4 blocks from Cragin Hall. Make a sketch showing the locations of Kate's dormitory, the library, and Cragin Hall for each of the following scenarios.

a. Best-case scenario: Kate's trip is as short as possible.

b. Worst-case scenario: Kate's trip is as long as possible.

c. Kate's trip is somewhere between the best and worst cases.

Name

LESSON MASTER 4-9 B **Questions on SPUR Objectives**

Representations Objective L: Graph equations of the forms $y = ax + b$ and $y = ax - b$ by making a table of values.

In 1–3, use the following information: At an all-you-can-eat buffet, the Pasta Emporium charges children under twelve $2 plus $0.50 for each year of age.

1. a. Complete the table showing the age of the child a and the cost of the child's meal c.

Age a	Cost c	(a, c)
0		
1		
2		
3		
4		
5		

b. Graph the ordered pairs (a, c).

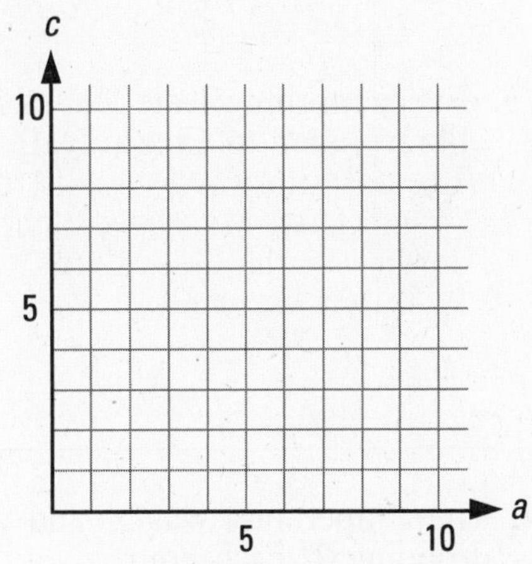

c. Write an equation that represents c in terms of a. ____________

d. What would be a suitable domain for this graph? ____________

In 2 and 3, use this information: Pasta Emporium decides to charge more for children. For each plan given below, complete the table, make a graph, and write an equation. Then describe how the graph is different from the first graph.

2. Plan A: Raise the basic charge to $3, but continue to charge $0.50 per year.

Age a	Cost c	(a, c)
0		
1		
2		
3		
4		
5		

c
10
5
a
5
10

equation: ____________

____

Name ______________________________

▶ LESSON MASTER 4-9 B *page 2*

3. Plan B: Keep the basic charge at \$2, but charge \$0.75 per year.

Age a	Cost c	(a, c)
0		
1		
2		
3		
4		
5		

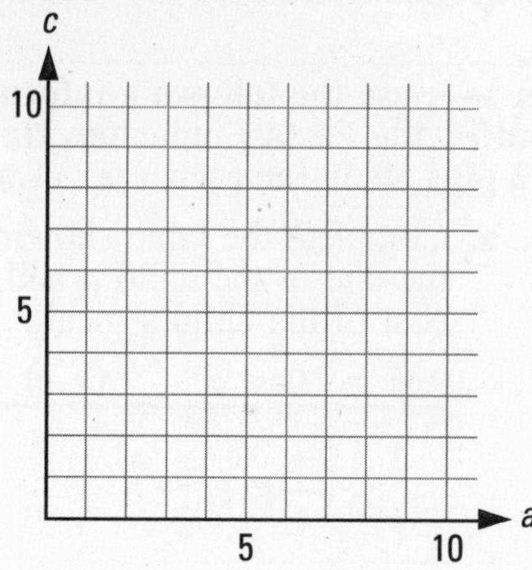

equation: ______________________

4. The temperature was 5° and was dropping 2° each hour.

a. Complete the table.

Hours h	Temperature c
0	
1	
2	
3	

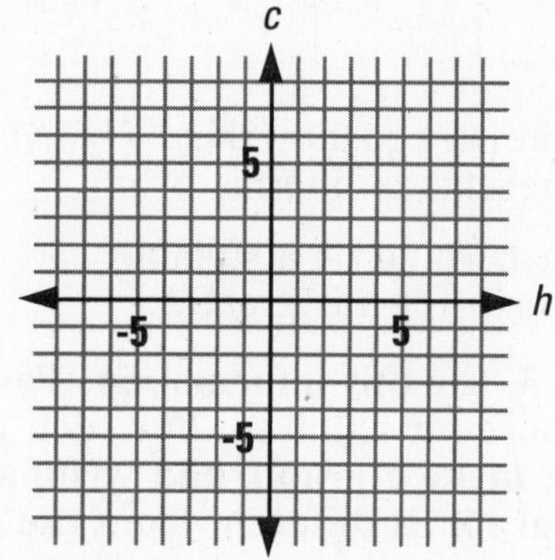

b. Draw the graph.

c. Write an equation to describe the temperature in terms of hours that have passed. ______________________

5. Consider the equation $y = -3x + 4$.

a. Make a table of values.

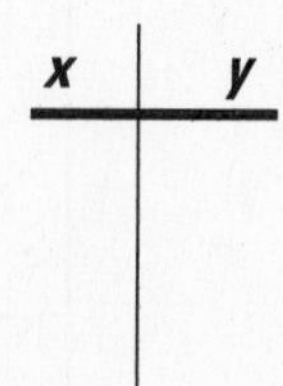

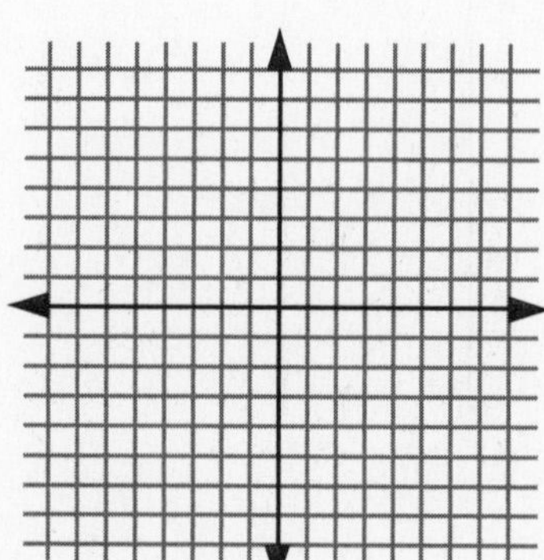

b. Draw the graph.

Name

LESSON MASTER

Questions on SPUR Objectives

Representations Objective H: Graph horizontal and vertical lines.

In 1–3, an equation is given. a. Give the coordinates of three points that satisfy the equation. b. Graph the equation.

1. $x = -2$ **2.** $y = 1$ **3.** $y = -3.5$

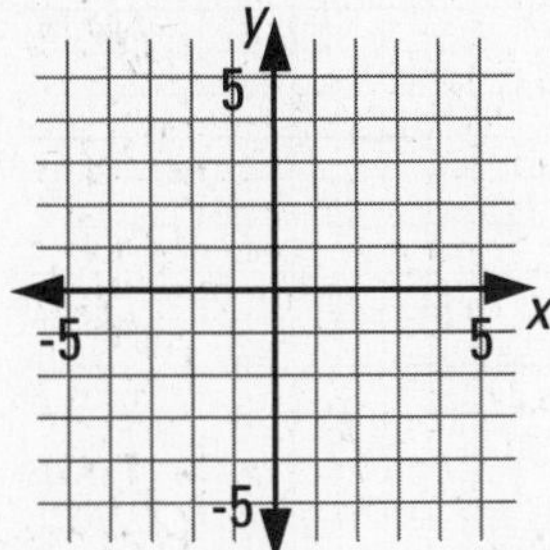

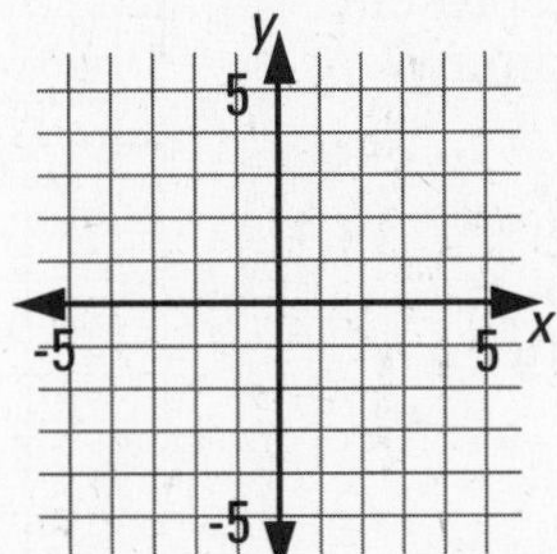

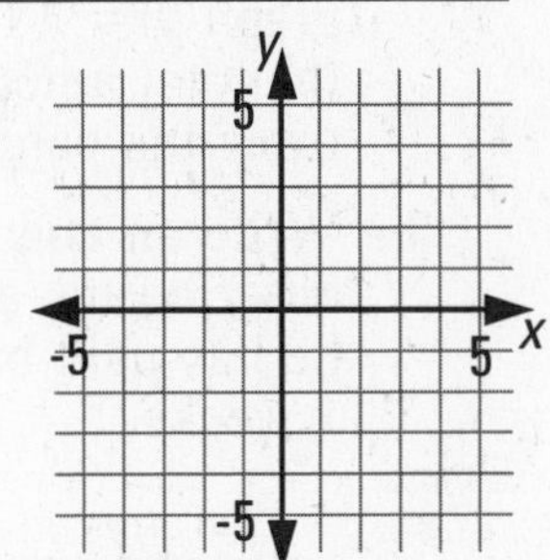

In 4–6, graph the given line and the point (-1, 4). Tell where (-1, 4) lies in relation to the line: *on*, *above*, *below*, *to the left*, or *to the right*.

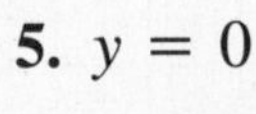

4. $y = 4$ ________ **5.** $y = 0$ ________ **6.** $x = 4$ ________

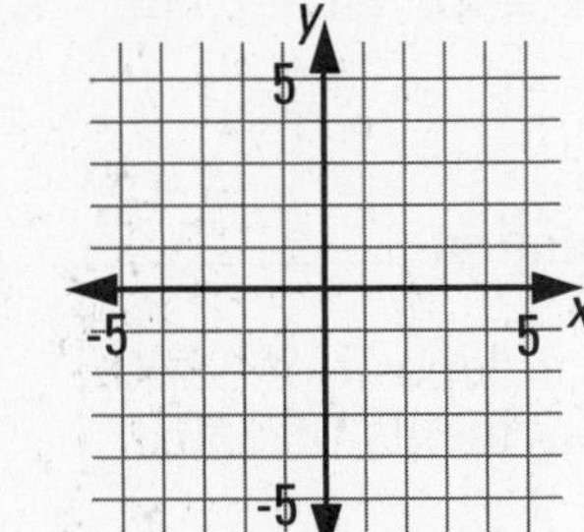

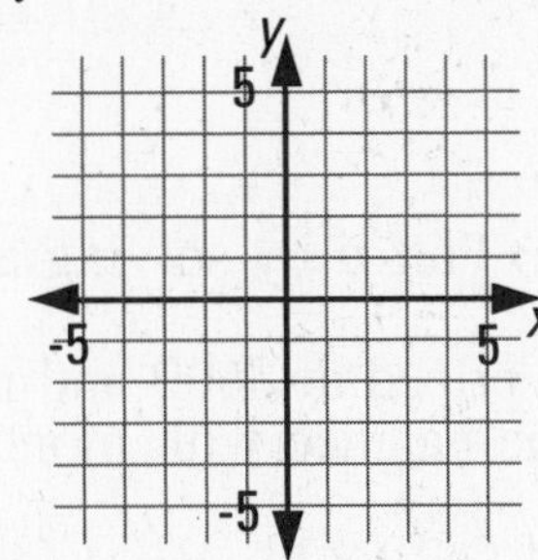

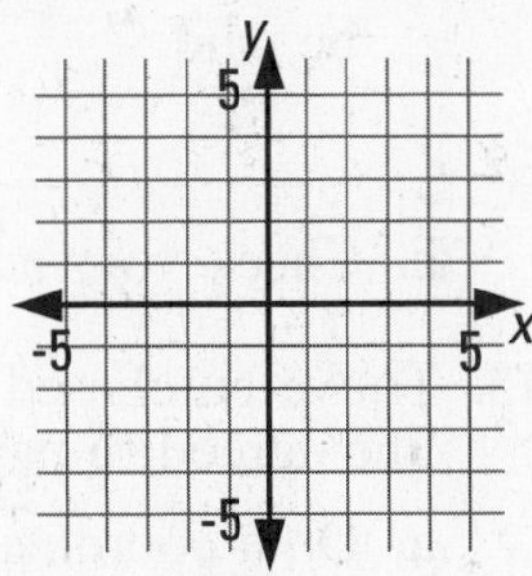

In 7–11, give an equation for the line shown or described.

7.

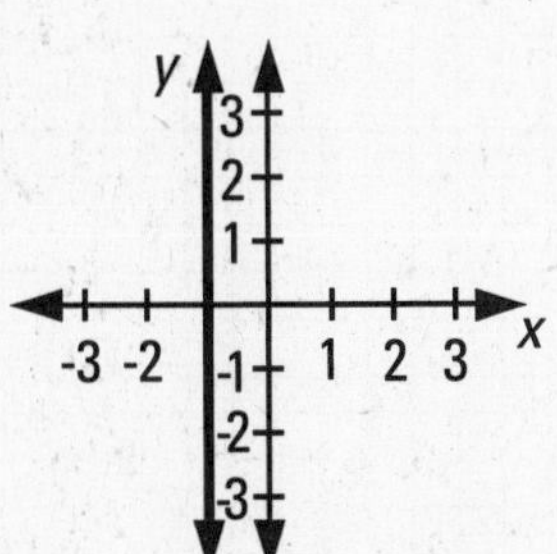

8.

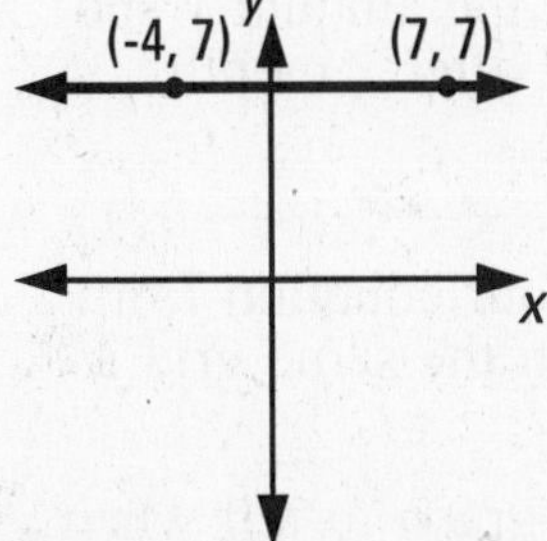

9. the horizontal line through (-6, 8) ________

Name

10. the vertical line through (0, 4) __________

11. the line through (3, 3), (3, -4.1) and (3, 0) __________

Representations Objective I: Use graphs to solve problems involving linear equations.

12. Tommy owes his parents \$140. He gave them \$36 and promised to pay back another \$8 each week.

a. On a coordinate grid, graph $y = 140$ to represent the total amount Tommy owes his parents.

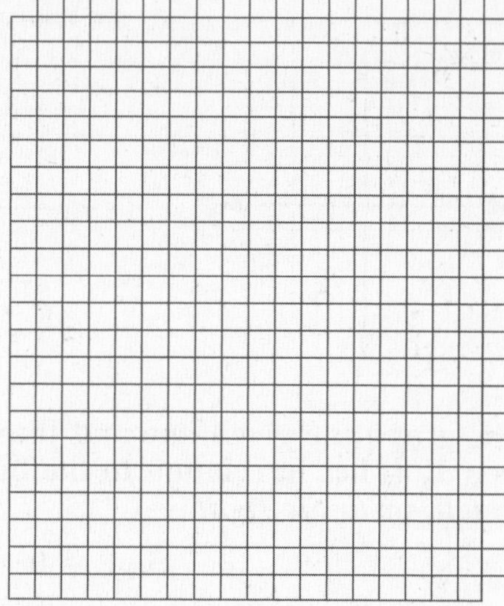

b. Write an equation to describe the amount y he has paid back after x weeks.

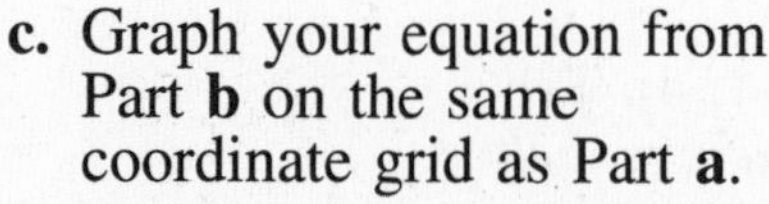

c. Graph your equation from Part **b** on the same coordinate grid as Part **a**.

d. Use the graph to estimate when Tommy's debt will be paid.

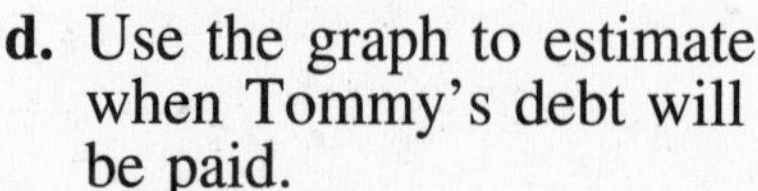

e. Check your answer to Part **d** by solving an equation. __________

13. Tonya purchased a sofa priced at \$600 and made a deposit of \$300. She agreed to pay off the balance with monthly payments of \$50.

a. On a coordinate grid, graph $y = 600$ to represent the total cost of the sofa.

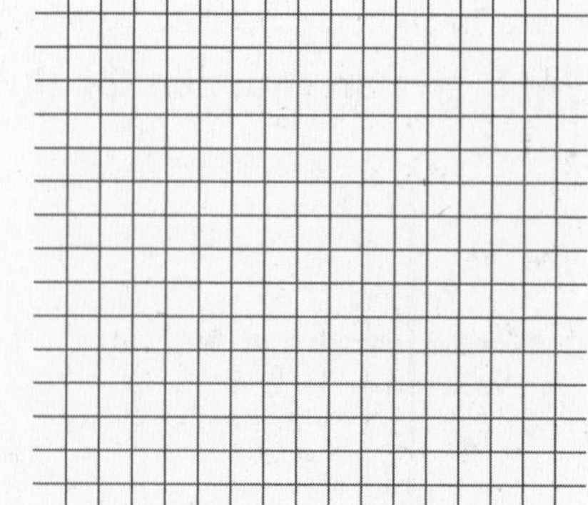

b. Write an equation to describe the amount y she has paid after x months.

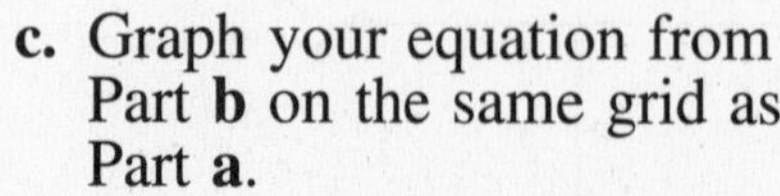

c. Graph your equation from Part **b** on the same grid as Part **a**.

d. Use the graph to tell when Tonya will have completed her payments.

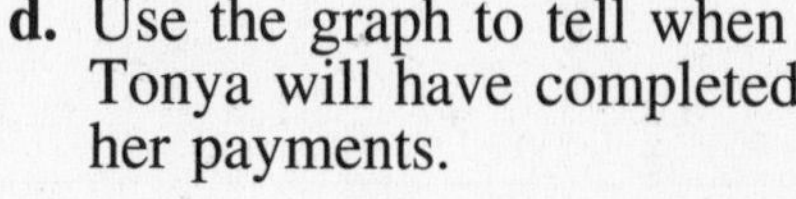

e. Check your answer to Part **d** by solving an equation. __________

Name

LESSON MASTER

Questions on SPUR Objectives

Representations Objective G: Use tables or spreadsheets to solve real-world problems involving linear situations.

1. At the Children's Museum, children can watch chicks and ducks hatch. Today there are 40 baby chicks and 25 ducks. Each day, 4 chicks and 7 ducks are expected to hatch.

a. Complete the table below.

DAY	CHICKS	DUCKS
0	40	25
1		
2		
3		
4		
5		
6		

b. At the end of 6 days, will there be more chicks or ducks? ____________

c. Write an equation for the number of chicks C in terms of the day d. ____________

d. Write an equation for the number of ducks D in terms of the day d. ____________

e. What equation could be used to find when there will be an equal number of chicks and ducks? ____________

2. Marta uses a spreadsheet (shown on the next page) to compare the salaries between two companies that have offered her a job. The O'Connell Company offers $29,000 the first year with annual raises of $900. Tri-Tech, Inc. pays $27,800 the first year and gives annual raises of $1,200. The cells of the spreadsheet contain yearly salaries.

a. What formula could be used in cell B3? ____________

b. What formula could be used in cell C3? ____________

c. Complete the spreadsheet.

Name

	A	B	C
1	YEAR	O'CONNELL	TRI-TECH
2	1	29,000	27,800
3	2		
4	3		
5	4		
6	5		
7	6		

d. Describe how the two jobs compare over a six-year period.

3. Over the years, the O'Connell Company has been switching from typewriters to computers. At one time the company had 815 typewriters which were wearing out at a rate of about 60 per year. At the same time, they had 500 computers and were adding 75 per year. Assume that the company continues buying computers and eliminating typewriters at the same rate.

a. Write an expression for the number of typewriters after y years.

b. Write an expression for the number of computers after y years.

c. Make a table and use it to find the number of years it takes for O'Connell to have an equal number of typewriters and computers.

d. Write an inequality of the form $y < k$ or $y > k$ to describe when there are more computers than typewriters.

Name

LESSON MASTER

Questions on SPUR Objectives

Skills Objective A: Solve linear equations of the form $ax + b = cx + d$.

1. a. Write the equation that is represented by this drawing.

____

b. Solve the equation to find the weight w of one box.

____

In 2–7, solve the equation and check the result.

2. $m + 12 = 2m + 77$

3. $7w = 2w + 45$

4. $5g + .6 = -3g - 4.4$

5. $\frac{1}{6}m + 33 = 5 - m$

6. $7(8h - 3) + 2h = 72 - 4h$

7. $-3(a + 14) = 6(2a + 3)$

Name ____

Properties Objective E: Apply and recognize properties associated with linear equations.

In 8 and 9, tell what should be done to both sides of the equation first in order to solve.

8. $10u + 16 = 5 - 5u$

____

9. $7x + 18 = 20x$

____

10. Fill in each blank with a number or operation to explain the steps in the solution shown below. Then complete the solution and check your result.

$1.6n + 4.2 = 0.7n + 6.9$ Add ________ to each side.

$0.9n + 4.2 = 6.9$ Add ________ to each side.

$0.9n = 2.7$ ________ each side by ________.

Uses Objective F: Use linear equations of the form $ax + b = cx + d$ to solve real-world problems.

11. A mountain climber is injured. His partner radios for help, then the two begin to descend from the 12,500-foot mountain at a speed of about 200 feet per hour. The rescue team starts at an altitude of 6,500 feet and climbs 1,000 feet per hour.

a. Write an equation to show that the rescuers meet the climbers after *h* hours. (In other words, their altitudes are the same.) ____________________

b. How long does it take the rescuers to reach the climbers? ____________________

c. At what height will they meet? ____________________

12. Raul and Tom both wish to wrestle at the same weight. Raul, who weighs 148 pounds, plans to gain a pound a week. Tom who weighs 166 pounds, plans to lose two pounds a week.

a. Write an equation to tell when the boys will have reached the same weight. ____________________

b. How long will it take the boys to reach the same weight? ____________________

c. At what common weight will the boys wrestle? ____________________

Name

LESSON MASTER

Questions on SPUR Objectives

Uses Objective F: Use linear equations of the form $ax + b = cx + d$ to solve real-world problems.

Representations Objective I: Use graphs to solve problems involving linear expressions.

1. The graph below shows the price of buying a vase of roses at two florists. Each shop charges a certain amount for a vase and then adds an additional charge per rose.

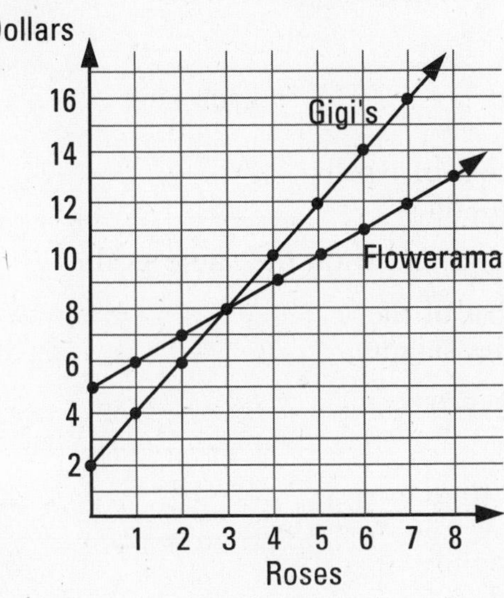

a. How much does an empty vase cost at Gigi's Flowers?

____

b. Brad wants to send his fiancée a half-dozen roses. Which shop would have a lower price? How much lower?

____

c. For how many roses do the two shops charge the same amount?

____

d. For how many roses is Flowerama more expensive?

____

2. The graph below shows the estimated enrollment of two universities t years from now.

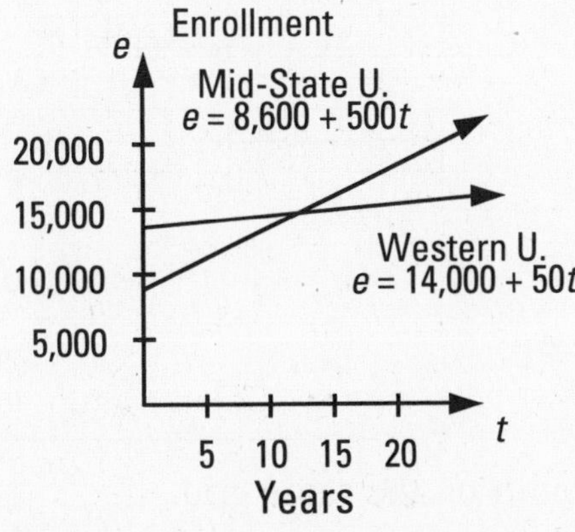

a. Use an equation to find in how many years the estimated enrollments will be equal. Use the graph to check your answer.

____

____

b. When is Mid-State's estimated enrollment less than Western's?

____

c. When is Mid-State's estimated enrollment greater than Western's?

____

Name

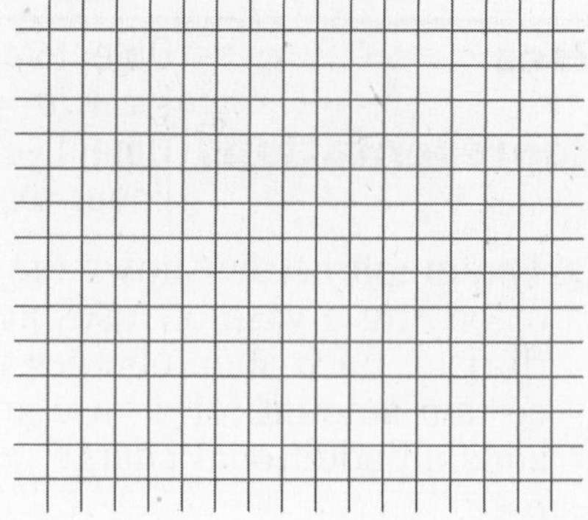

3. Downtown Deli normally charges 55¢ for an onion roll. But they also offer the rolls at 15¢ each with the purchase of a pound of salami at $4.80.

Let r = the number of rolls purchased and c = cost.

a. Write an equation describing the cost of r rolls at the regular price.

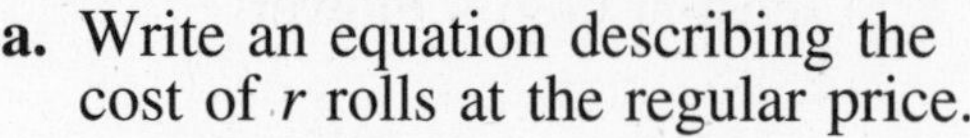

b. Write an equation describing the cost of r rolls with the purchase of a pound of salami. ______________

c. Graph the two equations from Parts **a** and **b** on the same grid.

d. Use your graph to tell when the cost of the rolls is the same with or without the salami. ______________

e. What equation could be used to answer the question in Part **d**? ______________

f. Lucas needs 15 rolls. Is it cheaper to get the salami also? ______________

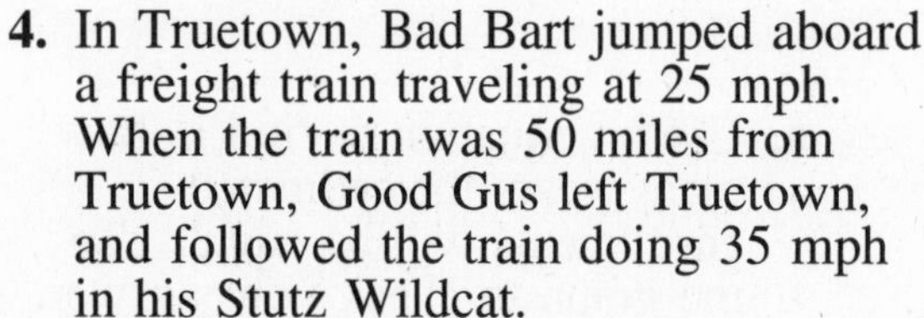

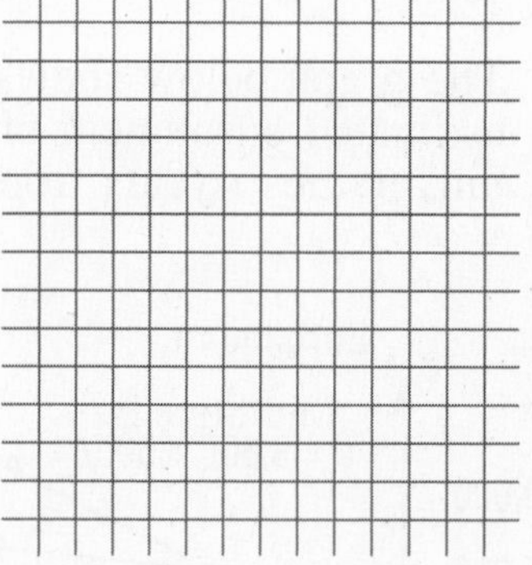

4. In Truetown, Bad Bart jumped aboard a freight train traveling at 25 mph. When the train was 50 miles from Truetown, Good Gus left Truetown, and followed the train doing 35 mph in his Stutz Wildcat.

Let r = the speed in mph and t = the time in hours.

a. Write an equation describing Good Gus's distance from Truetown t hours after starting out.

____

b. Write an equation describing the distance of the train from Truetown t hours after Good Gus started out. ______________

c. Graph the two equations from Parts **a** and **b** on the same grid.

d. Use your graph to tell when Good Gus will catch up to the train. Then write and solve an equation to verify your answer.

______________	______________	______________
answer in graph	equation	solution

Name

LESSON MASTER

Questions on SPUR Objectives

Representations Objective L: Given an equation, be able to use an automatic grapher to draw and interpret a graph.

In 1–3, use the window at the right.

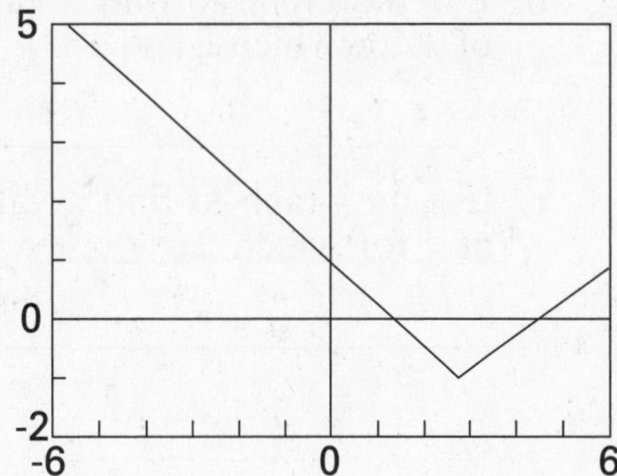

1. Write two inequalities to describe this window.

2. As you move from $x = -5$ to $x = 1$ on the graph, what happens to the height of the graph?

3. What are the coordinates of the point where the graph crosses the y-axis?

4. What are the coordinates of the lowest point on the graph?

5. Describe a window that would show the lowest point in the center of the graph.

In 6–7, graph $y = x^2 - 4x - 12$ on an automatic grapher, using the given window. Sketch the graph, being sure to show the limits of the window and the axes, if they appear.

6. window: $-5 \le x \le 5$
$-5 \le y \le 5$

7. window: $-10 \le x \le 10$
$-20 \le y \le 40$

Name ______________________________

► **LESSON MASTER 5-5 B** *page 2*

8. a. Use the window $-10 \le x \le 10$, $-10 \le y \le 10$, and graph the two equations $y = 2x$ and $y = x^2$. Sketch the graph.

b. Use the graph to find a value of x for which $2x \neq x^2$.

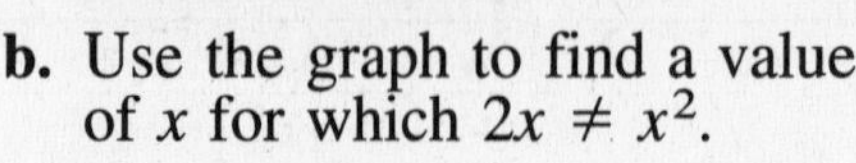

____

c. Use the graph to find a value of x for which $2x = x^2$

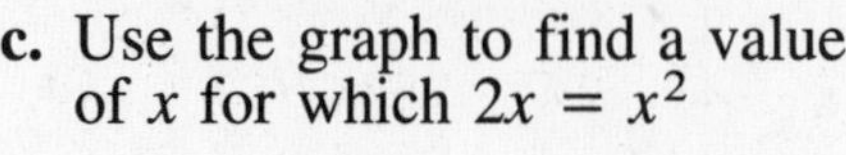

____

9. a. Use the window $-15 \le x \le 15$, $-10 \le y \le 10$, and graph the two equations $y = 5 - x$ and $y = x - 5$. Sketch the graphs.

b. Use the graph to find a value of x for which $x - 5 \neq 5 - x$.

____

c. Use the graph to find a value of x for which $x - 5 = 5 - x$.

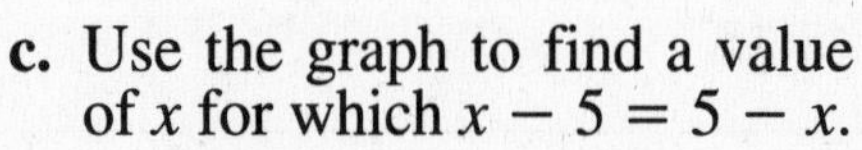

____

10. Use an automatic grapher to graph the two equations $y = -6x + 31$ and $y = .3x - 80$ on the same window of $-100 \le x \le 100$, $-100 \le y \le 100$.

a. Use the trace and zoom features to estimate the value of x for which $-6x + 31 = .3x - 80$. ______________________

b. For what values of x is $-6x + 31 < .3x - 80$? ______________________

Name ______________________

Questions on SPUR Objectives

Skills Objective B: Solve linear inequalities of the form $ax + b < cx + d$.

1. Write an inequality to find the values of x that make $12x + 14$ less than $20x - 8$. ______________

In 2–5, solve and check.

2. $5a + 7 < 2a + 13$

3. $6x > 11x + 35$

4. $6m + 8 + 2m \geq 4(3m + 2)$

5. $-1.6e - 8 < 2.2e + 30$

In 6 and 7, solve the inequality and graph all solutions on a number line.

6. $u + 19 \leq 3u - 1$

7. $45 - 7b < 30 - 10b$

Properties Objective E: Apply and recognize properties associated with linear inequalities.

8. Solve for $6x - 10 > 18 - 2x$ as directed. Show your work.

   a. Add $-6x$ to both sides.

   b. Add $2x$ to both sides.

9. Which solution method above do you prefer, and why?

____

____

Uses Objective F: Use linear inequalities of the form $ax + b < cx + d$ to solve real-world problems.

10. To ship an order weighing 10 pounds or less, McGann's charges \$4 plus 90¢ per pound of merchandise. Northern Traders charges \$6 plus 50¢ per pound.

a. For what size order will the two shipping charges be the same?

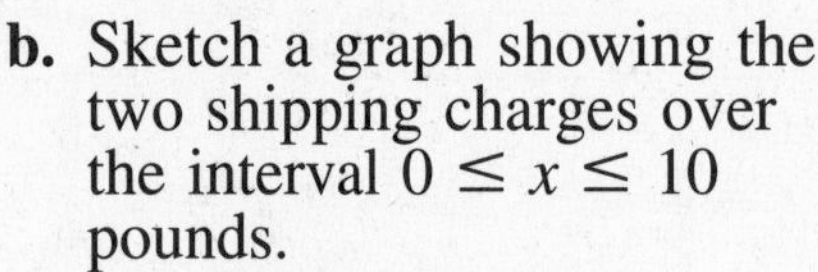

b. Sketch a graph showing the two shipping charges over the interval $0 \le x \le 10$ pounds.

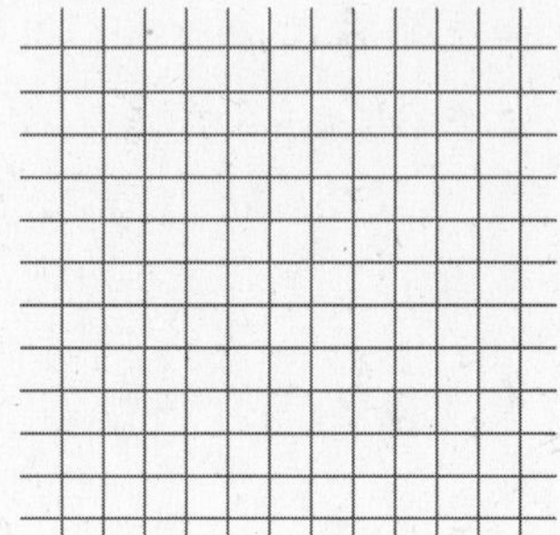

c. For what weight of merchandise does McGann's charge less?

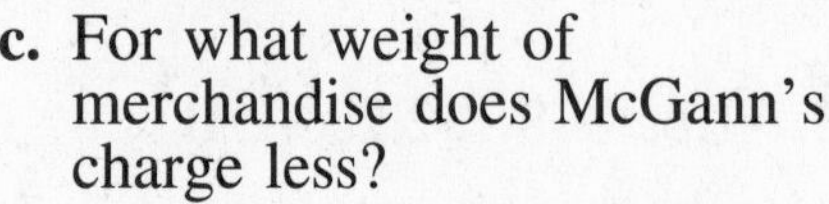

11. For a long-distance call, Dash charges 20¢ for the first minute plus 15¢ for each additional minute. AB&C charges 26¢ for the first minute plus 13¢ for each additional minute.

a. For what length of time will the two companies charge the same amount for a long-distance call?

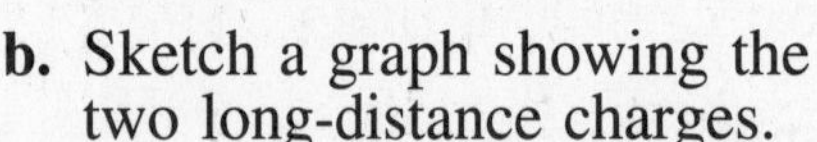

b. Sketch a graph showing the two long-distance charges.

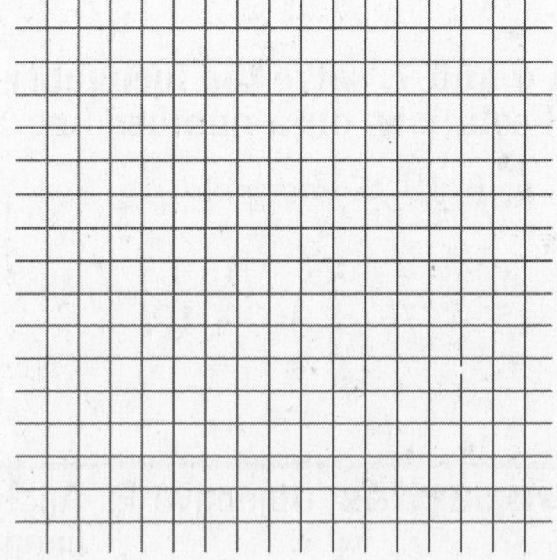

c. For what lengths of time does AB&C charge less?

Name

LESSON MASTER 5-7 B

Questions on SPUR Objectives

Skills Objective D: Find equivalent forms of formulas and equations.

In 1–10, solve the formula for the given variable.

1. $C = K - 273$ for K

2. $d = 7w$ for w

3. $p = 2a + b + c$ for a

4. $C = \pi d$ for d

5. $p = 2(\ell + w)$ for w

6. $V = \frac{1}{3}Bh$ for B

7. $F + V = E + 2$ for E

8. $I = prt$ for p

9. $s = \frac{n}{2}(f + \ell)$ for f

10. $S = (n - 2)180$ for n

11. The formula $C = p\left(\frac{\ell w}{5000}\right)$ gives the cost C of fertilizing a lawn with length ℓ ft and width w ft, where p = price per bag of fertilizer. Solve $C = p\left(\frac{\ell w}{5000}\right)$ for w. ____________

In 12–17, solve the equation for *y*.

12. $9x + y = 15$

13. $8 = x - y$

14. $12 = 6x - 3y$

15. $-5x + 2y = 7$

Properties Objective E: Apply and recognize properties associated with linear sentences.

16. Tech Tasks puts a customer's snapshot prints onto CDs for use with CD-Rom. The formula $C = 2.5p + 14$ relates the cost in dollars C to the number of prints p.

a. Find the cost for 29 prints. ______________

b. Solve $C = 2.5p + 14$ for p. ______________

c. Use your answer to find the number of prints in an order that cost $59. ______________

17. Fill in the blanks to explain the steps taken to solve $T = .15(C - S)$ for C.

$T = .15(C - S)$

$T = .15C - .15S$ ______________ Property

$T + .15S = .15C$ ______________ to each side.

$\frac{T}{.15} + S = C$ ______________ each side by ____.

Review Objective A, Lesson 3-7

In 18–23, write the expression without parentheses.

18. $12\left(\frac{7x}{12} + \frac{9x}{4}\right)$ ______________

19. $-18\left(\frac{4u}{9} + \frac{11u}{6}\right)$ ______________

20. $-8\left(\frac{5e}{3} + -\frac{3e}{8}\right)$ ______________

21. $5\left(v + \frac{v}{5}\right)$ ______________

22. $100(.3c + .15c + .05c)$ ______________

23. $.5(8m + 12m + 10m)$ ______________

Name

LESSON MASTER 5-8 B

Questions on SPUR Objectives

Skills Objective A: Clear fractions or multiply through by a fraction to solve linear equations of the form $ax + b = cx + d$.

In 1–6, solve the equation.

1. $\frac{3a}{4} + 4 = 13$

2. $\frac{4}{5}h + \frac{1}{6} = \frac{11}{30}$

3. $\frac{5x}{4} - 8 = 3 + \frac{3x}{4}$

4. $\frac{1}{9}x + \frac{5}{6} = \frac{1}{2}x - \frac{1}{3}$

5. $6m - .3 = 2.8m + 2.9$

6. $.5(2x + 7) = .2x - 2.1$

Skills Objective A: Clear fractions or multiply through by a fraction to solve linear inequalities of the form $ax + b < cx + d$.

In 7–12, solve the inequality.

7. $\frac{7b}{8} + 4 \le 3b - \frac{1}{4}$

8. $4 - \frac{w}{3} < w$

9. $\frac{a}{2} + \frac{a}{5} - \frac{3}{10} > \frac{4a}{5} + \frac{1}{4}$

10. $400n + 600 \ge 1500 - 200n$

11. $1.3a + 1 < 2 - .7a$

12. $55y + 44 > 22y + 66$

Properties Objective E: Apply and recognize properties associated with linear sentences.

In 13 and 14, write the equation or inequality that results from multiplying through by the given number.

13. $\frac{11}{12}u + \frac{1}{4} = 8$ Multiply both sides by 12. ______________

14. $1.66 - 3.8r > .92 + .95r$ Multiply both sides by 100. ______________

Name ______

15. Consider the equation $\frac{x}{3} + \frac{5}{6} = \frac{5}{2}$.

a. Multiplying through by 6 is an application of which property?

______

b. Give two other numbers by which you could multiply through.

______ ______

16. Tell what to multiply each side by to solve more easily.

a. $12{,}000e + 16{,}000 = 19{,}000e - 3{,}000$ ______

b. $1.6 - .5u \leq 2.2$ ______

c. $\frac{1}{5}(12y + 7) > \frac{3y}{4}$ ______

Uses Objective F: Use linear equations of the form $ax + b = cx + d$ and linear inequalities of the form $ax + b < cx + d$ to solve real-world problems.

17. For an upcoming election, $\frac{1}{4}$ of the registered voters support Candidate A, $\frac{2}{5}$ support Candidate B, and the rest, 7,700, are undecided.

a. Write an equation to find the number of registered voters. ______

b. How many registered voters are there? ______

c. Check your answer to Part **b** by finding the number of registered voters who support each candidate.

______

18. In Adeline County, 22% of the elementary-school children attend Jackson School, 18% attend Traynor School, and 240 students attend Claridge School. The students at these three schools make up more than 50% of the county's elementary-school children.

a. Write an inequality to describe this situation. ______

b. How many elementary-school children live in Adeline County? ______

c. How many children attend the other schools in Adeline County? ______

Name ______________________

LESSON MASTER 5-9 B

Questions on SPUR Objectives

Skills Objective C: Use chunking to simplify or evaluate expressions and to solve equations.

1. If $6x = 5$, find the value of

   a. $12x$. ________ b. $60x$. ________ c. $3x$. ________

2. If $2c = 3.3$, find the value of $10c + 2$. ________

3. If $25y + 4 = 817$, find the value of $25y + 5$. ________

4. If $.77p - .3 = 21.9$, find the value of $10(.77p - .3)$. ________

5. If $3n = 8$, find the value of $(3n)^2$. ________

6. If $5c + 4 = 19$, find the value of $25c + 20$. ________

7. If $12t - 4a = 16$, find the value of $3t - a$. ________

8. If $2s = 3$, find the value of $(2s)^3 + 8$. ________

In 9–20, use chunking to simplify.

9. $3(2a + 7) + 6(2a + 7)$ ________

10. $7(r + 6) - 10(r + 6)$ ________

11. $-2(x^2 + 1) + 4(x^2 + 1) - 8(x^2 + 1)$ ________

12. $9\sqrt{6} + 3\sqrt{6} - \sqrt{6} - 4\sqrt{6}$ ________

13. $\frac{2}{7m - 4} + \frac{5}{7m - 4}$ ________

14. $\frac{-8}{5abc} + \frac{4}{5abc}$ ________

15. $\frac{8}{12d - 1} - \frac{11}{12d - 1} + \frac{5}{12d - 1}$ ________

16. $\frac{6u + 1}{d - 2} + \frac{2u}{d - 2} - \frac{5u + 3}{d - 2}$ ________

17. $\frac{e + 9}{8} \cdot \frac{5}{e + 9}$ ________

18. $\frac{x^2 + 7}{3} \cdot \frac{9}{x^2 + 7}$ ________

19. $\frac{4}{3(b - 5)} \cdot \frac{5(b - 5)}{9}$ ________

20. $\frac{2}{\sqrt{7} + 2} \cdot \frac{3(\sqrt{7} + 2)}{10}$ ________

Name ______________________________

In 21–28, solve the equation.

21. $2(4a + 6) + 6(4a + 6) = 80$

22. $(2a + 3)^2 = 49$

23. $(x + 3)^2 = 36$

24. $(m - 8)^2 = 121$

25. $(u^2)^2 = 625$

26. $3(x^2 + 1) - 4(x^2 + 1) = -26$

27. $10(w + 1) - 5(w + 1) + (w + 1) = -42$

28. $12(2w^2 + 4) - 5(2w^2 + 4) - (2w^2 + 4) = 24$

29. If $\sqrt{x + 3} = 81$, what is the value of $x + 3$? ______________

30. If $\sqrt{x + 3} = 81$, what is the value of x? ______________

31. If $\sqrt{x + 3} = 81$, what is the value of $3\sqrt{x + 3}$? ______________

32. If $14y + 21 = 17$, what is the value of $2y + 3$? ______________

Name

LESSON MASTER 6-1 B

Questions on SPUR Objectives

Skills Objective A: Divide real numbers and algebraic fractions.

In 1–15, fill in the blanks or boxes.

1. $\frac{7}{a}$ = ________ ÷ ________

2. -5 ÷ 8 = ________ · ________

3. $\frac{5}{12}$ = ________ · ________

4. $\frac{x}{y}$ = ________ · ________

5. $b \cdot \frac{1}{3} = \frac{\square}{\square}$

6. $c \cdot \frac{1}{e} = \frac{\square}{\square}$

7. $10 \cdot \frac{1}{7} = \frac{\square}{\square}$

8. $\frac{\frac{5}{6}}{\frac{2}{3}}$ = ________ ÷ ________

9. $\frac{\frac{e}{2r}}{\frac{w}{x}}$ = ________ · ________

10. $\frac{1}{2} \div \frac{7}{8}$ = ________ · ________

11. $\frac{a}{b} \div \frac{2}{7c}$ = ________ · ________

12. $\frac{1}{m} \div -27 = \frac{1}{m} \cdot$ ________

13. $\frac{s}{\frac{x}{y}}$ = ________ · ________

14. $3d \div \frac{4}{7 + u} = \frac{3d}{\square}$

15. $21 \cdot \frac{3y}{8} = \frac{\square}{\square}$

Multiple choice. **Tell which expression is *not* equivalent to the others.**

16. (a) $\frac{-6}{-5}$ (b) $-\frac{6}{5}$ (c) $\frac{-6}{5}$ (d) $\frac{6}{-5}$ ________

17. (a) $\frac{x}{a + b}$ (b) $x\left(\frac{1}{a + b}\right)$ (c) $\frac{1}{x}(a + b)$ (d) $x \div (a + b)$ ________

Name ____

► **LESSON MASTER 6-1 B** *page 2*

In 18–29 simplify.

18. $\frac{1}{6} \div \frac{4}{9}$ ______ **19.** $\frac{7}{8} \div 10$ ______ **20.** $\frac{a}{b} \div \frac{2a}{b}$ ______

21. $-y \div \frac{3}{m}$ ______ **22.** $\frac{3 + n}{8} \div \frac{3 + n}{10}$ ______ **23.** $\frac{7}{3bc} \div \frac{2b}{5c}$ ______

24. $\frac{\frac{3}{4}}{\frac{1}{12}}$ ______ **25.** $\frac{\frac{y}{6}}{\frac{y}{12}}$ ______ **26.** $\frac{\frac{m}{2}}{m}$ ______

27. $\frac{\frac{7}{b}}{ac}$ ______ **28.** $\frac{-4\frac{1}{3}}{\frac{5}{6}}$ ______ **29.** $\frac{\frac{\pi}{6}}{\frac{2\pi}{3}}$ ______

Review Objective J, Lesson 3-4

For 30–33, use the grid at the right.

30. Graph $P'Q'R'S'$, the image of sliding quadrilateral $PQRS$ 6 units left and 8 units up.

31. Slide $P'Q'R'S'$ 1 unit left and 2 units down. Label the image $P''Q''R''S''$.

32. Give the coordinates of Q''.

____

33. The coordinates of P and R are (3, 4) and (7, -4), respectively. Explain how to find the coordinates of each point without using a graph.

a. point P' ____

____

b. point R'' ____

____

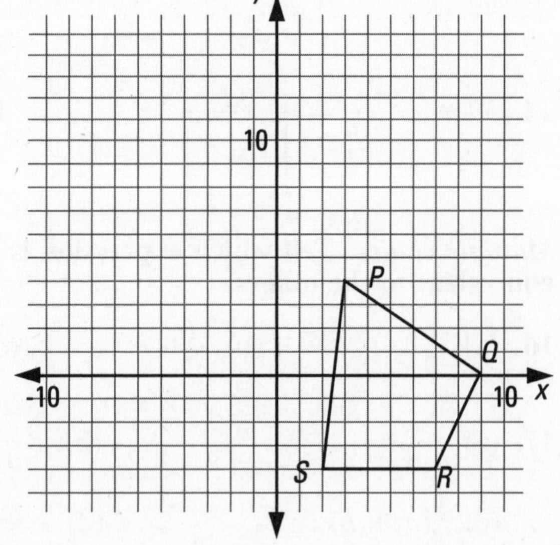

Name ______________________________

LESSON MASTER

Questions on SPUR Objectives

Uses Objective E: Use the rate model for division.

1. Automobile racing first appeared as a sport in 1894. Only 15 of the 21 starting vehicles completed the race. It took the winner about 5.2 hours to complete the 125-km run between Paris and Rouen, France.

a. What was the winner's average speed in kilometers per hour? ______________

b. How long did it take the winning car to travel 1 kilometer? ______________

2. During a meteor shower, some meteors approach the earth's atmosphere at speeds of 95 kilometers per second. Give the reciprocal rate and explain its meaning.

____

____

3. Explain how considering a rate of $\frac{12 \text{ miles}}{0 \text{ seconds}}$ illustrates that dividing by zero is impossible.

____

____

In 4–13, calculate a rate for the situation described.

4. Clarissa drove 135 miles in 3 hours. ______________

5. The car traveled 315 miles on 15 gallons of gasoline. ______________

6. In 15 almonds there are about 90 calories. ______________

7. The roast weighed 5.6 pounds and cost $21.22. ______________

8. Craig answered 186 questions in 12 minutes. ______________

9. There were 19,500 bushels of corn grown on 300 acres of farmland. ______________

10. The tree grew 18 feet in 5 years. ______________

11. On January 8, 26 inches of snow fell in 6 hours. ______________

Name ________________________________

12. In 1990, the population of Alaska was 550,403 and its area was 656,424 square miles. Give two rates suggested by this information. ____________ ____________

13. Mr. Santos stuffed 4200 envelopes in 3 hours. Give two rates, one using hours and one using minutes. ____________ ____________

14. For each situation, give a rate.

a. The committee made 144 bean bags in 6 hours. ____________

b. The committee made 200 bean bags in *h* hours. ____________

c. The committee made *b* bean bags in $\frac{1}{2}$ hour. ____________

15. A 20-oz jar of lotion costs $4.09 and a 12-oz jar costs $2.49.

a. Find the unit cost (cost per ounce) for 20 ounces. ____________

b. Find the unit cost of the smaller bottle. ____________

c. Which is the better buy? ____________

16. If it takes 7 minutes to call the names of 100 graduates, how long will it take to call the names of 448 graduates? ____________

In 17–19, give the density (weight per volume) of each item.

		WEIGHT	VOLUME	DENSITY
17.	aluminum	8,097 grams	3,000 cubic centimeters	
18.	copper	4,928 grams	550 cubic centimeters	
19.	gold	4,338 grams	225 cubic centimeters	

20. Which is faster, typing $5p$ pages in $4h$ hours or $4p$ pages in $3h$ hours? Explain your answer.

____

____

21. Which is less expensive, $6c$ cases of juice for $10 or $4c$ cases of juice for $6? Explain your answer.

____

____

Name

LESSON MASTER 

Questions on SPUR Objectives

Vocabulary

1. There are 14 teachers for 280 students. What is the ratio of teachers to students? __________

2. Out of 26 kindergartners, 15 are girls. What is the ratio of girls to boys? __________

3. A farm has 800 acres of corn and 2,000 acres of wheat. What is the ratio of corn to wheat? __________

4. In a survey, 125 people out of 300 said they like spring best. What ratio is this? __________

Uses Objective F: Use ratios to compare two quantities.

5. *Multiple choice.* Which of the following is (are) *not* equal to the ratio of 5 to 4? __________

   (a) $\frac{20}{16}$ (b) $\frac{5x}{4x}$ (c) $\frac{4}{5}$

   (d) 80% (e) 400 to 500 (f) 30 ft to 24 ft

6. *Multiple choice.* Which of the following is (are) *not* equal to the ratio of a to b? __________

   (a) $\frac{a}{b}$ (b) $\frac{ax}{bx}$ (c) $100b$ to $100a$ (d) a miles to b miles

7. At the pool, there were 118 swimmers in the morning, 420 in the afternoon, and 258 in the evening. What is the ratio of morning swimmers to all swimmers? __________

8. At Central Electronics, the ratio of black-and-white TVs to all TVs is 1 to 24. What is the ratio of color TVs to all TVs? __________

9. During his 17 years in the major leagues, Lou Gehrig was at bat 8,001 times and made 2,721 hits. Give his *batting average*, the ratio of hits to times at bat, as a decimal rounded to the nearest thousandth. __________

10. The children's section of a library has 8,410 books, of which 3,145 are fiction. The adult section has 98,875 books and 27,218 of them are fiction. Which section has more fiction books in relation to the total number of books in the section? __________

Name

11. A punch recipe calls for 3 parts juice, 2 parts soda, and 3 parts sherbet. How much of each ingredient is needed for 2 gallons of punch? (1 gallon = 16 cups)

______

12. In a "taste-test," 77 people out of 120 preferred smooth peanut butter to crunchy. Out of 4,000 jars of peanut butter purchased, how many were probably smooth? ______

Uses Objective H: Solve percent problems in real situations.

In 13–18, give a ratio comparing the first quantity to the second. Then give the ratio as a percent.

13. 16 questions correct out of 20 ______ ______

14. 2,044 voters out of 6,820 for Candidate A ______ ______

15. $56 discount on a coat regularly priced at $224 ______ ______

16. 2 hours for homework and 30 minutes for practicing ______ ______

17. 3 defective light bulbs out of 500 tested ______ ______

18. 64 germinated seeds out of 70 planted ______ ______

19. According to the 1900 census, the U.S. population was 76,212,168. Find the percent of the U.S. population that lived in each of these states.

a. Iowa 2,231,853 ______

b. New York 7,268,894 ______

c. Louisiana 1,381,625 ______

20. According to the 1990 census, the U.S. population was 248,709,873. Find the percent of the U.S. population that lived in each of these states.

a. Iowa 2,776,755 ______

b. New York 17,990,455 ______

c. Louisiana 4,219,973 ______

21. An electronic note pad originally costing $259 is on sale for $207.20. After tax is added, the price is $223.78.

a. What is the percent of discount? ______

b. What is the percent of tax? ______

Name ____

LESSON MASTER 6-4 B

Questions on SPUR Objectives

Uses Objective G: Calculate relative frequencies or probabilities in situations with a finite number of equally likely outcomes.

1. A fair six-sided die was tossed 60 times. The number 5 came up 13 times.

a. What was the relative frequency of tossing 5? ____________

b. What is the probability of tossing 5? ____________

c. Are your answers to Parts **a** and **b** the same? Explain why this is the case.

____

____

____

2. In Franklin Heights, 1,300 of the 4,200 residents bought season passes to the swimming pool. Give the relative frequency of residents who bought passes

a. as a fraction. ____________ **b.** as a percent. ____________

3. In 1993, it was estimated that out of 91,238,000 households in the United States that had television sets, 1,862,000 had only black-and-white television sets.

a. What was the relative frequency, as a percent, of households with only black-and-white television sets? ____________

b. How many households had color sets? ____________

c. What was the relative frequency, as a percent, of households with color television sets? ____________

4. A survey asked students to name their favorite class. Give the relative frequency, as a fraction, of students who like art best if

a. 68 students were polled and 59 did *not* pick art. ____________

b. 187 students were polled and 161 did *not* pick art. ____________

c. 275 students were polled and x did *not* pick art. ____________

d. s students were polled and n did *not* pick art. ____________

Name ______________________________

5. A teacher filled a box with 700 yellow and 400 green centimeter cubes. A student randomly grabbed a handful of 22 cubes and found that 16 were yellow.

a. Give the probability of randomly selecting a yellow cube. ______________

b. Give the student's relative frequency of randomly selecting a yellow cube. ______________

6. Describe the complement of each event.

a. Toss a number cube and get a number greater than 4.

____

b. The lake is frozen.

____

c. The name of a state begins with a vowel.

____

7. Music Boosters sold 814 raffle tickets. One ticket will be drawn at random, and the winner will receive tickets to a concert. Rose bought 12 tickets. Let the event E = Rose wins and S = set of outcomes. Find each of the following.

a. $N(E)$ ______________

b. $N(S)$ ______________

c. $P(E)$ ______________

d. P(Rose does not win.) ______________

8. A card is drawn at random from a regular deck. Find each of the following.

a. P(four) ______________

b. P(four of diamonds) ______________

c. P(four, five, six, seven, or eight) ______________

d. P(spade) ______________

9. Consider tossing a die. Give an example of an event

a. with probability 0. ______________________________

b. with probability 1. ______________________________

Name

LESSON MASTER

Questions on SPUR Objectives

Skills Objective B: Solve percent problems.

1. 24 out of 200 is what percent? __________

2. What is 7% of 613? __________

3. 2.6 is what percent of 9.6? __________

4. 19% of what number is 57? __________

5. What is 14.3% of 400? __________

6. 84 is what percent of 56? __________

7. $2\frac{1}{2}$% of what number is 75? __________

8. What is 0.7% of $42,000? __________

9. 9 is what percent of 14,000? __________

10. $3\frac{1}{3}$% of 600 is what number? __________

11. 7.44% of what number is 18.6? __________

12. What is 475% of 88? __________

Uses Objective H: Solve percent problems in real situations.

13. Last year 42% of the students at Roosevelt rode the bus. If there were 350 students, how many rode the bus? __________

14. Refer to the headline below.

CITY SCHOLARSHIPS AWARDED TO 12% OF SENIOR CLASS 36 Students Proudly Accept Grants

How many students are in the senior class? __________

15. About 2.2% of Tennessee's total area is water. The total area of Tennessee is 42,146 square miles.

a. What is the water area in Tennessee? __________

b. What is the land area in Tennessee? __________

Name ____________________

16. Between 1980 and 1990 the population of Columbus grew 12%.

a. *Fill in the blank.* If the 1980 population was P, then the 1990 population was ____________

b. The 1990 population of Columbus was 632,910. Write an equation and find the 1980 population.

____________ equation ____________ population

17. Between 1980 and 1990 Baltimore's population dropped 6.4%.

a. *Fill in the blank.* If the 1980 population was P, then the 1990 population was ____________

b. The 1990 population of Baltimore was 736,014. Write an equation and find the 1980 population.

____________ equation ____________ population

18. The total cost of head phones, including 7% sales tax, was $35.15. What was the price of the head phones without tax? ____________

19. A coat is on sale for 40% off. The sale price is $172.80. What is the regular price? ____________

20. During the summer, the population of Golden Beach Shores increased 32% to 1,023. What was the population during the other seasons? ____________

21. Mrs. Jin invested $4,500 in bonds. After 1 year, her investment was worth $5017.50. By what percent did her investment grow? ____________

22. In a 14-gram serving (1 tablespoon) of a certain brand of mayonnaise, there are 11 grams of fat. What percent of the mayonnaise is fat? ____________

23. In an 8th-grade class, 8 students have birthdays in fall, 6 in winter, 7 in spring, and 7 in summer. What percent of the students do not have summer birthdays? ____________

24. The figure at the right shows two rectangles. What percent of the larger rectangle is shaded?

4
6
10
15

____

Name ____________________

LESSON MASTER **Questions on SPUR Objectives**

Representations Objective J: Find probabilities involving geometric regions.

In 1 and 2, give the probability that the spinner will land in region X.

1.

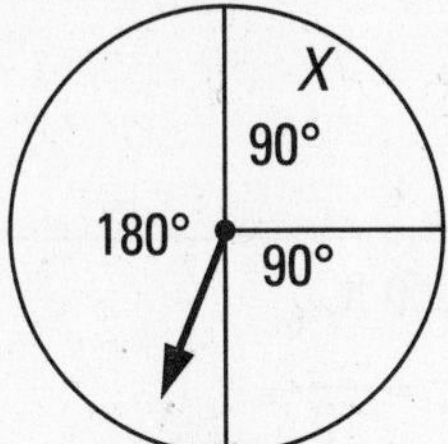

____

2.

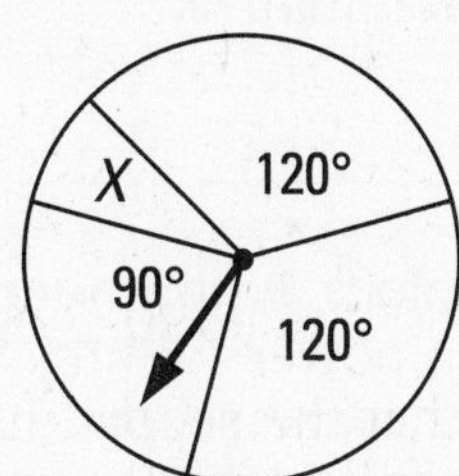

____

In 3–5, the target at the right is made up of circles with radii of 10, 20, and 30 cm.

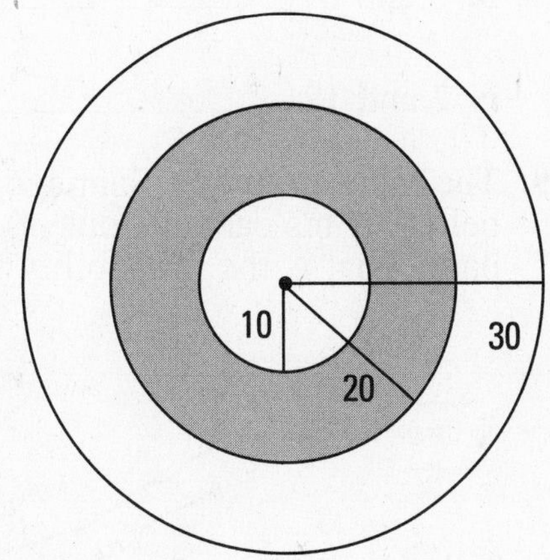

3. Find the area of each circle. ____________________

4. Find the area of the shaded ring. ____________________

5. If a dart thrown at random hits the target, what is the probability that it will land in

a. the smallest circle? ____________________

b. the shaded ring? ____________________

c. the outermost ring? ____________________

6. The land area of the United States is about 3,536,000 square miles and the water surface area is about 251,000 square miles. If a meteor hits the United States, what is the probability that it will

a. fall on land? ____________________

b. fall on water? ____________________

Name ______________________________

▶ LESSON MASTER 6-6 B *page 2*

7. A park 200 ft by 300 ft contains a fountain 60 ft in diameter. Kelly, a sky diver, parachutes into the park. If Kelly lands at random, what is the probability she will land in the fountain?

____

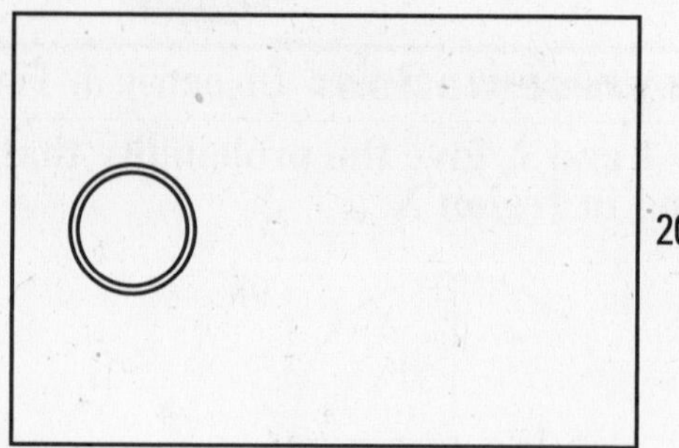

8. An electric clock with a second hand is stopped by a power failure. What is the probability that the second hand stopped between the following two numerals?

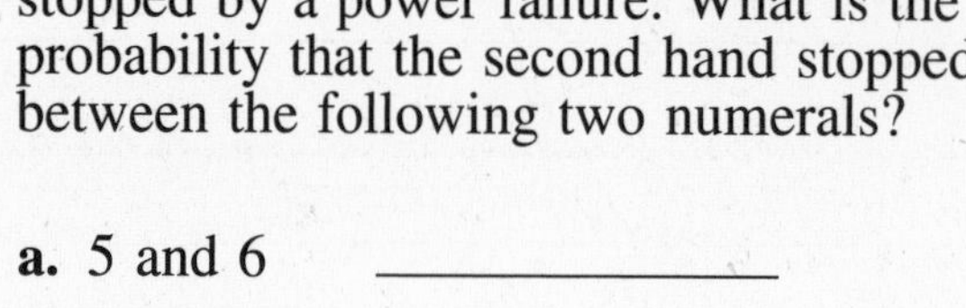

a. 5 and 6 ______________

b. 3 and 6 ______________

c. 7 and 12 ______________

9. The route from Mr. Santiago's office to his home is shown below. If his car runs out of gas at a random point on the path, what is the probability that it will be on the freeway?

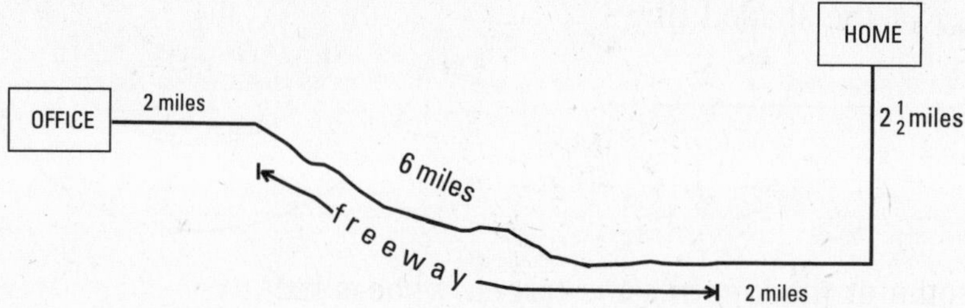

____

10. In baseball, the width of the strike zone is the 17-in. width of home plate. The height of the strike zone is the distance between the batter's chest and knees. The strike zones for two batters are shown as shaded areas in the diagrams below. Suppose a pitcher throws a ball within a square region 36 in. on a side which contains the strike zone. If the placement of the ball within this square is random, what is the probability that the ball will be in the strike zone of each batter?

a.

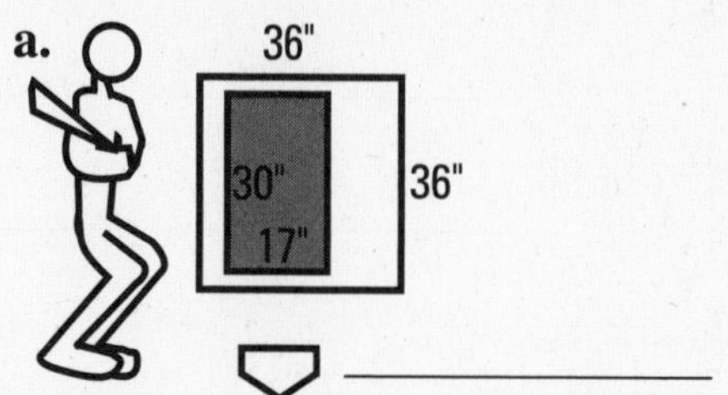

____

b.

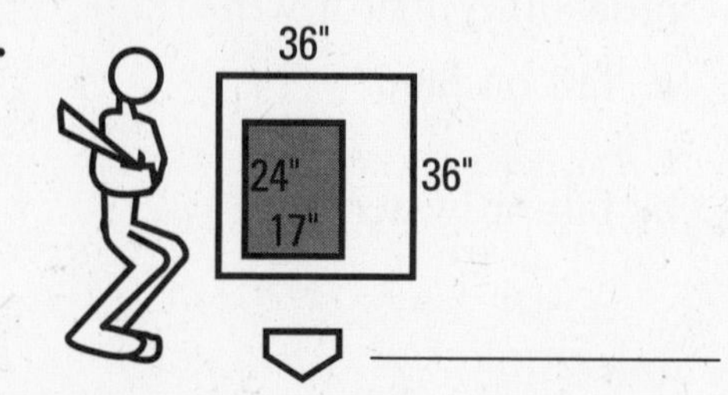

____

Name

LESSON MASTER 6-7 B

Questions on SPUR Objectives

Vocabulary

1. If a size change is an *expansion*, what is true of the size-change factor?

____

2. If a size change is a *contraction*, what is true of the size-change factor?

____

Uses Objective H: Solve percent problems from real situations.

3. Gwen enlarged cartoon A on a photocopy machine by a factor of 150%. The result was cartoon B. Then she enlarged cartoon B by a factor of 125% to get cartoon C.

Find the widths of the other two cartoons if the width of

a. cartoon A is 12 cm. **b.** cartoon B is 12 cm. **c.** cartoon C is 27 cm.

a.	b.	c.
B ________	A ________	A ________
C ________	C ________	B ________

4. Jo's Catalog charges $3\frac{1}{2}$ times the normal cost to ship an order overnight. If it normally costs \$4.50 to ship a jacket, what is the cost for overnight shipment? ________

Name

Representations Objective K: Apply the Size Change Model for Multiplication.

5. **a.** Graph quadrilateral *ABCD* with $A = (6, -2)$, $B = (3, 3)$, $C = (0, 6)$, and $D = (0, 0)$.

   b. Graph $A'B'C'D'$, the image of *ABCD* under a size change of magnitude $\frac{2}{3}$.

   c. Graph $A''B''C''D''$, the image of *ABCD* under a size change of magnitude -2.

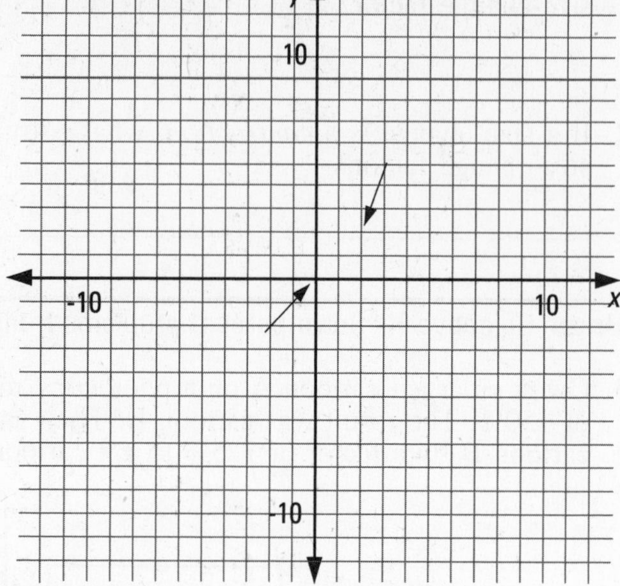

In 6–10, tell if the size change described is an *expansion*, a *contraction*, or *neither*. Then tell whether or not the original figure has been rotated 180°.

6. $k = 8$ __________ _____

7. $k = -1$ __________ _____

8. $k = -.75$ __________ _____

9. The image of (7, -2) is (3.5, -1). __________ _____

10. The image of (-4, 6) is (6, -9). __________ _____

In 11 and 12, consider two figures, Figure 1 and Figure 2. Figure 1 is the image of a triangle under a size change k_1. Figure 2 is the image of the same triangle under a size change k_2. Tell how the two images are <u>different</u> if

11. $k_1 = 6$ and $k_2 = 2$.

____

____

12. $k_1 = 3$ and $k_2 = -3$.

____

Name

LESSON MASTER 6-8 B

Questions on SPUR Objectives

Skills Objective C: Solve proportions.

In 1–10, use the Means-Extremes Property to solve.

1. $\frac{5}{12} = \frac{x}{30}$

2. $\frac{-4}{5} = \frac{12}{a}$

3. $\frac{5m}{14} = \frac{6}{21}$

4. $\frac{1}{y + 7} = \frac{8}{72}$

5. $\frac{3}{x} = \frac{x}{12}$

6. $\frac{b}{8} = \frac{18}{b}$

7. $\frac{2e + 9}{24} = \frac{e + 1}{8}$

8. $\frac{3(s + 4)}{2} = \frac{14s}{4}$

9. $\frac{4a - 2}{3} = 2a$

10. $\frac{c + 12}{c + 2} = 6$

In 11 and 12, a proportion is given. a. Give the exact solution. b. Give the solution to the nearest hundredth.

11. $\frac{5}{x} = \frac{x}{2}$

a. ______________________

b. ______________________

12. $\frac{k}{8} = \frac{3}{4k}$

a. ______________________

b. ______________________

Properties Objective D: Use the language of proportions and the Means-Extremes Property.

In 13 and 14, identify the means and the extremes in each proportion.

13. $\frac{7}{8} = \frac{5}{40}$

__________ means __________ extremes

14. $\frac{u + 2}{10} = \frac{3u}{12}$

__________ means __________ extremes

Name

15. Explain how you can use the Means-Extremes Property to determine if the fractions $\frac{4.5}{6}$ and $\frac{12}{16}$ are equal.

____

____

____

Uses Objective I: Solve problems involving proportions in real situations.

16. In three hours, 1,650 gallons were drained out of a swimming pool. At this rate, how many gallons will be drained out in 8 hours? ______

17. One of the heaviest rainfalls ever recorded occurred in Holt, Missouri, when 12 inches of rain fell in 42 minutes. At this rate, how much rain would fall in an hour? ______

18. A pollster found that 73 out of 120 people were in favor of an upcoming school referendum. If 4,500 people turn out to vote, how many can be expected to vote for the referendum? ______

19. Jimmy counted 23 raisins in 2 cups of his favorite cereal. At this rate, how many are in the entire box containing 11 cups of cereal? ______

20. As a library employee, Dawn found she was able to shelve 100 books in 3 hours. At this rate, how many books can she shelve in an 40-hour work week? ______

21. A ranger caught, tagged, and released 150 deer in a state park. Three months later, the ranger caught 80 deer. Of these, 6 had tags. Based on these findings, estimate the total number of deer in the park. ______

22. If an animator needed to draw 3,600 frames for a $2\frac{1}{2}$-minute cartoon, how many frames would be needed for a 6-minute cartoon? ______

Name

LESSON MASTER

Questions on SPUR Objectives

Vocabulary

1. *Similar* figures have the same ________________.

Representations Objective L: Find lengths and ratios of similitude in similar figures.

In 2–4, ΔARM is similar to ΔLEG with corresponding sides parallel.

2. Which side in ΔARM corresponds to

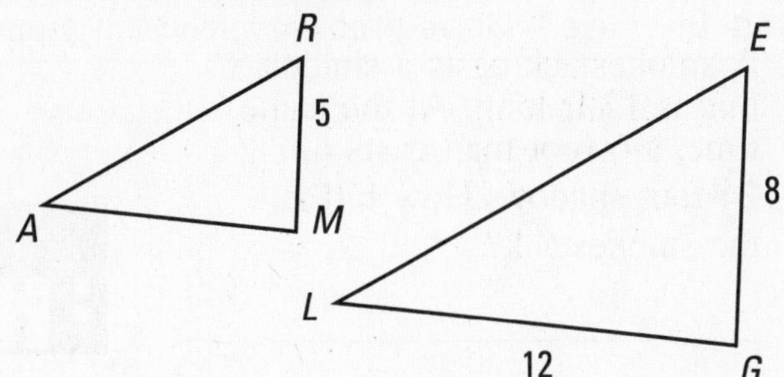

a. $\overline{LG}$? ________

b. $\overline{LE}$? ________

c. $\overline{GE}$? ________

3. Write and solve a proportion to find the length of $\overline{AM}$.

________________ proportion ________________ solution

4. Give the two possible ratios of similitude. ________________

5. Lilly made a 5-inch-by-7-inch enlargement of a $3\frac{1}{2}$-inch-by-5-inch snapshot. Are the two pictures similar? Why or why not?

____

____

In 6–8, the two quadrilaterals are similar. Find each length.

6. $\overline{PQ}$ ________

7. $\overline{QR}$ ________

8. $\overline{RS}$ ________

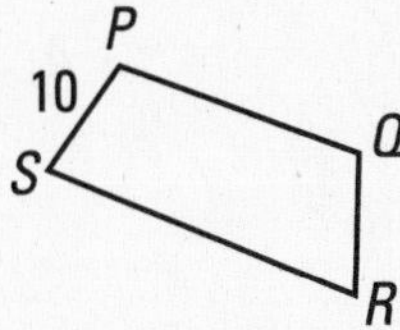

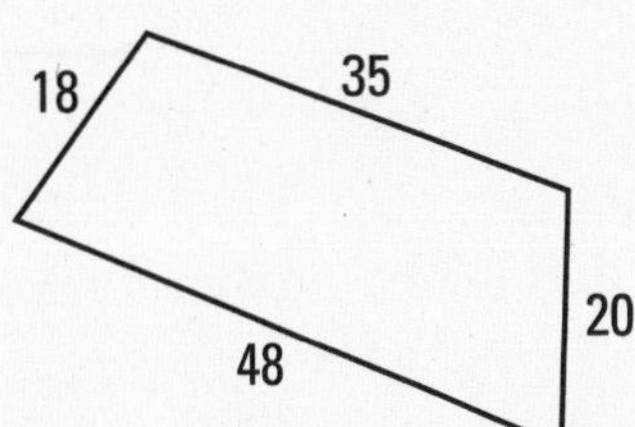

▶ **LESSON MASTER 6-9 B** *page 2*

9. These two rectangles are similar. Find the dimensions of the smaller rectangle.

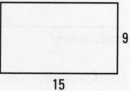

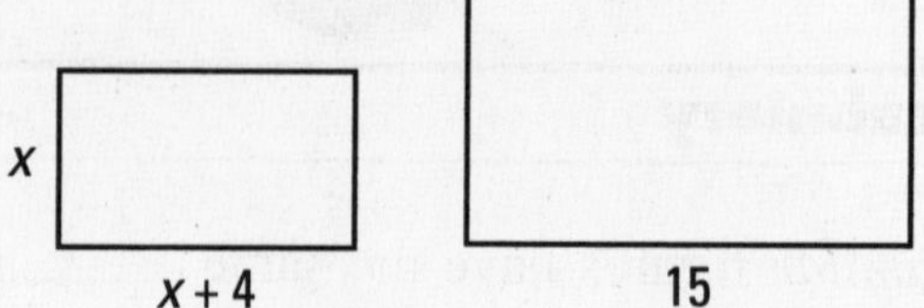

____

10. A smokestack casts a shadow that is 12 ft long. At the same time, a 6-foot man casts a $2\frac{1}{2}$-foot shadow. How tall is the smokestack?

____

11. Quadrilaterals *BIRD* and *LAMB* are similar. $\overline{LA}$ is shown and corresponds to $\overline{BI}$. Complete a drawing of *LAMB*.

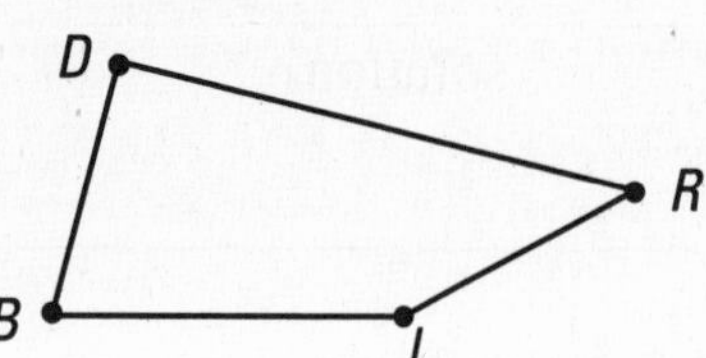

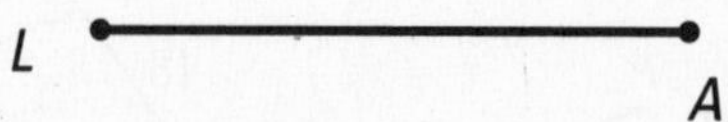

Name ____________________

LESSON MASTER 7-1 B

Questions on SPUR Objectives

Uses Objective E: Calculate rates of change from real data.

In 1–3, fill in the blanks to give the rate of change for each situation.

1. A vine grew 30 inches in 10 weeks. ________ inches per ________

2. Mr. Logan lost 15 pounds in 6 months. ________ pounds per ________

3. Over a 3-year period, the company bought 7,500 new computers. ________ computers per ________

In 4–7, use the chart below which shows the number of subscribers to the *Granville Gazette*.

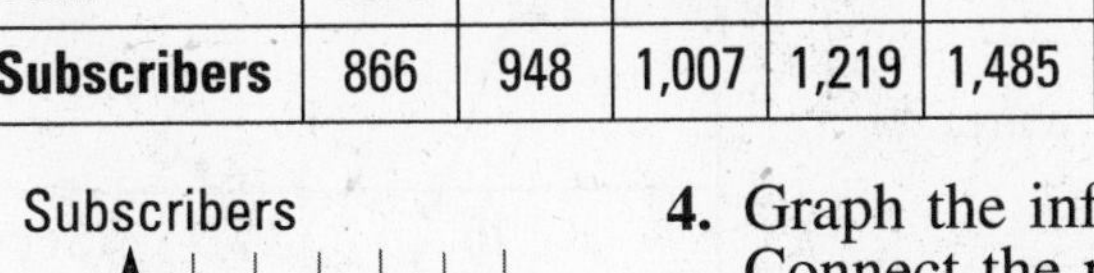

Year	1970	1975	1980	1985	1990
Subscribers	866	948	1,007	1,219	1,485

Subscribers

Year

4. Graph the information on the grid at the left. Connect the points.

5. a. Which segment is steeper, the one connecting (1975, 948) to (1980, 1,007), or the one connecting (1980, 1,007) to (1985, 1,219)?

____

b. Explain what this means.

____

____

____

6. What was the rate of change of the number of subscribers

a. from 1970 to 1975? ________________

b. from 1985 to 1990? ________________

7. For the years shown, was the rate of change ever negative? ________________

Name ________________________________

In 8 and 9, use the table at the right. It shows some of the rental charges for a chain saw.

HOURS	COST
2	$20
3	$28
8	$45

8. **a.** What is the rate of change from a 2-hour rental to a 3-hour rental? ____________

   b. What is the unit of the rate of change? ____________

9. Is the rate of change from 2 hours to 3 hours the same as the rate of change from 3 hours to 8 hours? ____________

In 10–12, use the graph at the right. It shows the altitude of an otter on rocks and in the water.

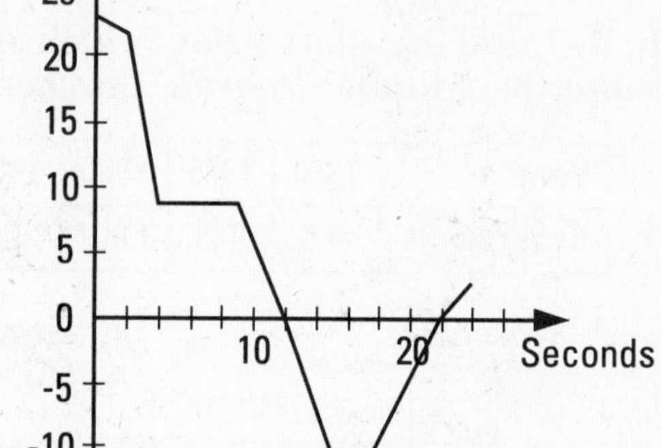

10. How many seconds pass before the otter enters the water?

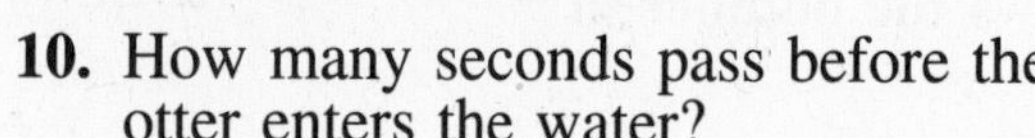

____

11. How long is the otter in the water?

____

12. The otter rested on the rocks for several seconds.

    a. During what time interval did this occur?

    ____

    b. Give the rate of change during this time interval. ____________

13. Use the spreadsheet below, which shows the average number of cars produced each month in Mexico.

	A	B	C
1	YEAR	CARS PER MONTH (in thousands)	RATE OF CHANGE PER YEAR (in thousands)
2	1987	19.0	
3	1988	29.0	120.0
4	1989	37.9	106.8
5	1990	51.2	
6	1991	61.1	

a. What formula could be in cell C5? ____________

b. Complete the spreadsheet.

Name

LESSON MASTER 

Questions on SPUR Objectives

Skills Objective A: Find the slope of the line through two given points.

In 1–6, calculate the slope of a line through the two points.

1. (4, 8) and (6, 12) __________

2. (-3, 2) and (5, -1) __________

3. (0, 11) and (6, 14) __________

4. (-8, -1) and (-6, -4) __________

5. (4, 9) and (7, 9) __________

6. (3, 4) and (4, -18) __________

In 7–10, find the slope of the line.

7.

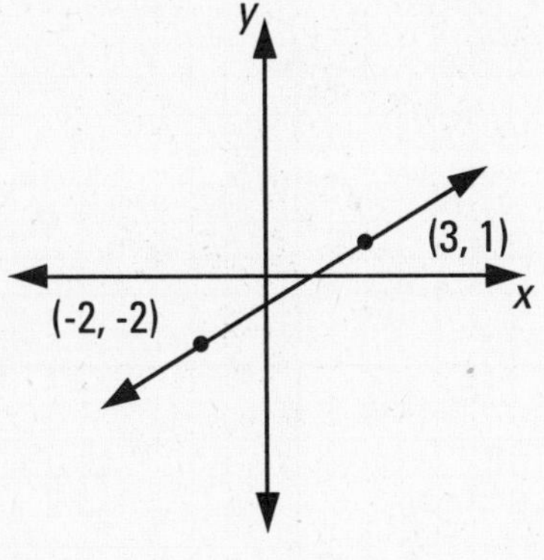

____

8.

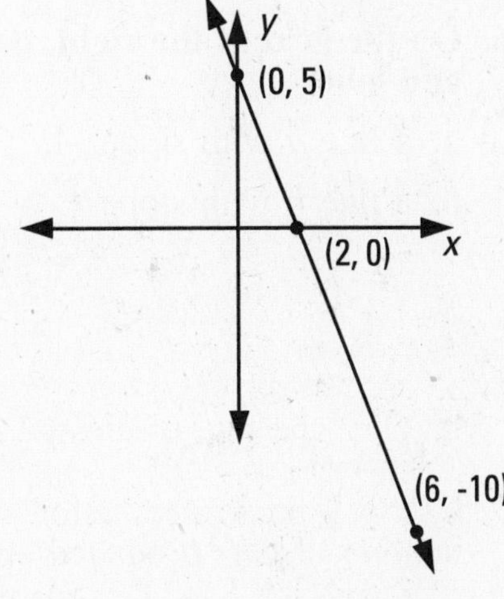

____

9.

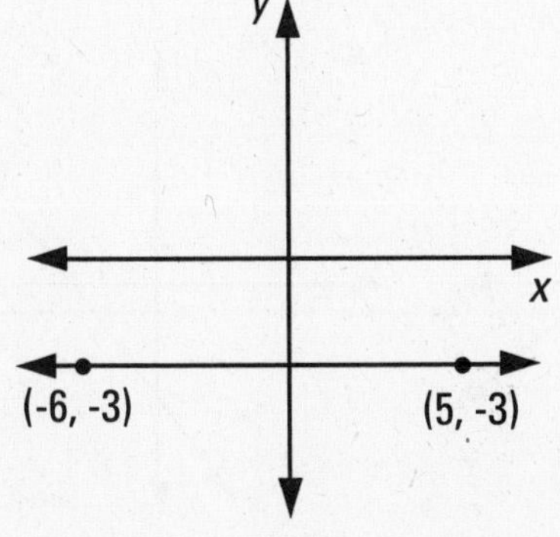

____

10.

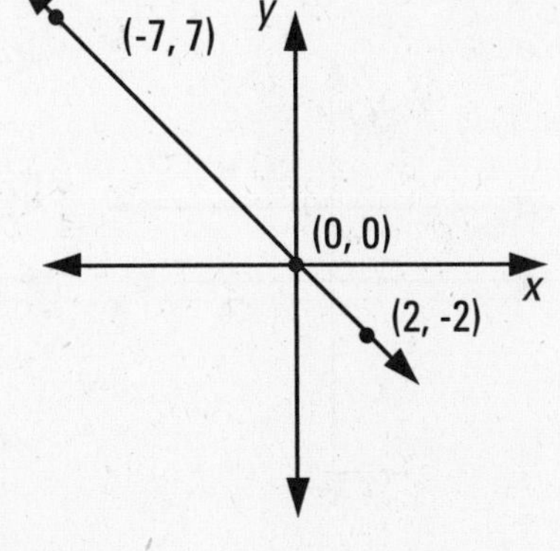

____

Name ______________________________

11. The points (2, -3) and (n, 6) are on a line with slope -3. Find the value of n. ____________

12. The points (0, c) and (-4, -4) are on a line with slope $\frac{1}{2}$. Find the value of c. ____________

In 13 and 14, an equation is given. a. Find two points on the line. b. Find the slope of the line.

13. $x - y = 11$

a. ______________________

b. ______________________

14. $4x + 3y = 2$

a. ______________________

b. ______________________

Properties Objective D: Use the definition of slope.

15. Give the slope of the line passing through the points (p, q) and (r, s). ____________

16. On the grid at the right, draw and label

a. a line a with slope -4.

b. a line b with slope $\frac{3}{2}$.

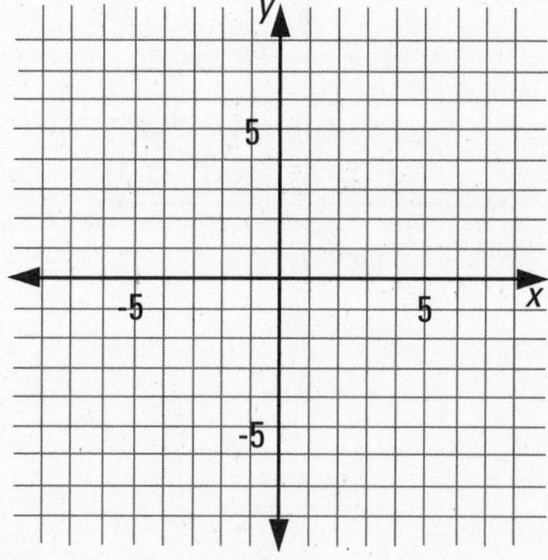

17. Tell if the slope of each line is *positive*, *negative*, or *zero*.

a.

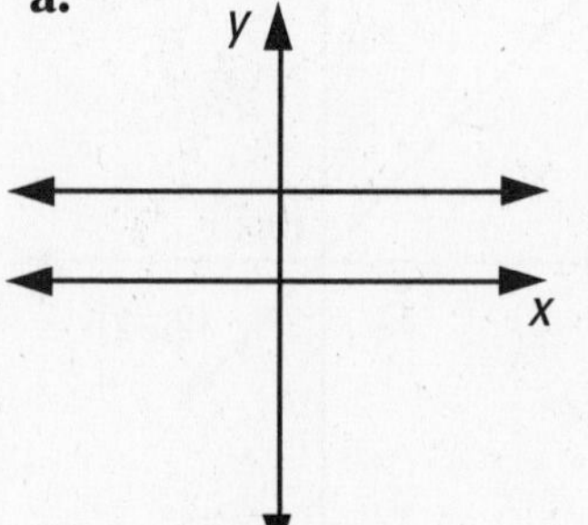

b.

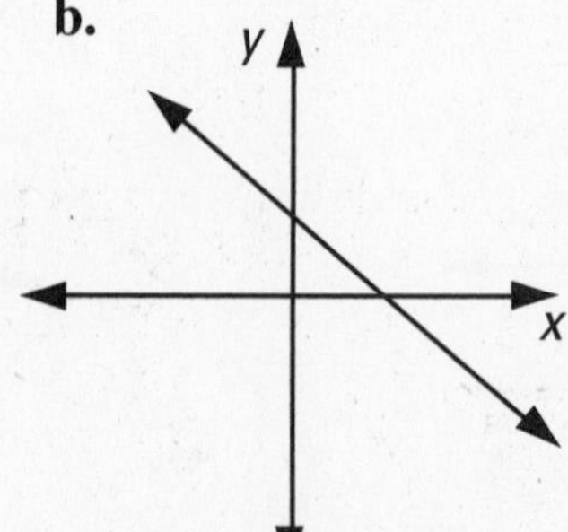

c.

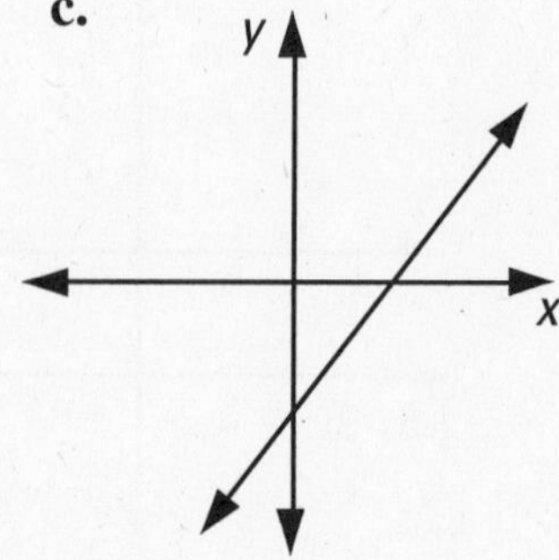

____________ ____________ ____________

Name ______________________________

LESSON MASTER 7-3 B

Questions on SPUR Objectives

Properties Objective D: Use the definition and properties of slope.

1. Consider a line with slope -3. Describe the change in the height of the line when it moves one unit to the right.

____

____

2. a. Suppose points *A* and *B* lie on the same horizontal line and *A* = (4, 2). Give possible coordinates of *B*.

____

b. Give the slope of $\overleftrightarrow{AB}$ and explain why the line must have this slope.

____

____

3. a. Suppose points *A* and *C* lie on the same vertical line and *A* = (4, 2). Give possible coordinates of *C*.

____

b. Give the slope of $\overleftrightarrow{AC}$ and explain why the line must have this slope.

____

____

In 4–9, tell if the slope of the line is *positive*, *negative*, *zero*, or *undefined*.

4. line *l* ____________

5. line *m* ____________

6. line *n* ____________

7. line *p* ____________

8. *x*-axis ____________

9. *y*-axis ____________

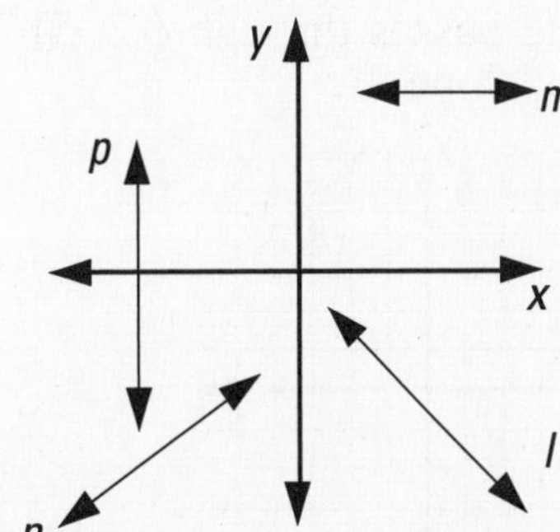

Name ______________________

In 10–12, consider a line which goes through the point (-7, 5) and has the given slope. Give another point with integer coefficients that lies on the line.

10. $\frac{5}{2}$ ________ **11.** -4 ________ **12.** 1 ________

Uses Objective E: Calculate rates of change from real data.

13. The cost of upholstering a sofa is given in the table below.

YARDS OF FABRIC	COST
8	$560
9	$585
10	$610
11	$635
12	$660

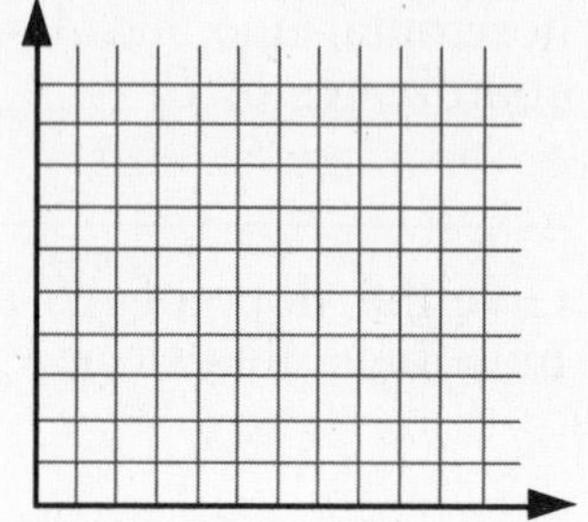

a. What is the rate of change in cost from 8 yards to 12 yards? ________

b. Graph the data in the table and draw a line through the points.

c. Find the slope of the line from Part **b**. ________

d. How is the slope related to the rate of change in Part **a**?

____

Representations Objective H: Graph a straight line given a point and the slope.

In 14 and 15, graph the line described.

14. The line passes through (-2, 5) and has slope -3.

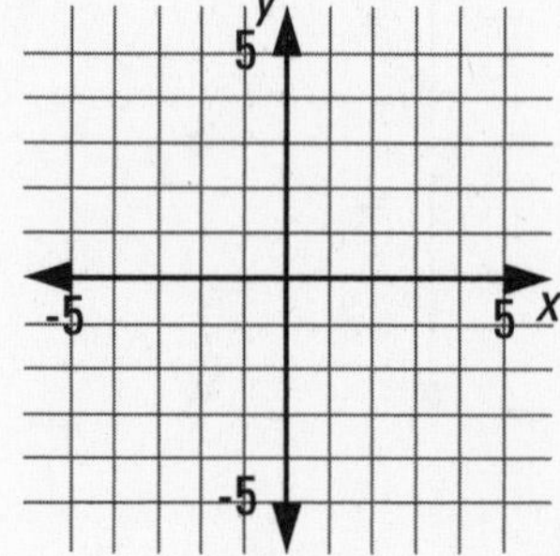

15. The line passes through (1, 0) and has slope $\frac{3}{4}$.

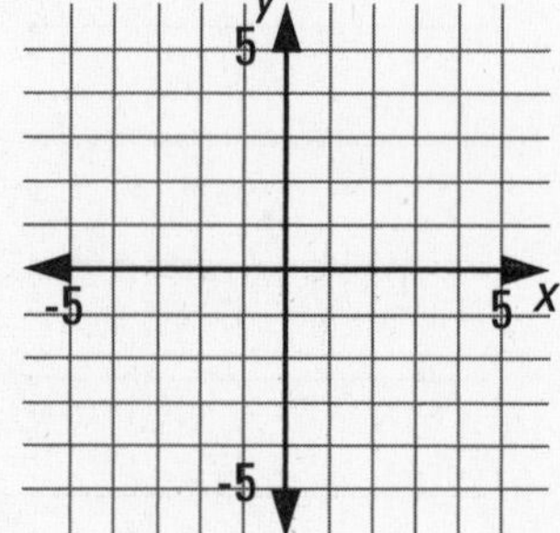

Name

LESSON MASTER **7-4 B**

Questions on SPUR Objectives

Vocabulary

1. What is the *y-intercept* of a line?

2. Write the *slope-intercept* form for the equation of a line and tell what m and b represent.

Skills Objective B: Find an equation for a line given its slope and one point on it.

In 3–9, a line is described. Write its equation in slope-intercept form.

3. slope $\frac{5}{6}$, y-intercept 2

4. slope -8, y-intercept -1

5. slope -1, y-intercept 0

6. slope 3, x-intercept 4

7. passes through (-1, 1), slope $\frac{1}{2}$

8. passes through (-8, -4), slope -2

9. passes through (3, 5), slope 0

In 10 and 11, a line is graphed. a. Give the slope of the line. b. Give the y-intercept. c. Write an equation for the line.

10.

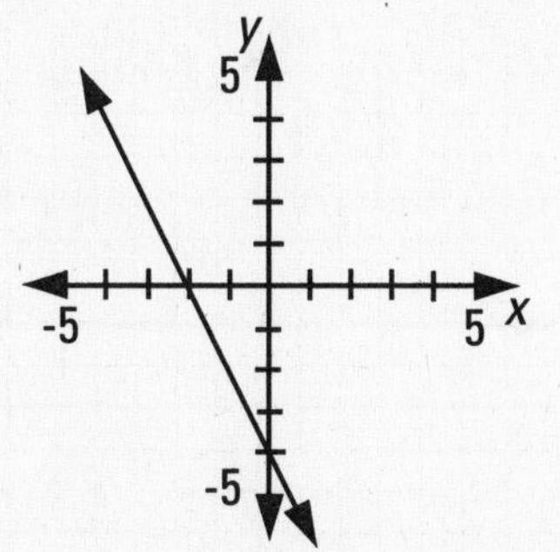

a. ________ **b.** ________

c. ________

11.

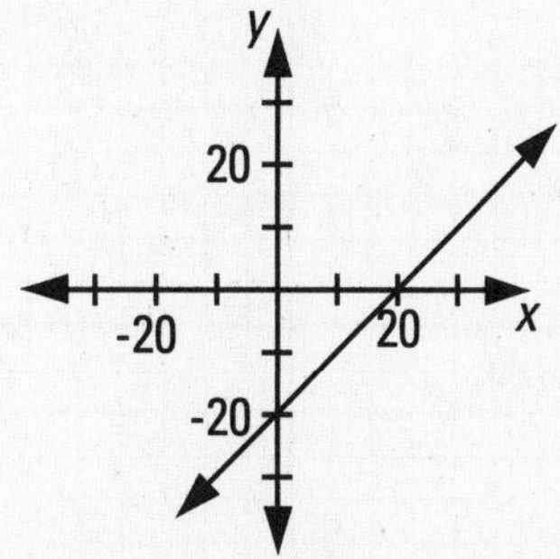

a. ________ **b.** ________

c. ________

Name ______________________________

▶ **LESSON MASTER 7-4 B** *page 2*

Skills Objective C: Write an equation for a line in slope-intercept form, and find its slope and y-intercept.

In 12–14, an equation of a line is given. a. Write it in slope-intercept form. b. Give the slope. c. Give the y-intercept.

12. $3x + y = 36$ **13.** $-5x + 2y = -8$ **14.** $x - y = 6$

a. ________ **a.** ________ **a.** ________

b. ________ **b.** ________ **b.** ________

c. ________ **c.** ________ **c.** ________

Uses Objective F: Use equations for lines to describe real situations.

In 15 and 16, a situation is given that can be described by a line. a. Give the y-intercept. b. Find the slope. c. Write an equation for the line.

15. Margie has 88 CDs. Through a club, she will purchase 3 new CDs per month.

a. ________ **b.** ________ **c.** ________________

16. Engraving costs \$18 plus .75 per letter.

a. ________ **b.** ________ **c.** ________________

Representations Objective H: Graph a straight line given its equation, or given a point and the slope.

In 17 and 18, graph the equation.

17. slope $-\frac{3}{2}$, y-intercept -4

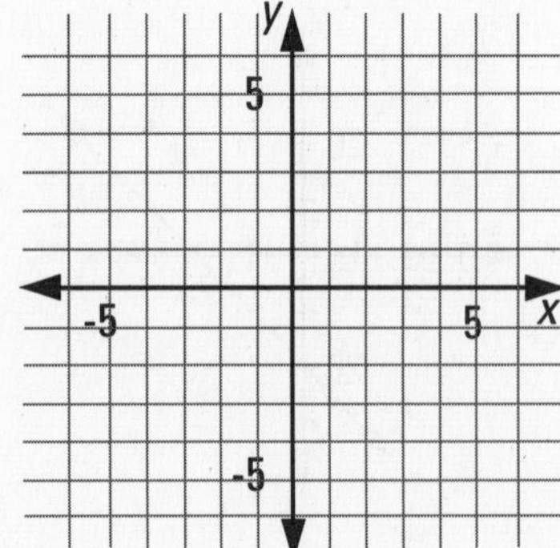

18. $-3x + y = 1$

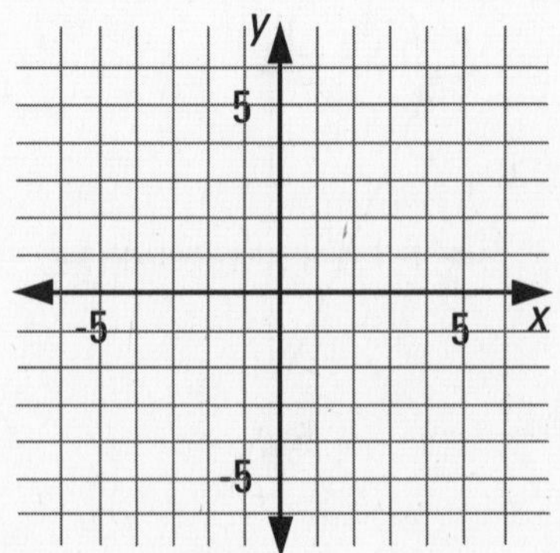

Name

LESSON MASTER  **Questions on SPUR Objectives**

Skills Objective B: Find an equation for a line given its slope and one point on it.

In 1–6, a point and slope are given. Write an equation of the line given its slope and one point.

1. slope $\frac{2}{3}$, point (3, 5) ______

2. slope -6, point (1, 0) ______

3. slope -1, point (0, 3) ______

4. slope 2, point (0, 0) ______

5. slope 0, point (-3, 8) ______

6. slope -3.5, point (-4, 5) ______

7. a. Write an equation for the line graphed at the right.

______

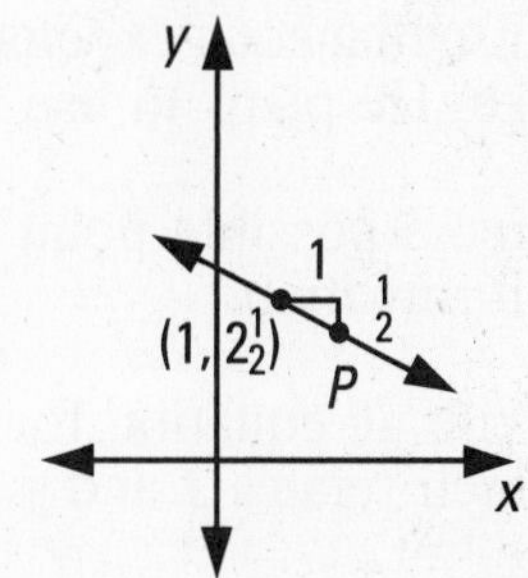

b. What are the coordinates of point P?

______

c. Show that the coordinates of point P satisfy your equation from Part **a**.

______

d. At what point will the line cross the y-axis? ______

8. Match each line r, s, t, and u with its equation below.

a. $y = -x$ ______

b. $y = -x + 3$ ______

c. $y = 3x - 6$ ______

d. $y = 3x$ ______

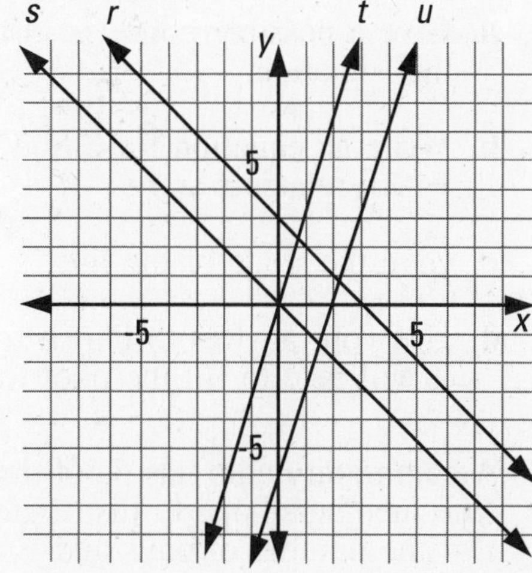

Uses Objective F: Use equations for lines to describe real situations.

9. The cost for renting a car for a day is \$36 per day plus 22¢ per mile. Let x = the number of miles and y = the cost.

a. Give a possible point (x, y). __________

b. Write an equation for a line which relates x and y. __________

c. Give the slope of the line. __________

d. Use your answer to Part **b** to find the cost if you rent a car for a day and drive 180 miles. __________

10. Koyi set aside \$850 he earned over the summer to use for miscellaneous expenses while he is away at college. He plans to use \$20 each week.

a. Give a possible point (x, y) which fits this situation. __________

b. Write an equation for a line which relates x and y. __________

c. Give the slope of the line. __________

d. Use your answer to Part **b** to find how long Koyi's money will last. __________

11. The water in a 3-foot deep pool is 6 inches deep. A hose is filling the pool at the rate of 3 inches per hour.

a. Give a possible point (x, y) which fits this situation. __________

b. Write an equation for a line which relates x and y. __________

c. Give the slope of the line. __________

d. Use your answer to Part **b** to find how long it will take to fill the pool to 34 inches deep. __________

12. A community club has 5,500 leaflets to deliver. The club members hope to distribute 400 a day. Let x = the number of days and y = the number of leaflets still available. Write an equation relating x and y. __________

Name

LESSON MASTER 7-6 B

Questions on SPUR Objectives

Skills Objective B: Find an equation for a line given two points on it.

In 1–10, find the equation in slope-intercept form for the line containing the two points.

1. (1, 3) and (-2, 1) ______________

2. (-6, -6) and (0, -4) ______________

3. (1, 4) and (-2, -5) ______________

4. (-3, 13) and (-1, -1) ______________

5. (3, 12) and (-4, -16) ______________

6. (-3, 7) and (6, -8) ______________

7. (9, 2) and (18, 11) ______________

8. (1, 1) and (5, 4) ______________

9. (8, 6) and (-3, 6) ______________

10. (100, -300) and (101, -299) ______________

In 11 and 12, two points are given. a. Write an equation in slope-intercept form for the line containing the two points. b. Graph the line from Part a and check that both points are on the line.

11. (-3, 7) and (5, -1)

a. ______________

b.

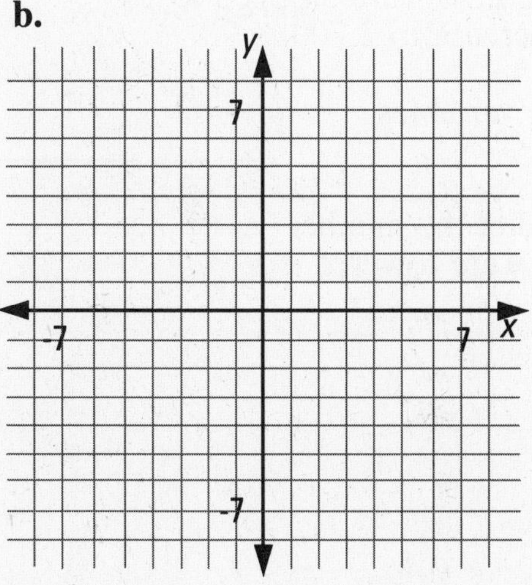

12. (6, -3) and (0, -3)

a. ______________

b.

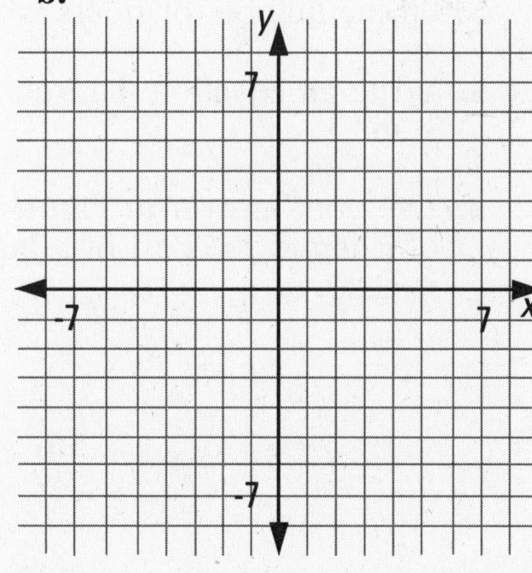

Name

Uses Objective F: Use equations for lines to describe real situations.

13. If Abby uses 2 cups of flour, she can make 24 muffins. If she uses $3\frac{1}{2}$ cups, she can make 42 muffins. Let c = number of cups of flour and m = number of muffins.

a. Write the two ordered pairs (c, m) described. ______________

b. Write an equation for the line through the two points. ______________

c. If she uses 5 cups of flour, how many muffins can she make? ______________

14. At Sew-n-Sew Windows, there is a linear relationship between the width of a window and the width of the fabric before it is pleated into draperies. A window 44 inches wide requires a 120-inch width of fabric. A 60-inch window requires 160 inches. Let x = the width of the window and y = the width of the drapery fabric.

a. Write the two ordered pairs (x, y) described. ______________

b. Write an equation for the line through the two points. ______________

c. If a window is 38 inches wide, how wide should the fabric be before it is pleated? ______________

15. The Blueport Bus Company finds that if they lower their prices, more people will ride the bus. Right now they charge $1.25 per ride and average 2,400 customers per day. Analysts feel that there is a linear relationship between the cost x and the number of riders y and that if the cost were dropped to $1.00 the number of riders would increase to 2,700.

a. Write an equation that relates the variables x and y. ______________

b. Use your answer to Part **a** to predict the number of riders if the cost of a bus ride were lowered to $.80. ______________

Name

LESSON MASTER

Questions on SPUR Objectives

Uses Objective G: Given data whose graph is approximately linear, find a linear equation to fit the graph.

1. *Multiple choice.* In which of these scatterplots is the data almost linear? ______

(a)

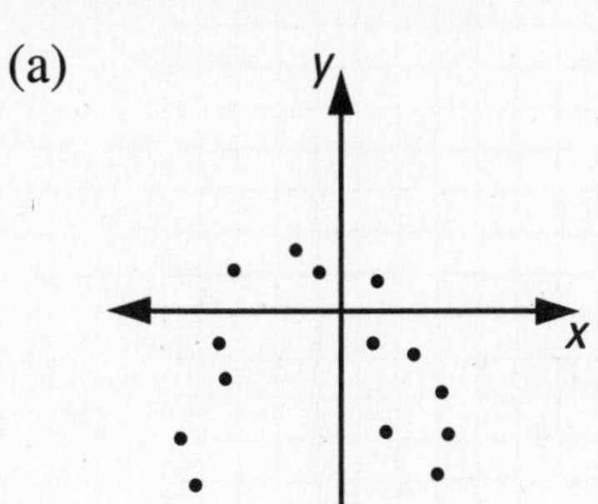

(b)

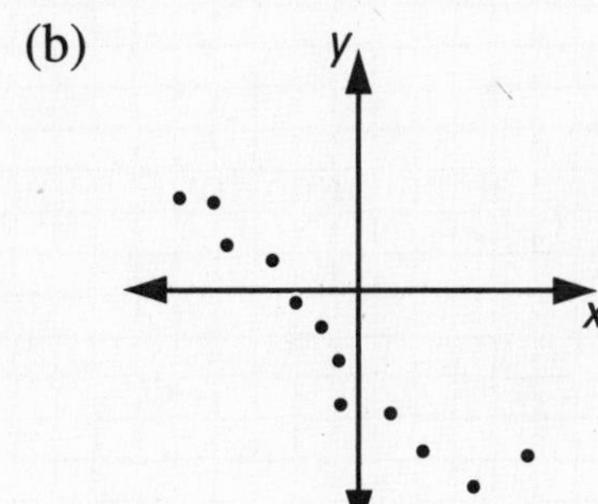

(c)

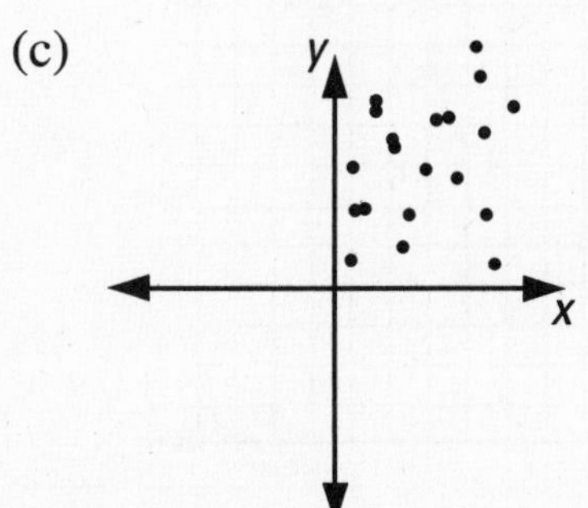

(d)

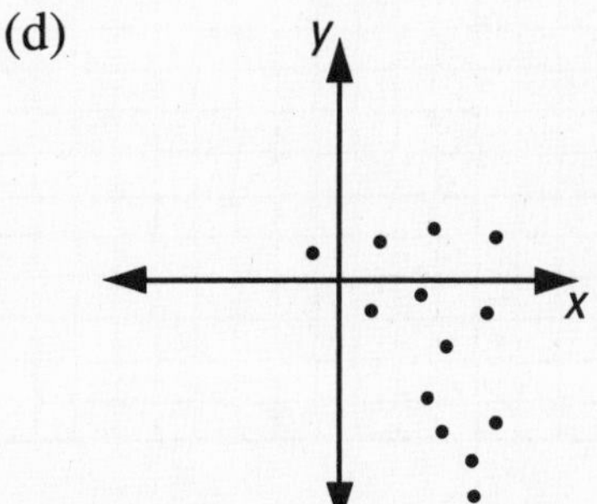

2. Based on a study of 200 dishwasher purchases, the table below shows the age of the dishwashers and the number of repairs needed by this group of dishwashers each year.

Age in Years	1	2	3	4	5	6	7	8	9	10
Number of Repairs	2	3	4	6	7	8	10	11	13	16

a. Use the grid on the next page, and carefully draw a scatterplot of points (age, number of repairs).

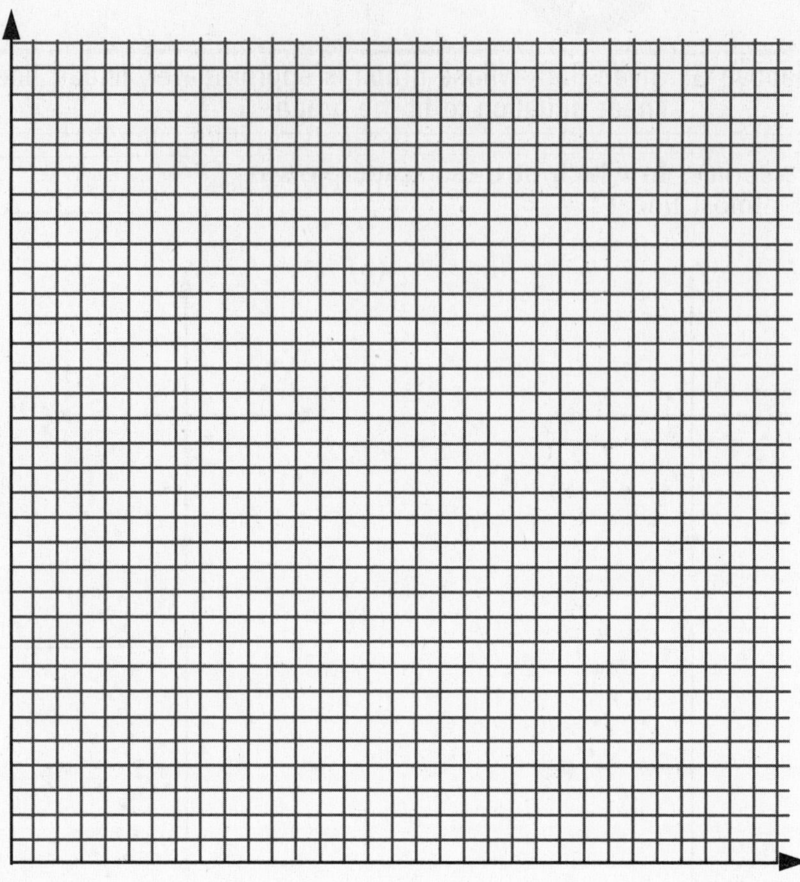

b. Fit a line to the data and draw it with a ruler.

c. Give the coordinates of two points on the line you drew. ____________

d. Use your two points to find an equation of your line. ____________

e. According to your equation, what happens to the number of repairs as the dishwashers get older?

____

f. Use your equation to find the number of repairs when the dishwashers are 12 years old. ____________

Review Objective B, Lesson 5-6

In 3 and 4, solve each inequality and graph all solutions on the number line provided.

3. $2m + 14 \leq 6m - 2$

4. $25 - 5b < 50 - 8b$

Name

LESSON MASTER 7-8 B

Questions on SPUR Objectives

Skills Objective C: Write an equation for a line in standard form, and from that form find its slope and *y*-intercept.

1. Write the standard form for an equation of a line. Then identify the constants.

____

2. Are there any lines that cannot be described by an equation in standard form? If so, which ones?

____

____

In 3–12, tell if the equation is in standard form.

3. $7y + 2x = 18$ ________ 4. $x + y = -8$ ________

5. $4x - 2y = 5$ ________ 6. $y = 3x + 8$ ________

7. $-x + 3y = -8$ ________ 8. $4x + 2y + 9 = 0$ ________

9. $0x - 2y = 7$ ________ 10. $22x + 0y = 44$ ________

11. $y = -x + 0$ ________ 12. $15y - x = 19$ ________

In 13–20, a. rewrite the equation in standard form with integer coefficients, and b. give the values of *A*, *B*, and *C*.

13. $y = -2x + 5$ a. ____________ b. ________

14. $y = \frac{4}{3}x + 1$ a. ____________ b. ________

15. $y = -\frac{7}{8}x - \frac{1}{3}$ a. ____________ b. ________

16. $2y + 3x = 9$ a. ____________ b. ________

17. $y = 4x$ a. ____________ b. ________

18. $-\frac{1}{2}x = 14$ a. ____________ b. ________

19. $2.1x - .8y = .6$ a. ____________ b. ________

20. $\frac{5}{6}y = \frac{3}{4}x$ a. ____________ b. ________

Name

Uses Objective F: Use equations for lines to describe real situations.

21. In a math competition, a team gets -2 points for wrong answers and 5 points for right answers. The Acute Anglers got x wrong answers and y right answers. Their final score was 67.

a. Write an equation in standard form describing the relationship between x and y. __________

b. Give three solutions to your equation in Part **a**.

____

22. Jeff and Sally sold books for the school book sale. Some cost \$15 and some cost \$20. They forgot to keep track of the number of each type they sold, but they do know that they collected \$900. Let x = number of \$15 books and y = number of \$20 books sold.

a. Find the number of \$20 books sold if only \$20 books were sold. __________

b. Find the number of \$20 books sold if 24 \$15 books were sold. __________

c. Write an equation in standard form describing the relationship between x and y. __________

Representations Objective H: Graph a straight line given its equation.

In 23 and 24, graph the line described.

23. $6x + 3y = 9$

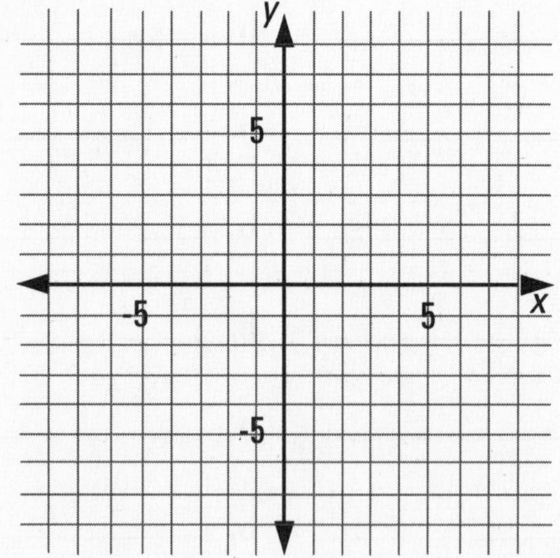

24. $5x - 2y = 8$

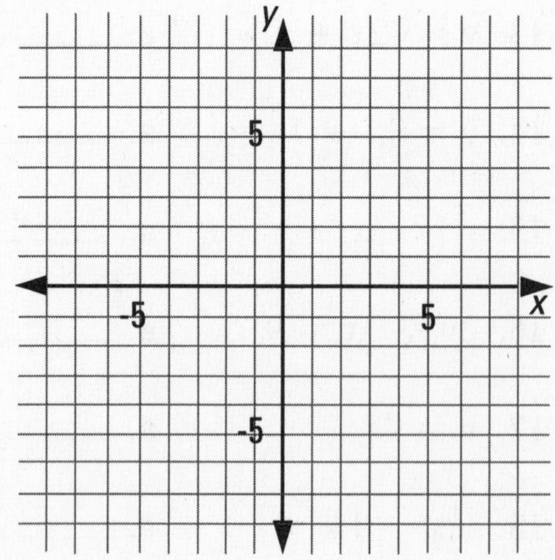

Name

LESSON MASTER 7-9 B

Questions on SPUR Objectives

Representations Objective I: Graph linear inequalities.

In 1–4, write an inequality that describes the graph.

1.

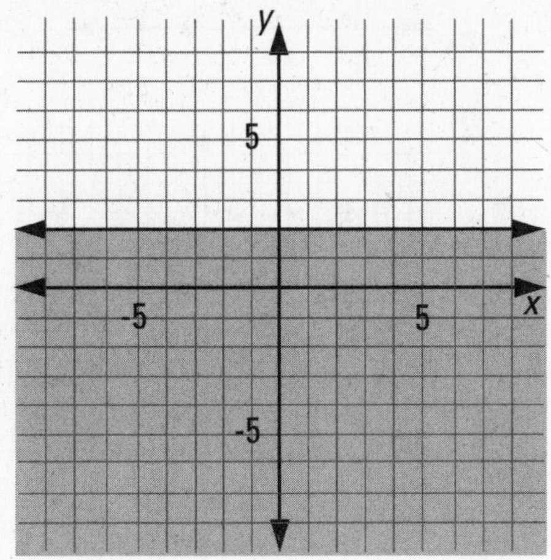

2.

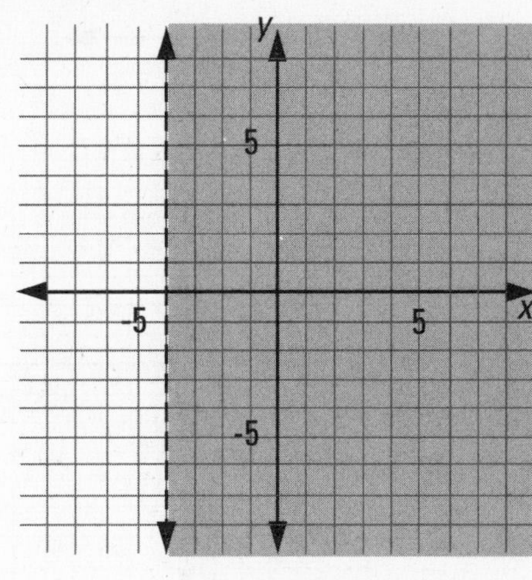

3.

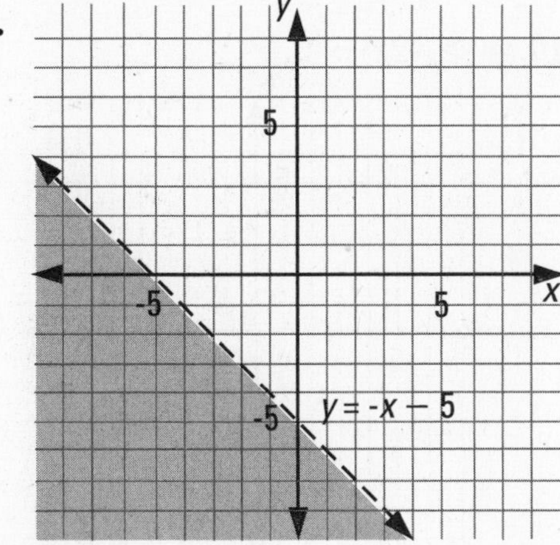

4.

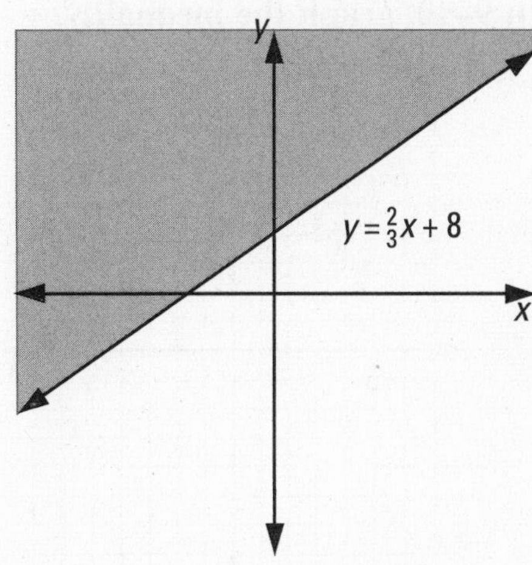

In 5 and 6, an inequality is given. a. Tell if you should shade above or below the boundary line. b. Tell if the boundary line should be solid or dashed.

5. $y < x - 11$

a. ______

b. ______

6. $y \geq 5x + 4$

a. ______

b. ______

Name ___

In 7 and 8, graph the inequality a. on the number line and b. on the coordinate grid.

7. $y > -4$

a. 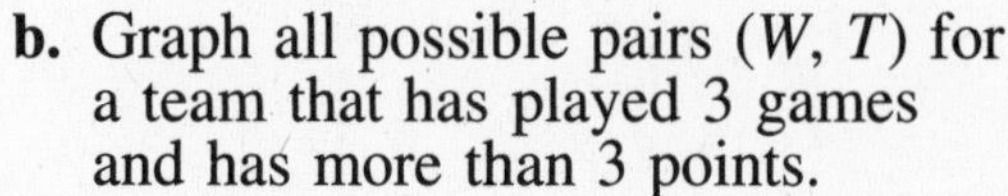

b.

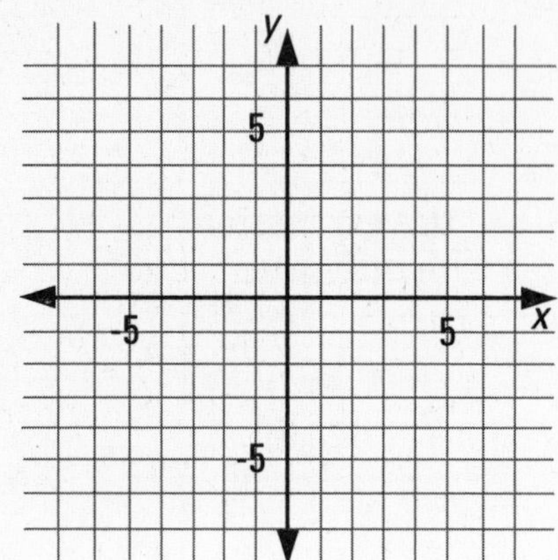

8. $x \leq 5$

a.

b.

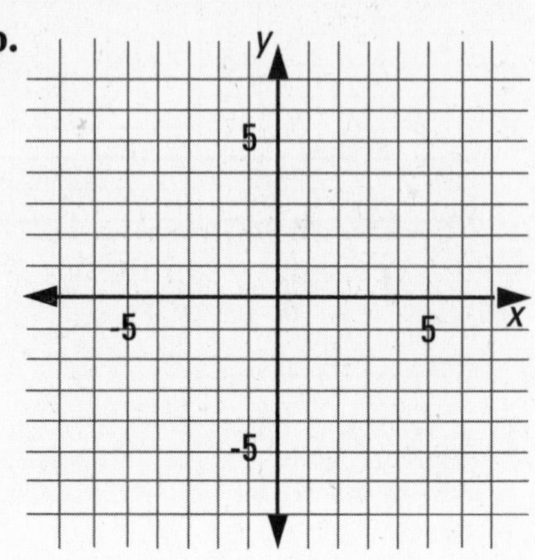

In 9–10, graph the inequality.

9. $y \leq x + 4$

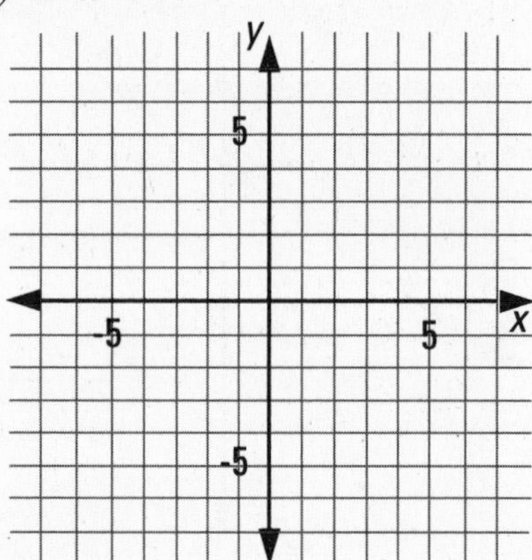

10. $y > -2x - 3$

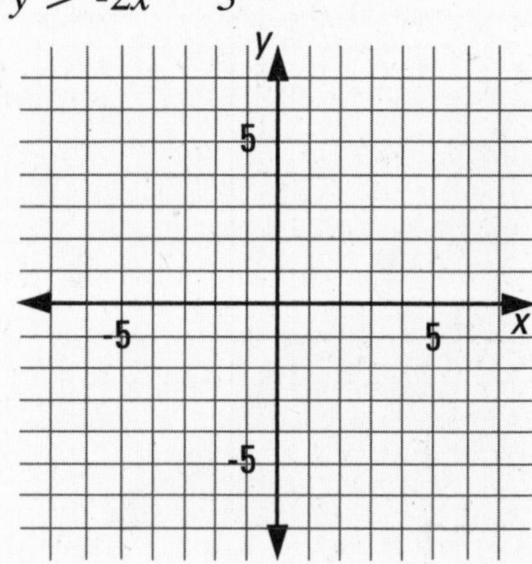

11. In World-Cup Soccer, a team gets 3 points for a win and 1 point for a tie. Let W be the number of wins and T be the number of ties.

a. If a team has more than 3 points, what inequality must W and T satisfy?

___

b. Graph all possible pairs (W, T) for a team that has played 3 games and has more than 3 points.

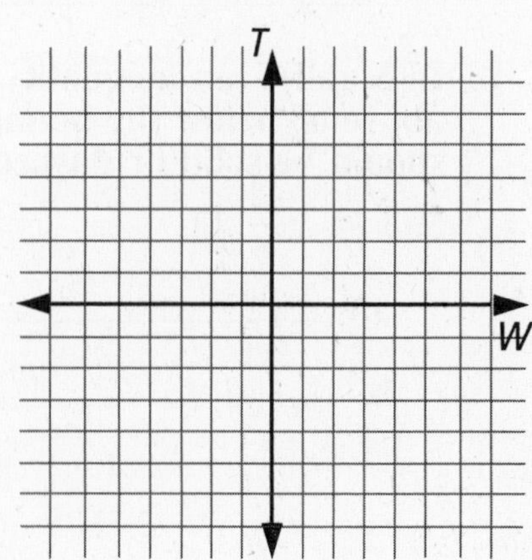

Name ________________

LESSON MASTER 8-1 B **Questions on SPUR Objectives**

Vocabulary

1. Consider a number of the form x^n.

a. x^n is called a ________________.

b. x is the ________________.

c. n is the ________________.

In 2 and 3, an expression is given. a. Write the expression using exponents. b. Identify the *base*(*s*). c. Identify the *exponent*(*s*). d. Identify the *coefficient*.

2. $38 \cdot c \cdot c \cdot c \cdot c$

a. ________________

b. ________________

c. ________________

d. ________________

3. $8 \cdot x \cdot x \cdot y \cdot y \cdot y \cdot y \cdot y$

a. ________________

b. ________________

c. ________________

d. ________________

4. The data below show the amount of money in a bank account.

Deposit		\$500.00
End of first year	500(1.07) =	\$535.00
End of second year	500(1.07)(1.07) =	\$572.45

a. What is the annual yield? ________________

b. What is the principal? ________________

c. What is the interest paid during the two-year period? ________________

Skills Objective A: Evaluate integer powers of real numbers.

In 5–10, evaluate the expression. Give answers rounded to the nearest ten-thousandth.

5. 5^3 ________________

6. 19^2 ________________

7. 3.4^2 ________________

8. 1.06^6 ________________

9. $(1 + .04)^7$ ________________

10. $200(1.085)^{12}$ ________________

Name ________________________________

Uses Objective F: Calculate compound interest.

11. a. Write an expression for the amount in an account after 18 years if $3,500 is invested at 7.2% annual yield.

____

b. Write a key sequence to enter this on your calculator.

____

c. To the nearest dollar, how much is in the account after 18 years? ________________

12. A bank uses the spreadsheet below to show the amount in a savings account earning 6% interest. The principal invested is $800.

	A	B	C
1	YEAR	BALANCE	YEARLY INTEREST
2	0	800.00	
3	1	848.00	48.00
4	2	898.88	50.88
5	3	952.81	53.93
6	4		

a. What formula can be entered in cell B6? ________________

b. What number should appear in cell B6? ________________

c. What formula can be entered in cell C6? ________________

d. What number should appear in cell C6? ________________

e. What trend do you notice in Column C? What do you think accounts for this?

____

____

13. Barb won $5,000 in a lottery and decided to put it in the bank for an emergency. An emergency never arose. How much was in the account after 15 years if the account had an annual yield of 9%? ________________

14. A department store charges 19.6% interest per year on unpaid monthly bills. How much would you owe if you did not pay a bill of $272 for 2 years? ________________

Name

LESSON MASTER 8-2 B

Questions on SPUR Objectives

Skills Objective A: Evaluate integer powers of real numbers.

In 1–10, evaluate.

1. 15^0
2. 27.4^0
3. $9^2 \cdot 9^0$
4. $(4.3 + 6)^0$
5. $\left(\frac{2}{3}\right)^4$
6. $\left(\frac{3}{4}\right)^4 + \left(\frac{6}{5}\right)^0$
7. $(y + 64)^0$ when $y = 10$
8. $4 \cdot 3^3 + 2 \cdot 8^1 + 12 \cdot 18^0$
9. $500(6^n)$ when $n = 0$
10. $133^{(7-7)}$

Properties Objective E: Use properties of exponents to explain operations with powers.

11. Suppose an investment of \$300 earns 8% interest each year.
    a. What does $300(1.08)^3$ represent?
    b. What does $300(1.08)^0$ represent?
    c. Use the expression from Part **b** to explain why $(1.08)^0$ equals 1.

Name

Uses Objective G: Solve problems involving exponential growth.

12. At the computer, Mrs. Gold enlarged a graphic 20%. She enlarged the resulting graphic 20%, and then enlarged this newest graphic another 20%. If the original graphic was 3 inches wide, how wide was the final graphic? ______________

13. A greenhouse purchased a dozen ivy plants. Periodically, new plants are started by taking *cuttings* of the old plant. It is estimated that the number of plants will be multiplied by 3 each month.

a. How many plants will there be after 6 months? ______________

b. How many plants will there be after n months? ______________

c. Do you think there will be enough space at the greenhouse for all the ivy plants if they continue the process for a year? Explain your answer.

____

____

Representations Objective I: Graph exponential relationships.

14. An analyst predicts that the number of subscribers to the *Bradley Sentinel* will increase 15% each year for the next five years. Today, there are 4,500 subscribers.

a. Make a table of values showing the number of subscribers 0, 1, 2, 3, 4, and 5 years from now.

b. Graph the number of subscribers for 0 through 5 years.

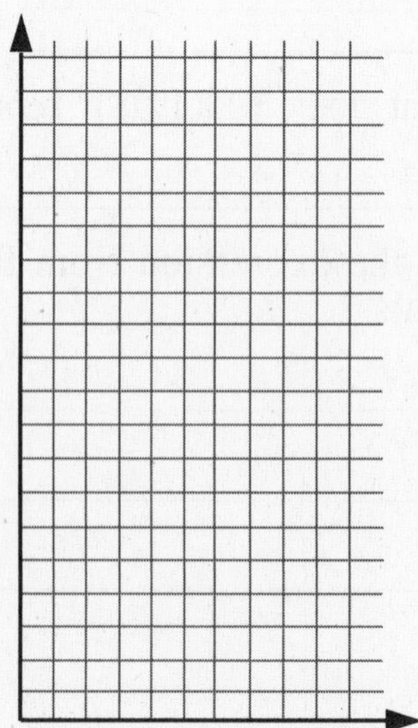

Name

LESSON MASTER **8-3 B**

Questions on SPUR Objectives

Uses Objective G: Solve problems involving exponential growth.
Representations Objective I: Graph exponential relationships.

1. The transportation department is studying two reports related to the predicted increase in the number of passengers at the airport. Report *A* predicts an increase of 1 million passengers each year, while Report *B* predicts that each year there will be a 6% increase. This year there are 14 million passengers at the airport. Let x = the number of years.

a. Write an expression for the number of passengers if that number increases by 1 million per year. ________________

b. Write an expression for the number of passengers if that number increases by 6% per year. ________________

c. Fill in the table below.

YEAR	INCREASE BY 1,000,000	INCREASE BY 6%
0	14,000,000	14,000,000
1		
2		
3		
4		
5		
6		
7		
8		
9		
10		

Name ________________________________

▶ LESSON MASTER 8-3 B *page 2*

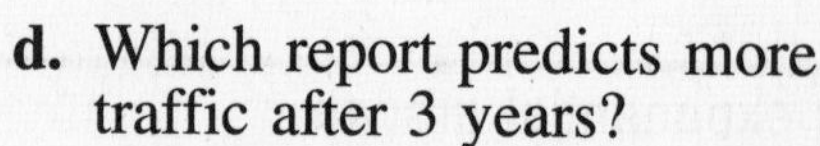

d. Which report predicts more traffic after 3 years?

____

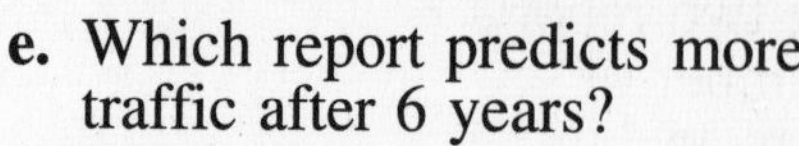

e. Which report predicts more traffic after 6 years?

____

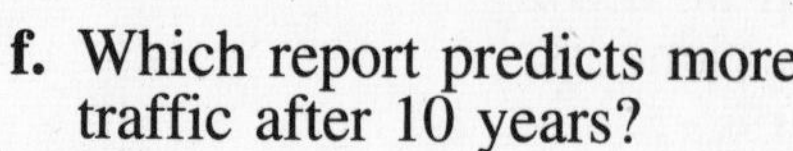

f. Which report predicts more traffic after 10 years?

____

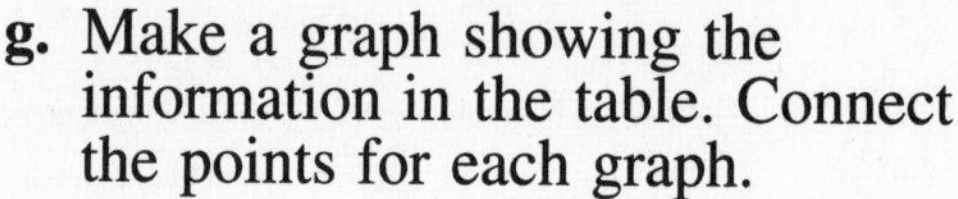

g. Make a graph showing the information in the table. Connect the points for each graph.

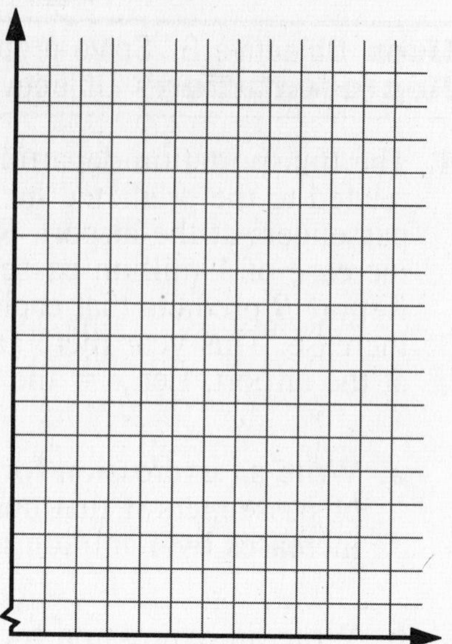

2. Sketch a possible graph below showing exponential growth.

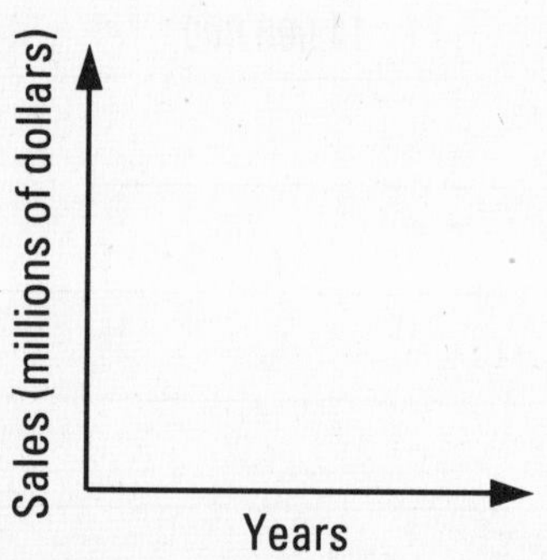

3. Sketch a possible graph below showing constant increase.

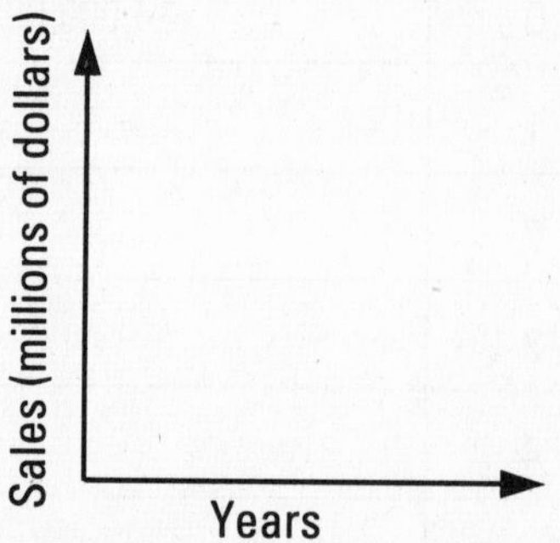

In 4–10, tell which is being described: *constant increase* or *exponential growth*.

4. Each year the enrollment increased by 200. ________________

5. Each year the enrollment increased by 4%. ________________

6. Each hour 2 more inches of snow fell. ________________

7. Each month the profits increased .5%. ________________

8. $210 \cdot 1.045^x$ ________________

9. $210 + 6x$ ________________

10. Each year the farm doubled its yield. ________________

Name

LESSON MASTER 8-4 B

Questions on SPUR Objectives

Uses Objective G: Solve problems involving exponential decay.

1. National Cables has launched a program to reduce its debt by 12% per year. The debt is currently $9,000,000.

YEAR	AMOUNT OF DEBT
0	$9,000,000
1	
2	
3	
4	
5	
6	

a. Fill in the table to show the amount of the company's debt for 0 through 6 years.

b. How much did the company reduce its debt during the first year?

____

c. How much did the company reduce its debt during the fifth year?

____

d. Write an expression for the amount of debt remaining after x years. ________________

e. Use trial and error to find how long it will take to reduce the debt to less than $1,000,000. ________________

2. A single thickness of one type of glass cuts down the emission of light by 10%. Consider a 60-watt light bulb which has an intensity of about 800 *lumens*.

a. By what number would you multiply to find the number of the light bulb's lumens emitted through a single thickness of the glass? ________________

b. How many lumens are emitted through a single thickness of the glass? ________________

c. How many lumens are emitted through two thicknesses of the glass? ________________

d. Let t = the number of thicknesses of glass. Write an expression to describe the number of lumens that are emitted through t thicknesses of the glass. ________________

e. How many lumens are emitted through five thicknesses of the glass? ________________

Name

3. Today, the Johnsville Lumber Company has 18,000 acres of trees available for lumber. They are cutting the trees at a faster rate than they are replacing them. As a result, they estimate that each year they will have 15% fewer acres of trees available for lumber.

a. Write and equation to describe this situation. ____________

b. How many acres of trees will be available for lumber after 15 years? ____________

In 4–7, *multiple choice*. Tell if the situation described is (a) exponential growth, (b) exponential decay, (c) constant growth, or (d) constant decrease.

4. The water level is going down 3 inches per day. ____________

5. The amount of mail increases 5% per year. ____________

6. Each year the company increases profits by $400,000. ____________

7. Each month the number of accidents is reduced 2%. ____________

Representations Objective I: Graph exponential relationships.

In 8–11, *multiple choice*. Match the graph to the equation.

(a) 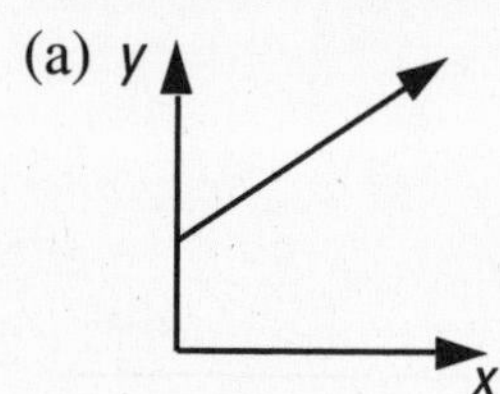

(b) 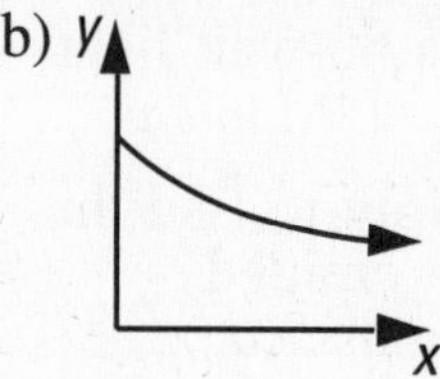

(c) 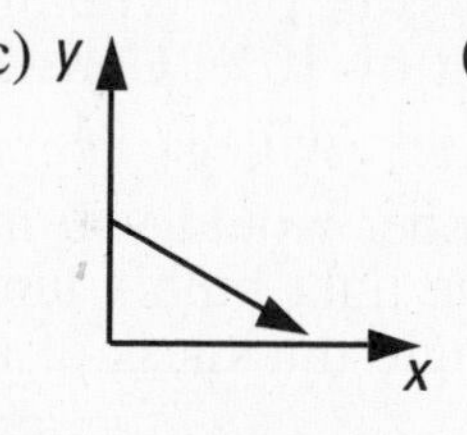

(d) 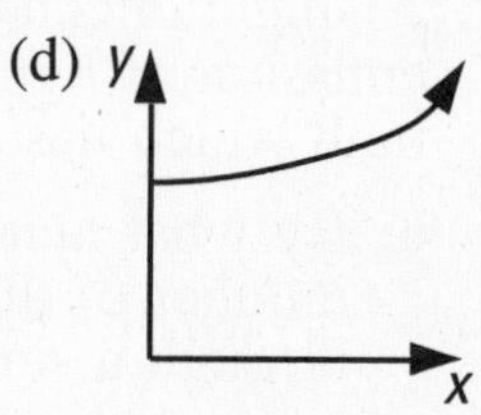

8. $y = -\frac{1}{2}x + 3$ ____________

9. $y = \frac{1}{2}x + 3$ ____________

10. $y = 3 \cdot 1.09^x$ ____________

11. $y = 3 \cdot .91^x$ ____________

12. Refer to Question 1. Graph the amount of the company's debt for 0 through 6 years. Connect the points of the graph with a smooth curve.

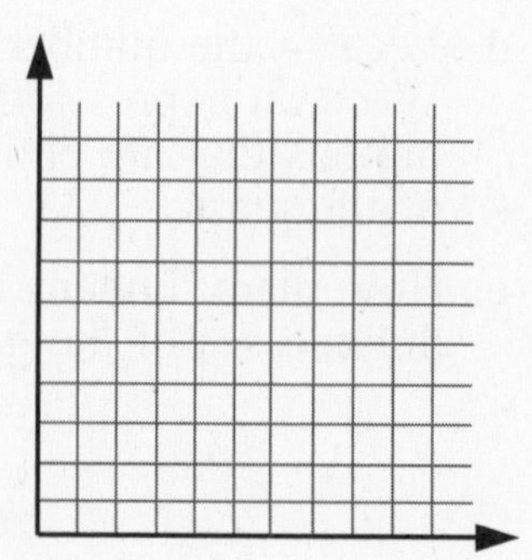

Name ______

LESSON MASTER 8-5 B

Questions on SPUR Objectives

Skills Objective B: Simplify products and powers of powers.

In 1–6, write each expression as a single power.

1. $8^4 \cdot 8^3$ ______

2. $10^2 \cdot 10^2$ ______

3. $5^6 \cdot 5^5 \cdot 5^2$ ______

4. $6 \cdot 6^3$ ______

5. $(3^4)^2$ ______

6. $(14^3)^5$ ______

7. a. Simplify $m^4 \cdot m^2$. ______

b. Check your answer by letting $m = 3$.

______

In 8–27, simplify each expression.

8. $m^2 \cdot m^3$ ______

9. $x^4 \cdot x^4$ ______

10. $(g^4)^3$ ______

11. $(a^5)^5$ ______

12. $r^3 \cdot r^4 \cdot r^2$ ______

13. $e \cdot e^3$ ______

14. $w^4 \cdot w \cdot w^5$ ______

15. $k^7 \cdot y^3 \cdot k \cdot y^3$ ______

16. $(n^3 \cdot n^5)^2$ ______

17. $(d \cdot d^2)^4$ ______

18. $4p^3 \cdot 5p^6$ ______

19. $-6x^2 \cdot 2x$ ______

20. $x^2 \cdot y \cdot x^4 \cdot y^3 \cdot y$ ______

21. $(h^0)^3$ ______

22. $5n(n^6)^3$ ______

23. $x^0 \cdot 2x^3$ ______

24. $a(a^6 - a^3)$ ______

25. $5x^2(x + 2x^4)$ ______

26. $m^2(m^3 - y^3)$ ______

27. $(b^4)^3 - (b^3)^4$ ______

Name

Properties Objective E: Identify properties of exponents and use them to explain operations with powers.

28. Show how to simplify $r^2 \cdot r^4$

a. by using repeated multiplication.

b. by using the Product of Powers Property.

29. Show how to simplify $(x^3)^4$

a. by treating x^3 as a chunk.

b. by using the Power of a Power Property.

30. Write a multiplication expression that uses the Product of Powers Property and has the value w^9.

31. Write an expression that uses the Power of a Power Property and has the value m^{18}.

In 32–37, solve for *x*.

32. $8^x \cdot 8^3 = 8^7$

33. $4^4 \cdot 4^x = 4^5$

34. $n^x \cdot n^3 = n^3$

35. $(5^4)^x = 5^{12}$

36. $(9^x)^5 = 9^{10}$

37. $e(e^8)^x = e^{17}$

Review Objective A, Lesson 3-1

38. In a magic square, each row, column, and diagonal has the same sum. Fill in the boxes at the right so each of these sums is -6*x*.

x	$-6x$	
		$-5x$

Name ______________________________

LESSON MASTER 8-6 B

Questions on SPUR Objectives

Skills Objective A: Evaluate integer powers of real numbers.

In 1–8, evaluate the expression. Give your answers as a simple fraction.

1. 7^{-1} __________ **2.** 11^{-2} __________

3. $\left(\frac{1}{5}\right)^{-1}$ __________ **4.** 6^{-3} __________

5. $2 \cdot 3^{-4}$ __________ **6.** $20^{-8} \cdot 20^{8}$ __________

7. $\left(\frac{2}{3}\right)^{-2}$ __________ **8.** $3^{-2} \cdot 3^{-3}$ __________

In 9–16, evaluate the expression. Give your answer as a decimal.

9. 10^{-1} __________ **10.** 10^{-4} __________

11. 10^{-2} __________ **12.** 10^{-10} __________

13. $6 \cdot 10^{-1}$ __________ **14.** $5 \cdot 10^{-3}$ __________

15. $2 \cdot 10^{3} + 8 \cdot 10^{2} + 6 \cdot 10^{1} + 6 \cdot 10^{0} + 3 \cdot 10^{-1} + 4 \cdot 10^{-2} + 5 \cdot 10^{-3}$

____

16. $9 \cdot 10^{5} + 4 \cdot 10^{4} + 3 \cdot 10^{2} + 8 \cdot 10^{0} + 2 \cdot 10^{-1} + 7 \cdot 10^{-4} + 1 \cdot 10^{-5}$

____

Skills Objective B: Simplify products of and powers of powers.

17. $m^{-3} \cdot m^{5}$ __________ **18.** $x^{2} \cdot x^{-8}$ __________

19. $a^{-2} \cdot a^{-6}$ __________ **20.** $(a^{-3})^{4}$ __________

21. $x^{3} \cdot x^{-9} \cdot x^{2}$ __________ **22.** $n \cdot n^{-6}$ __________

23. $uw^{4} \cdot u^{-2}w^{-8}$ __________ **24.** $(g^{-1})^{-5}$ __________

In 25–28, write each expression without negative exponents.

25. 4^{-x} __________ **26.** x^{-3} __________

27. $m^{-2}n^{5}$ __________ **28.** $7a^{-1}b^{-5}$ __________

Name ______

In 29–33, give examples of three different pairs of values of *a* and *b* that satisfy the equation.

29. $4^a \cdot 4^b = 4^3$ ______ ______ ______

30. $3^a \cdot 3^b = 3^1$ ______ ______ ______

31. $x^a \cdot x^b = x^2$ ______ ______ ______

32. $(5^a)^b = 5^6$ ______ ______ ______

33. $(y^a)^b = y^{-8}$ ______ ______ ______

Properties Objective E: Identify the Negative Exponent Property and use it to explain operations with powers.

34. Explain the relationship between b^n and b^{-n}.

______

35. Show how to simplify $m^{-4} \cdot m^4$

a. by first applying the Negative Exponent Property.

______

b. by first applying the Product of Powers Property.

______

Uses Objective G: Solve problems involving exponential decay.

36. Carl has $3276.99 in a saving account that earns 7% annually. Assuming no withdrawals or deposits were made, how much did he have in the account 4 years ago? ______

37. Crestburg's population doubled each of the last five decades. Today there are *p* people in Crestburg. How many people were there 50 years ago? ______

Uses Objective H: Use and simplify expressions with powers in everyday situations.

38. A test has 20 multiple-choice questions, each with 4 options. What is the probability of guessing all the correct answers? Express your answer using a negative exponent. ______

Name ______________________________

LESSON MASTER 8-7 B

Questions on SPUR Objectives

Skills Objective A: Evaluate quotients of integer powers of real numbers.

In 1–8, write as a single power.

1. $\frac{3^6}{3^4}$ ______________

2. $\frac{6^5}{6^9}$ ______________

3. $\frac{8^{-7}}{8^4}$ ______________

4. $\frac{12^6}{12^{-8}}$ ______________

5. $\frac{5^{-8}}{5^{-2}}$ ______________

6. $\frac{4^6}{4^6}$ ______________

7. $\frac{7^5 \cdot 7^2}{7^3}$ ______________

8. $\frac{2^8 \cdot 2^{-4}}{2^7}$ ______________

In 9 and 10, rewrite each equation using powers of 2.

9. $\frac{32}{8} = 4$ ______________

10. $\frac{16}{64} = \frac{1}{4}$ ______________

In 11–18, evaluate. Write the answer as a decimal.

11. $\frac{5^4}{5^2}$ ______________

12. $\frac{3^5}{3}$ ______________

13. $\frac{4^5}{4^7}$ ______________

14. $\frac{10^5}{10^{11}}$ ______________

15. $\frac{48 \cdot 10^5}{6 \cdot 10^2}$ ______________

16. $\frac{6.6 \cdot 10^7}{1.1 \cdot 10^{12}}$ ______________

17. $\frac{3 \cdot 10^6}{12 \cdot 10^4}$ ______________

18. $\frac{4.06 \cdot 10^9}{2 \cdot 10^2}$ ______________

Skills Objective B: Simplify quotients of powers.

19. Simplify $\frac{x^5}{x^{12}}$. Give your answer

a. as a fraction. ______________

b. using a negative exponent. ______________

Name

In 20–31, simplify. Write your answers without negative exponents.

20. $\frac{a^7}{a^2}$ ________

21. $\frac{x^5}{x^8}$ ________

22. $\frac{u^{-6}}{u^{-2}}$ ________

23. $\frac{a^4b^8}{ab^2}$ ________

24. $\frac{m^6n^8}{m^2n^{10}}$ ________

25. $\frac{15a^7}{3a^2}$ ________

26. $\frac{16d^4e^{11}}{20d^6e^4}$ ________

27. $\frac{-18cb^8}{6c^8b^2}$ ________

28. $\frac{9u^6}{4u^{-2}v^5}$ ________

29. $\frac{(y-5)^3}{(y-5)^4}$ ________

30. $\frac{(3v)^4}{(3v)^8}$ ________

31. $\frac{14c^3}{3x} \cdot \frac{6x^3}{c^{12}}$ ________

Properties Objective E: Identify the Quotient of Powers Property and use it to explain operations with powers.

32. Write an algebraic fraction that the Quotient of Powers Property can be used to simplify to b^5. ________

33. Explain how to use the Quotient of Powers Property to find the value of x in $\frac{6^x}{6^3} = 6^8$.

____

Uses Objective H: Use and simplify expressions with powers in everyday situations.

34. Pluto's average distance from the sun is $3.66 \cdot 10^9$ miles. Earth is about $9.3 \cdot 10^7$ miles from the sun. Pluto's distance from the sun is how many times Earth's distance? ________

35. In 1992, Colorado produced $7.26 \cdot 10^7$ bushels of wheat. What percent is this of that year's total U.S. wheat production of $2.46 \cdot 10^9$ bushels? ________

Name ______________________________

LESSON MASTER 8-8 B

Questions on SPUR Objectives

Skills Objective A: Evaluate integer powers of real number products and quotients.

In 1–6, tell if the number is *positive* or *negative*.

1. -13^5 ______________

2. -11^6 ______________

3. $(-8)^4$ ______________

4. $\left(-\frac{4}{5}\right)^7$ ______________

5. 17^3 ______________

6. $(-2.6)^{87}$ ______________

In 7–20, evaluate each expression.

7. -8^2 ______________

8. $(-9)^2$ ______________

9. -3^2 ______________

10. $(-6)^3$ ______________

11. -7^3 ______________

12. $(-4)^4$ ______________

13. $\left(\frac{1}{2}\right)^5$ ______________

14. $\left(-\frac{3}{10}\right)^4$ ______________

15. $-\left(\frac{4}{3}\right)^2$ ______________

16. $(-5.1)^2$ ______________

17. $(3 \cdot 4)^2$ ______________

18. $(3^{-2})^3$ ______________

19. $(1.8 \cdot 10^4)^2$ ______________

20. $(-7.66 \cdot 10^3)^2$ ______________

Skills Objective C: Rewrite powers of products and quotient.

In 21–28, simplify each expression.

21. $(4x)^2$ ______________

22. $(3a^5)^3$ ______________

23. $(3xyz)^0$ ______________

24. $\left(\frac{1}{6}a^4b\right)^4$ ______________

25. $4n(8n^5)^3$ ______________

26. $(5r^2)^4(-2r^3)^5$ ______________

27. $-\left(\frac{3a^2}{b}\right)^4$ ______________

28. $\left(\frac{3}{4}m\right)^2 \cdot (8m)^2$ ______________

Name

Properties Objective E: Identify the Product of a Power and Power of a Quotient Properties and use them to explain operations with powers.

29. Show how to simplify $(mx^{-3})^4$

a. by rewriting using repeated multiplication.

____

b. by rewriting using the Power of a Product Property.

____

30. Show how to simplify $\left(\frac{3}{u^e}\right)^4$

a. by rewriting using repeated multiplication.

____

b. by rewriting using the Power of a Quotient Property.

____

In 31–34, *multiple choice*. Identify the property that is illustrated.

(a) Power of a Power **(b) Power of a Product**

(c) Product of Powers **(d) Power of a Quotient**

(e) Quotient of Powers

31. $\left(\frac{a}{3}\right)^4 = \frac{a^4}{81}$ ____________

33. $m^3 \cdot m^6 = m^9$ ____________

33. $(e^5)^2 = e^{10}$ ____________

34. $\frac{x^3}{x^8} = x^{-5}$ ____________

Uses Objective H: Use and simplify expressions with powers in everyday situations.

35. Find the volume of each cube.

a. ____________

b. ____________

c. ____________

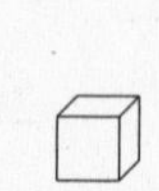

n cm

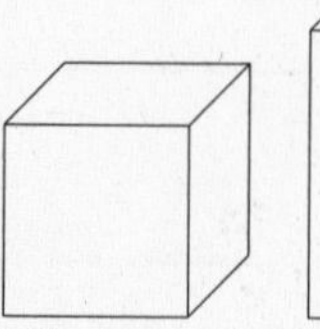

$3n$ cm

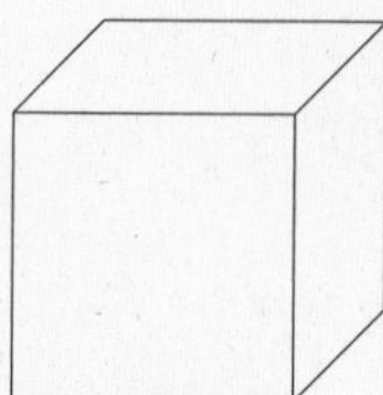

kn cm

Name

LESSON MASTER **8-9 B**

Questions on SPUR Objectives

Skills Objective A: Evaluate integer powers of real numbers.

In 1–6, simplify, giving the answer as a simple fraction.

1. $\left(\frac{3}{14}\right)^{-1}$ __________

2. $\left(\frac{2}{7}\right)^{-2}$ __________

3. $\left(\frac{4}{3}\right)^{-3}$ __________

4. $(-3)^{-4}$ __________

5. -3^{-4} __________

6. $\left(-\frac{1}{10}\right)^{-4}$ __________

7. *Multiple choice.* Which of the following equals $(3m^{-3})^{-4}$? Explain your reasoning.

(a) $81m^{12}$ (b) $\frac{m^{12}}{81}$ (c) $\frac{81}{m^{12}}$ (d) $\frac{1}{81m^{12}}$

____

Properties Objective D: Test a special case to determine whether a pattern is true.

8. Give a counterexample to the pattern $a^3 \cdot a^2 = a^6$.

____

9. For each value of a, tell if $\frac{a^3}{a^2} = a^4$ is *true* or *false*.

a. $a = 2$ __________ **b.** $a = 1$ __________

c. $a = .1$ __________ **d.** $a = 0$ __________

10. For each value of x, tell if $(-x)^5 = -(x)^5$ is *true* or *false*.

a. $x = 1$ __________ **b.** $x = 0$ __________

c. $x = -1$ __________ **d.** $x = 2$ __________

Name ______________________________

► **LESSON MASTER 8-9 B** *page 2*

In 11–14, *multiple choice*. Choose the simplified form of the given expression. Check your answer by testing a special case.

11. $(4x^3)^2$ (a) $16x^5$ (b) $16x^6$ (c) $4x^5$ (d) $16x^5$ ______

____
check

12. $5x^4 \cdot 3x^3$ (a) $15x^7$ (b) $8x^7$ (c) $15x^{12}$ (d) $16{,}875^{14}x^7$ ______

____
check

13. $\frac{x^{12}}{x^6}$ (a) x^2 (b) $\frac{1}{x^6}$ (c) x^6 (d) $\frac{1}{x^2}$ ______

____
check

14. $\left(\frac{2}{x^2}\right)^{-3}$ (a) $\frac{x^6}{8}$ (b) $\frac{x^6}{6}$ (c) $-\frac{x^6}{8}$ (d) $\frac{1}{8x}$ ______

____
check

15. Show two different ways to simplify $\left(\frac{x}{y}\right)^3\left(\frac{x}{y}\right)^{-1}$.

____

____

16. Consider the pattern $\sqrt{x^2 + y^2} = x + y$.

a. Test the case with four different pairs of numbers for x and y.

____

____

____

____

b. Do you think the pattern is true? Why or why not?

____

____

Name

LESSON MASTER

Questions on SPUR Objectives

Vocabulary

In 1–6, use the graphs of parabolas A and B pictured at the right.

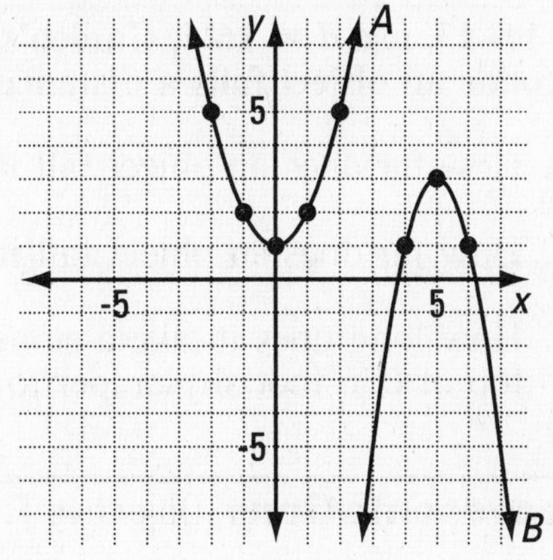

1. What seems to be the vertex of

a. parabola A? ______

b. parabola B? ______

2. What is the axis of symmetry of parabola A? ______

3. Give an equation for the axis of symmetry of parabola B. ______

4. Which parabola opens

a. up? ______ **b.** down? ______

5. Which parabola has a

a. maximum? ______ **b.** minimum? ______

6. Give the coordinates of the point that is the reflection image of the given point over the parabola's axis of symmetry.

a. (-2, 5) on parabola A ______

b. (6, 1) on parabola B ______

Skills Objective A: Solve quadratic equations of the form $ax^2 = k$.

In 7–10, find both values of x. If answers are not integers, round to the nearest hundredth.

7. $5x^2 = 180$ ______ **8.** $\frac{1}{4}x^2 = 36$ ______

9. $\frac{7}{6}x^2 = 14$ ______ **10.** $4.8x^2 = 912$ ______

Name ____

▶ **LESSON MASTER 9-1 B** *page 2*

Uses Objective E: Use quadratic equations to solve problems about paths of projectiles.

In 11–13, use $d = 16t^2$, Galileo's formula relating the time t in seconds an object falls a distance d in feet.

11. How far does an object fall in 8 seconds? ____________

12. How far does an object fall in $3t$ seconds? ____________

13. How long does it take a stone to fall from the top of 676-foot skyscraper to the ground below? ____________

Representations Objective F: Graph equations of the form $y = ax^2$ and interpret these graphs.

In 14 and 15, an equation is given. Make a table of values using x-values -3, -2, -1, 0, 1, 2, and 3. Graph the equation.

14. $y = \frac{3}{2}x^2$

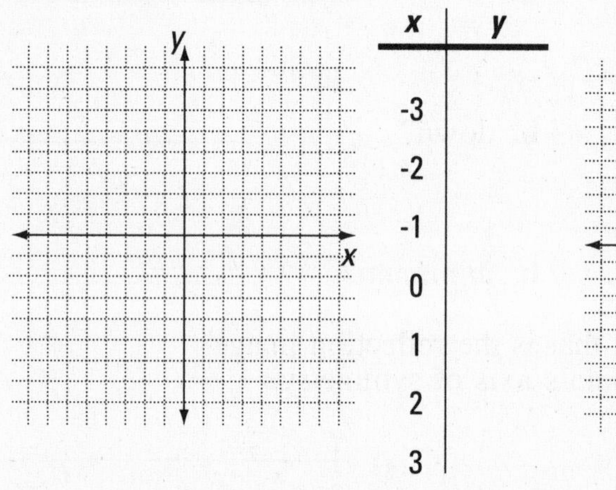

x	y
-3	
-2	
-1	
0	
1	
2	
3	

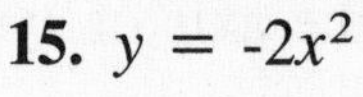

15. $y = -2x^2$

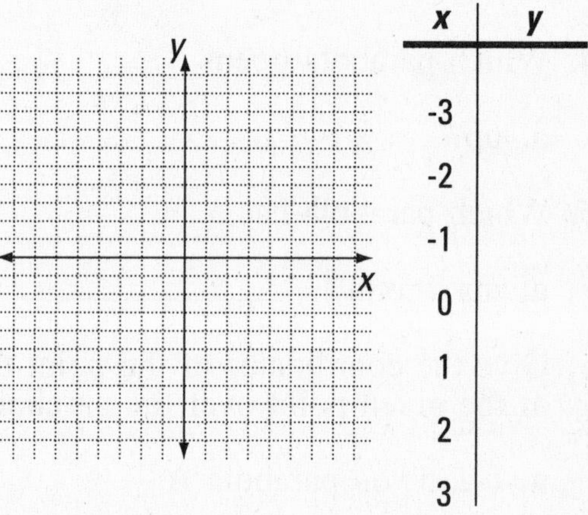

x	y
-3	
-2	
-1	
0	
1	
2	
3	

In 16 and 17, an equation is given. a. Tell if its graph opens *up* or *down*. b. Tell if it has a *maximum* or a *minimum*.

16. $y = \frac{2}{3}x^2$

a. ________ **b.** ____________

17. $y = -5x^2$

a. ________ **b.** ____________

Name

LESSON MASTER 9-2 B **Questions on SPUR Objectives**

Representations Objective F: Graph equations of the form $y = ax^2 + bx + c$ and interpret these graphs.

In 1 and 2, tell if the graph of the equation opens *up* or *down*.

1. $y = 3x^2 - 4x - 1$ ________ **2.** $y = -2x^2 + 3$ ________

In 3 and 4, the graph of a parabola is shown. a. Give the coordinates of the vertex. b. Give the *y*-intercept. c. Write an equation for the axis of symmetry.

3.

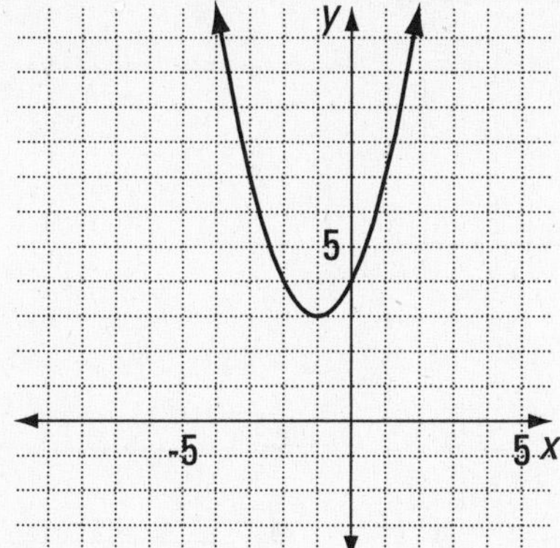

4.

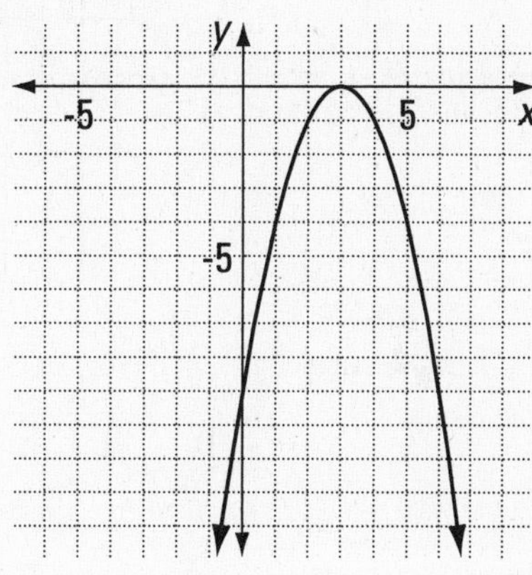

3. **a.** ____________ **b.** ____________ **c.** ____________

4. **a.** ____________ **b.** ____________ **c.** ____________

5. The table of values below is for a parabola.

x	-1	0	1	2	3	4	5	6	7
y	38	24	14	8	6	8			

a. Fill in the missing values.

b. What are the coordinates of its vertex? ____________

c. What is its *y*-intercept? ____________

d. Does this parabola open up? ____________

e. Does the parabola have a minimum value? ____________

Name

▶ LESSON MASTER 9-2 B *page 2*

In 6 and 7, an equation is given. a. Make a table of values using x-values -3, -2, -1, 0, 1, 2, and 3. b. Graph the equation. c. Give the coordinates of the vertex. d. Give the y-intercept. e. Write an equation for the axis of symmetry.

6. $y = x^2 - 4x + 5$

a. **b.**

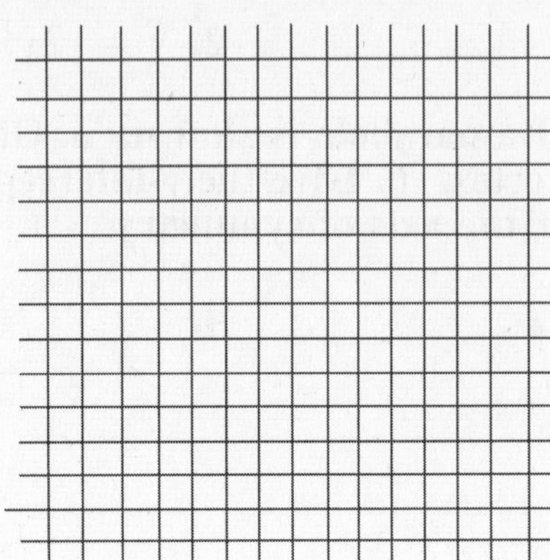

c. ____________

d. ____________

e. ____________

7. $y = -3x^2 + 1$

a. **b.**

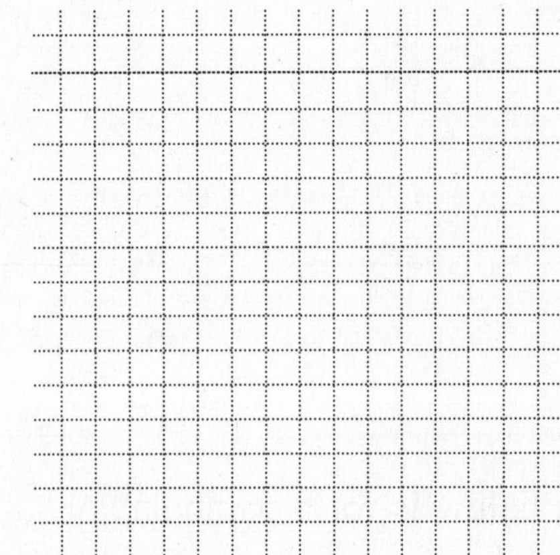

c. ____________

d. ____________

e. ____________

8. a. Use symmetry to complete the graph at the right.

b. Name its y-intercept.

____

c. Name its x-intercepts.

____

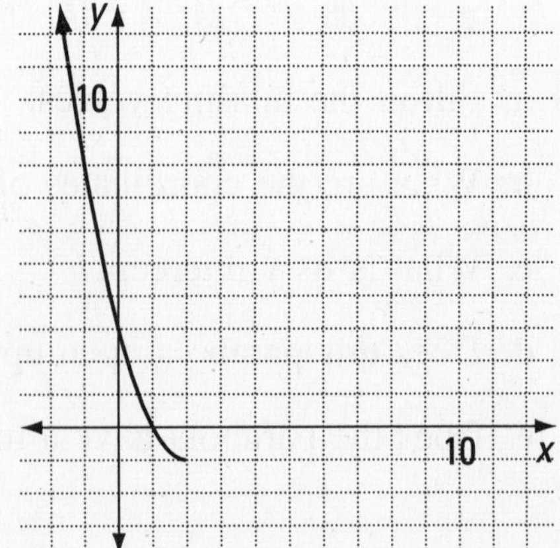

Name

LESSON MASTER **9-3 B** **Questions on SPUR Objectives**

Representations Objective F: Graph equations of the form $y = ax^2 + bx + c$ and interpret these graphs.

1. 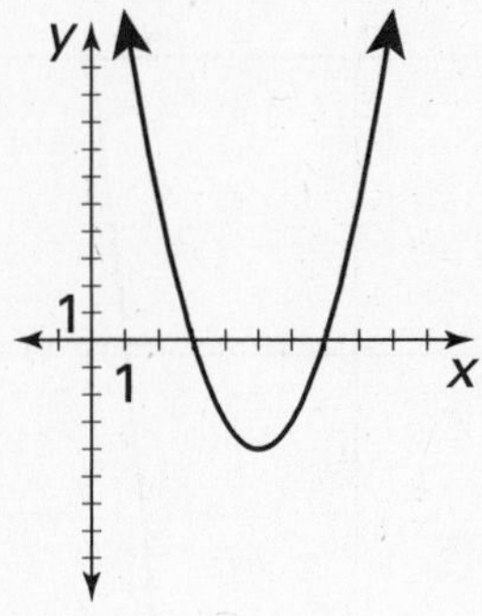

In the graph of the equation $x^2 - 10x + 21$ shown at the left, the x-intercepts are 3 and 7.

a. What is the x-coordinate of the vertex?

____

b. Use your answer to Part **a** to find the y-coordinate of the vertex.

____

c. Write an equation for the axis of symmetry.

____

2. **a.** On the default window of an automatic grapher, graph the four parabolas given. Then sketch them in the window at the right.

$y = -x^2 - 1$

$y = -2x^2 - 2$

$y = -3x^2 - 3$

$y = -4x^2 - 4$

b. Describe how the graphs are similar and how they are different.

____

____

____

____

c. Describe the graph of $-10x^2 - 10$.

____

____

____

Name ______________________________

▶ **LESSON MASTER 9-3 B** *page 2*

In 3 and 4, the graph of a parabola is given. Identify a different window that shows the vertex, the y-intercept, and both x-intercepts.

3. $y = x^2 - 8x - 22$

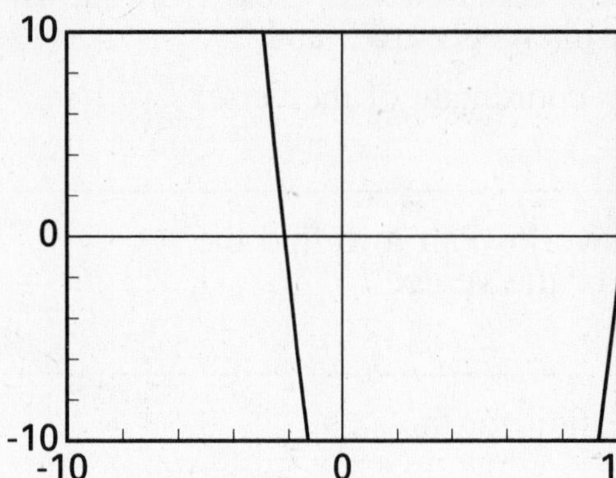

4. $y = -x^2 + 24x - 104$

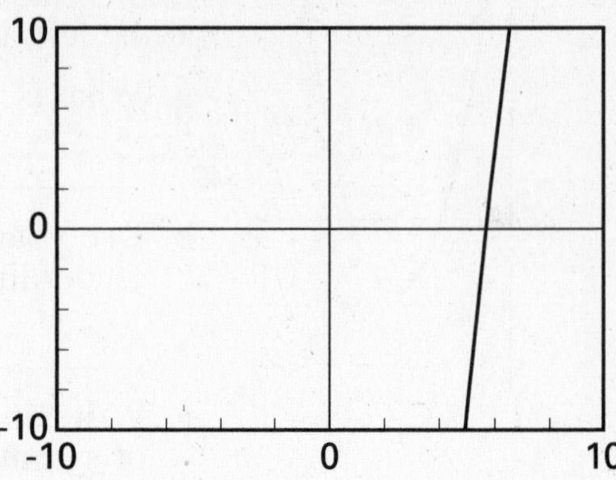

______________________________ ______________________________

______________________________ ______________________________

5. Identify a window for the graph of $y = -x^2 + 5$ so the graph will look like the graph at the right.

____

____

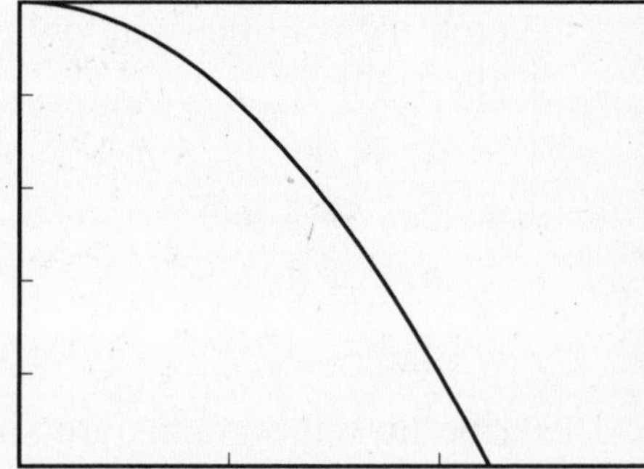

6. Graph $y = 2x^2 + 40x + 156$ on a window that shows the vertex and x-intercepts.

a. Estimate the coordinates of the vertex. ______________________________

b. Write an equation for the axis of symmetry. ______________________________

c. Estimate the x-intercepts. ______________________________

7. a. Use an automatic grapher and graph $y = x^2 + 1$ and $y = 2x + 4$ on the same set of axes.

b. Estimate the coordinates of the points where the two graphs intersect. ______________________________

Name ____________________

LESSON MASTER 

Questions on SPUR Objectives

Uses Objective E: Use quadratic equations to solve problems about paths of projectiles.

In 1–6, use the graph at the right. It shows the height *h* in feet of a small rocket *t* seconds after it is launched.

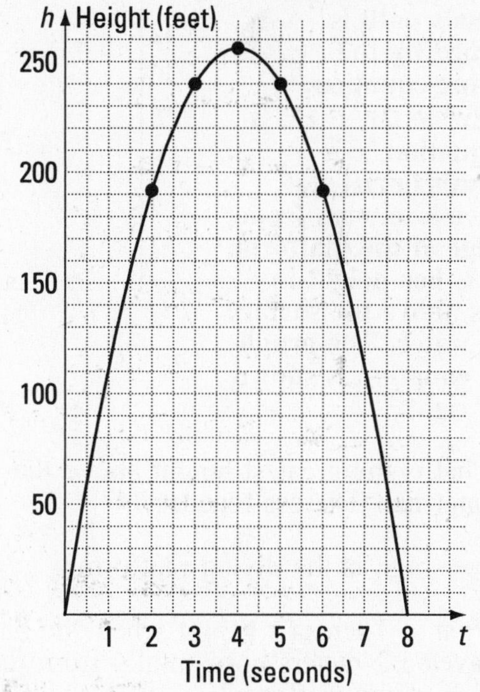

1. How long is the rocket in the air? ____________________

2. What is the greatest height the rocket reaches? ____________________

3. About how high is the rocket after 1 second? ____________________

4. After 2 seconds,

a. about how high is the rocket? ____________________

b. is the rocket *going up* or *coming down*? ____________________

5. After 6 seconds,

a. about how high is the rocket? ____________________

b. is the rocket *going up* or *coming down*? ____________________

6. Do you think the rocket is traveling faster from 0 to 1 second or from 3 to 4 seconds? Explain your thinking.

____

____

____

Name ______________________________

In 7–10, use this information. Theresa jumps off a diving platform into the swimming pool below. Theresa's path is described by the following equation: $y = -2x^2 + 2x + 15$. In this equation, x is Theresa's horizontal distance in meters from the edge of the platform, and y is her height in meters above the surface of the water. The graph of the equation is shown at the right.

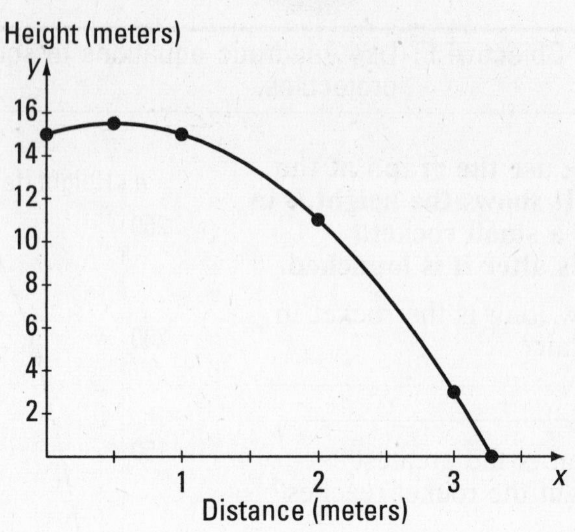

7. What is the greatest height above the water that Theresa reaches? ______________

8. How high is the diving platform? ______________

9. What is Theresa's height when she has traveled 2 meters horizontally from the edge of the platform? ______________

10. Use the equation to find Theresa's height when she has traveled 1.5 meters from the edge of the platform. ______________

Review Objective D, Lesson 1-6

In 11 and 12, a. give the exact square roots of the given number. b. Then approximate the square roots to the nearest hundred-thousandth.

11. 6 **a.** ______________ **b.** ______________

12. 342 **a.** ______________ **b.** ______________

In 13–16, evaluate without a calculator.

13. $-\sqrt{16}$ ______________ **14.** $3\sqrt{25}$ ______________

15. $\sqrt{36} + \sqrt{64}$ ______________ **16.** $\sqrt{36 + 64}$ ______________

Name

LESSON MASTER  **Questions on SPUR Objectives**

Skills Objective A: Solve quadratic equations using the Quadratic Formula.

1. Write the *quadratic formula* and explain what a, b, and c represent.

In 2–7, find the two values of the expression. Round answers that are *not* integers to the nearest tenth.

2. $\frac{-2 \pm 8}{2}$

3. $\frac{9 \pm 5}{4}$

4. $\frac{-6 \pm 15}{-6}$

5. $\frac{0 \pm \sqrt{81}}{3}$

6. $\frac{-4 \pm \sqrt{24 - -120}}{2}$

7. $\frac{-2 \pm \sqrt{4 - -10}}{2 \cdot 15}$

In 8–13, write each equation in standard form.

8. $x^2 + 40 + 4x = 0$

9. $3t^2 + 9t = 2$

10. $4v^2 = 80 + 6v^2 - 14v$

11. $3w^2 - 4w - 18 = -w^2 + w + 1$

12. $12y - y^2 = 0$

13. $16x - x^2 + 3 = 16x$

Name ______________________________

In 14–17, an equation in standard form is given. a. Identify *a*, *b*, and *c*. b. Give the solutions rounded to the nearest hundredth.

14. $x^2 - 10x + 16 = 0$

a. $a =$ ____ $b =$ ____ $c =$ ____

b. ______________________

15. $-v^2 + 14v + 33 = 0$

a. $a =$ ____ $b =$ ____ $c =$ ____

b. ______________________

16. $2s^2 + 5s - 3 = 0$

a. $a =$ ____ $b =$ ____ $c =$ ____

b. ______________________

17. $y^2 + 12y = 0$

a. $a =$ ____ $b =$ ____ $c =$ ____

b. ______________________

In 18–21, an equation is given. a. Rewrite the equation in standard form. b. Give the solutions rounded to the nearest hundredth.

18. $a^2 - 9a = 18$

a. ______________________

b. ______________________

19. $-2d^2 = 3d - 15$

a. ______________________

b. ______________________

20. $x^2 + 36 = 12x$

a. ______________________

b. ______________________

21. $4(n^2 + 2n) + 3 = 10$

a. ______________________

b. ______________________

22. Write a check for your solutions to Question 16.

____

____

Uses Objective E: Use quadratic equations to solve problems about paths of projectiles.

In 23–25, use this information: A rocket is launched from a cliff 30 feet above the ground. Its height *h* in feet above the ground *t* seconds after it is launched is given by the equation $h = -16t^2 + 192t + 30$.

23. At what two times is the rocket 100 feet above the ground? ______________

24. When is the rocket 606 feet above the ground? ______________

25. When does the rocket hit the ground? ______________

Name

LESSON MASTER 

Questions on SPUR Objectives

Vocabulary

1. What is the *discriminant* of the quadratic equation $ax^2 + bx + c = 0$?

____

Properties

Objective D: Identify and use the discriminant of a quadratic equation.

In 2–4, tell if the discriminant is *positive*, *negative*, or *zero*.

2. A quadratic equation has exactly one real solution. __________

3. A quadratic equation has exactly two real solutions. __________

4. A quadratic equation has no real solutions. __________

In 5–7, use the graph at the right. It shows the height y of a rocket in meters when it has been launched from a cliff and has been in the air for t seconds, where $y = 55 + 33t - 5t^2$. In 5–7, a height is given.

a. Write a quadratic equation that could be used to find the time when the rocket reaches that height.

b. Use the graph to predict whether the discriminant of the equation is *positive*, *negative*, or *zero*.

c. Check your answer to Part b by finding the value of the discriminant.

5. 80 feet

a. ______________________ **b.** __________ **c.** __________

6. 100 feet

a. ______________________ **b.** __________ **c.** __________

7. 110 feet

a. ______________________ **b.** __________ **c.** __________

Name ______________________________

In 8–15, a quadratic equation is given. a. Find the value of the discriminant. b. Give the number of real solutions. c. Find the real solutions, rounded to the nearest hundredth. If there are none, write "no solution."

8. $r^2 + 6r + 4 = 0$

a. ______________

b. ______________

c. ______________

9. $u^2 + 4u + 20 = 0$

a. ______________

b. ______________

c. ______________

10. $-w^2 + 22w - 121 = 0$

a. ______________

b. ______________

c. ______________

11. $-2x^2 - 8x + 12 = 0$

a. ______________

b. ______________

c. ______________

12. $y^2 + 3y = 0$

a. ______________

b. ______________

c. ______________

13. $-4z^2 - 4z = 21$

a. ______________

b. ______________

c. ______________

14. $b^2 + 38 = 0$

a. ______________

b. ______________

c. ______________

15. $3(n^2 - 7n) = -30$

a. ______________

b. ______________

c. ______________

16. For what value of h does $x^2 + 6x + h$ have exactly one solution? ______________

17. Find a value of h such that $x^2 + 6x + h$ has no real solutions. ______________

18. Find a value of h such that $x^2 + 6x + h$ has exactly two real solutions.

Name

LESSON MASTER

Questions on SPUR Objectives

Skills Objective B: Simplify square roots.

1. Use the drawing at the right.

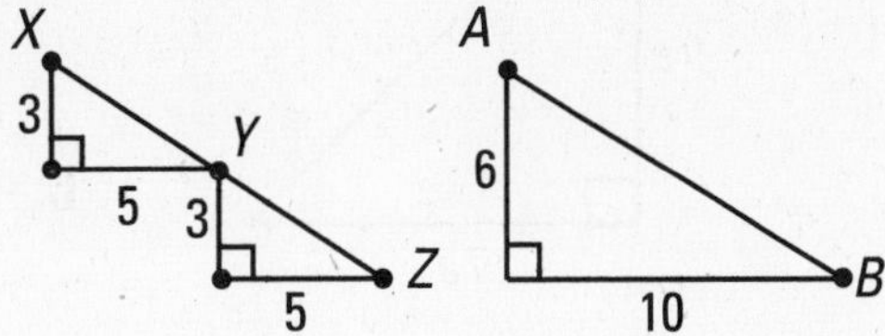

a. Calculate XY.

b. Express XZ as $2 \cdot XY$.

c. Find AB.

d. Use decimal approximations to show that your answers to Parts **b** and **c** are equal.

2. Which property states that if a and b are non-negative real numbers, then $\sqrt{a} \cdot \sqrt{b} = \sqrt{a \cdot b}$?

3. *Multiple choice*. Which of the expressions below equal $\sqrt{30}$?

(a) $2\sqrt{15}$ (b) $\sqrt{2} \cdot \sqrt{15}$ (c) $5\sqrt{6}$ (d) $\sqrt{5} \cdot \sqrt{6}$

4. *Multiple choice*. Which of the expressions below equal $\sqrt{32}$?

(a) $2\sqrt{8}$ (b) $16\sqrt{2}$ (c) $4\sqrt{2}$ (d) $2\sqrt{16}$

In 5–8, find the exact value of the variable in simplified form.

5.

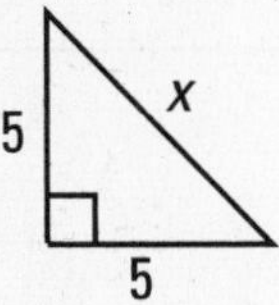

6.

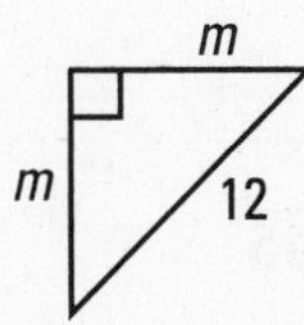

7.

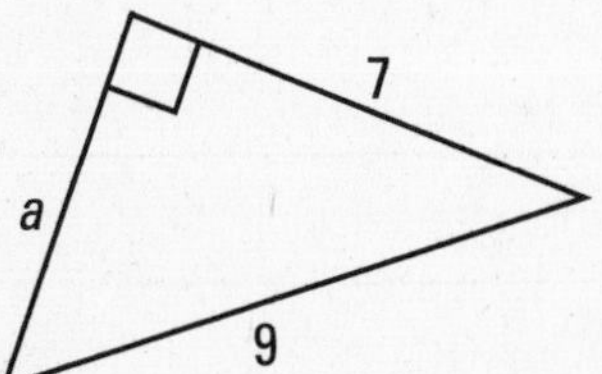

8.

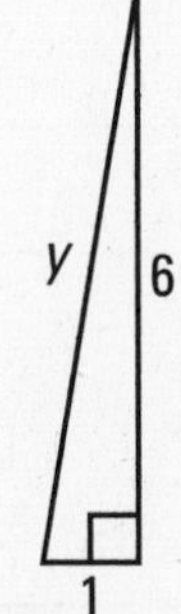

Name ______________________________

9. 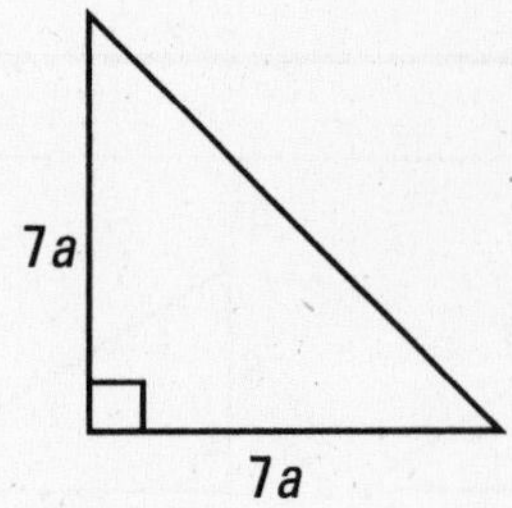

a. Use the Pythagorean Theorem to write an expression for the length of the hypotenuse of the triangle at the left. ______________

b. Simplify your answer to Part **a**. ______________

In 10–20, simplify. Do not use a calculator.

10. $\sqrt{2} \cdot \sqrt{18}$ ______________

11. $\sqrt{4} \cdot \sqrt{16}$ ______________

12. $\sqrt{14^2}$ ______________

13. $\sqrt{3^2 \cdot 7^2}$ ______________

14. $\sqrt{2a} \cdot \sqrt{5}$ where a is positive ______________

15. $\sqrt{2n} \cdot \sqrt{3n}$ where n is positive ______________

16. $2\sqrt{27}$ ______________

17. $\sqrt{200}$ ______________

18. $2\sqrt{75}$ ______________

19. $2\sqrt{6} \cdot 5\sqrt{24}$ ______________

20. **a.** $\sqrt{20}$ ______________

b. $\sqrt{45}$ ______________

c. $\sqrt{20} + \sqrt{45}$ ______________

In 21–24, give the exact solution in simplified form.

21. $x^2 = 300$ ______________

22. $(2y)^2 = 432$ ______________

23. $3x^2 + 18 = 165$ ______________

24. $\frac{6}{u} = \frac{u}{20}$ ______________

Name

LESSON MASTER  **Questions on SPUR Objectives**

Vocabulary

1. In terms of a number line, what is the *absolute value* of a number?

Skills Objective C: Evaluate expressions and solve equations using absolute value.

In 2–18, evaluate the expression.

2. $|-8|$

3. $|19|$

4. $|\frac{2}{3}|$

5. $|-0.72|$

6. $-|51|$

7. $|4^2|$

8. $|(-3)^2|$

9. $|-9^2|$

10. $-|\frac{4}{5}|$

11. $-|-\frac{7}{16}|$

12. ABS (0)

13. ABS $(-5 \cdot 7)$

14. $|4 - 12|$

15. $|4| - |12|$

16. $\sqrt{12^2}$

17. $\sqrt{(-12)^2}$

18. Give all values of m for which $|m|$ is *not* positive.

In 19–24, solve and check the equation.

19. $|x| = 20$

20. $|x + 4| = 13$

21. $|n - 8| = 5$

22. $|60 - x| = 14$

Name

▶ **LESSON MASTER 9-8 B** *page 2*

23. $|8n + 4| = 32$

24. $|-\frac{1}{2}x| = 28$

25. A carnival prize is given if someone guesses the number of marbles in a jar. There are actually 347 marbles and a guess is g. Write an expression for how far off the guess is

a. if the guess is too high. ________

b. if the guess is too low. ________

c. if you don't know whether the guess is too high or too low. ________

Representations Objective G: Calculate and represent distances on the number line.

In 26–28, find the distance between the given points.

26. -31 7

27. 

28. 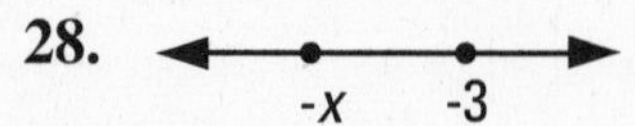

________ ________ ________

29. Give the coordinates of the two points on a number line that are 18 units from the point with coordinate 6. ________

30. Give the coordinates of the two points on a number line that are 40 units from the point with coordinate -65. ________

31. A manufacturer makes golf balls with a diameter of 1.68 inches and a tolerance of .05 in. This means they reject any balls they make whose diameter is outside the interval 1.68 ±.05 in.

a. What are the least and greatest acceptable diameters? ________

b. Is 1.677 an acceptable diameter? ________

c. Graph all acceptable diameters on a number line.

d. Let d be the diameter of an acceptable golf ball. Write an inequality relating $|d - 1.68|$ and .05 ________

Name

LESSON MASTER

Questions on SPUR Objectives

Representations Objective G: Calculate and represent distances in the plane.

In 1 and 2, each square represents a city block. Find how many blocks it take to travel from P to Q,
a. if you travel on the streets and go by way of R, or
b. if you travel as the crow flies.

1.

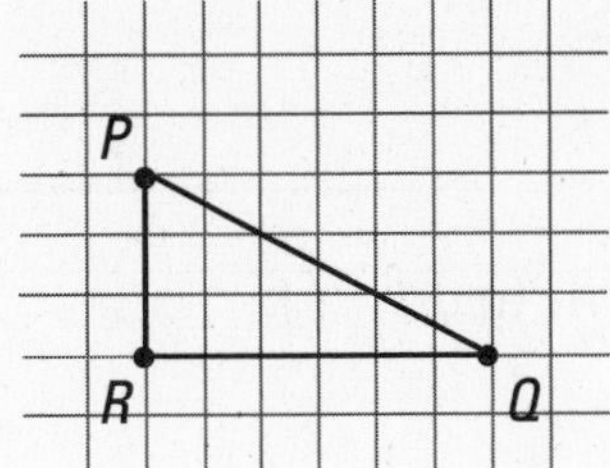

a. ____________

b. ____________

2.

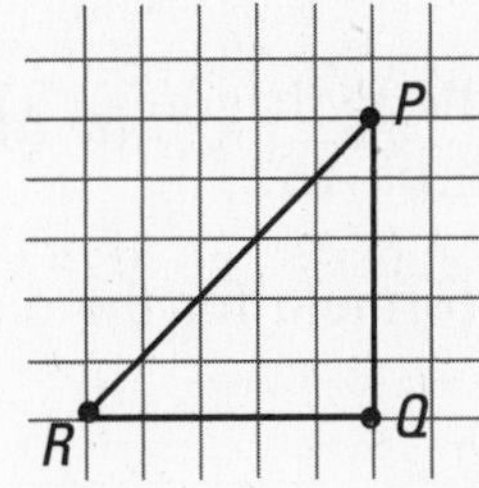

a. ____________

b. ____________

In 3–6, use the diagram at the right to find each length.

3. AB ____________

4. CD ____________

5. EF ____________

6. GH ____________

y
A = (1, 8)
B = (6, 8)
E = (-7, 4)
C = (8, 0)
x
G = (-2, -3)
H = (3, -3)
F = (-7, -4)
D = (8, -6)

7. In the diagram at the right, $P = (-2, 1)$. Points Q, R, S, and T are each 4 units from P on the horizontal or vertical line through P. Find the coordinates of each point.

Q ____________ R ____________

S ____________ T ____________

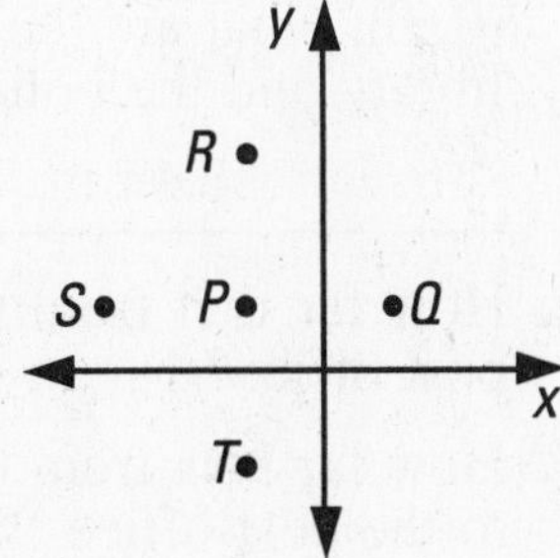

8. Find the coordinates of M in the diagram at the right.

____

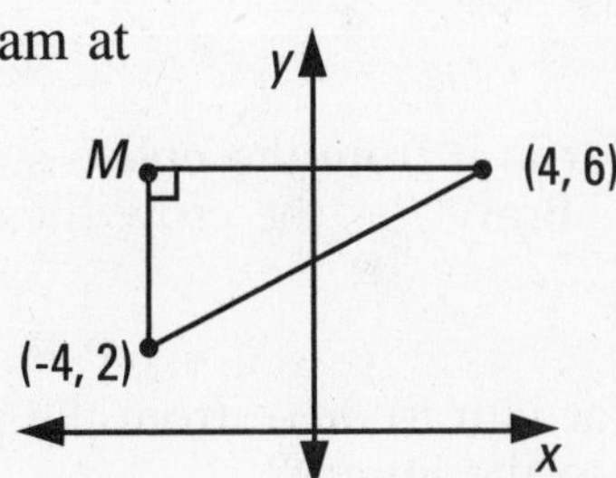

Name

▶ **LESSON MASTER 9-9 B** *page 2*

9. a. Find the coordinates of C.

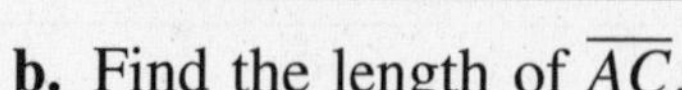

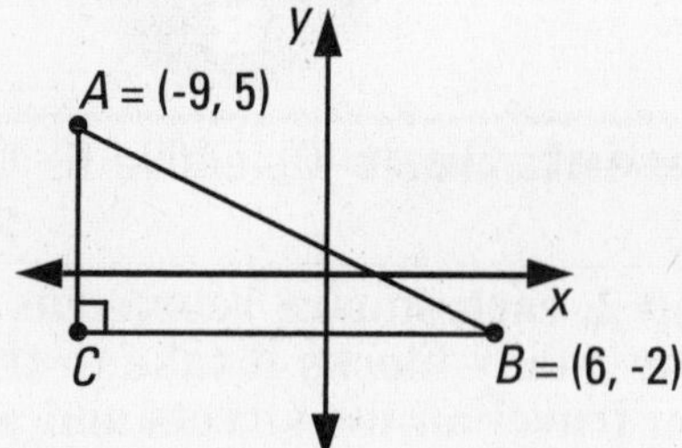

b. Find the length of $\overline{AC}$.

c. Find the length of $\overline{BC}$.

d. Use the Pythagorean Theorem to find the length of $\overline{AB}$.

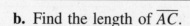

10. Write a formula for the distance between (m, n) and (r, s).

In 11–14, use the distance formula to find the distance between the two points. Round answers to the nearest hundredth.

11. (5, 6) and (12, 14)

12. (2, -7) and (-8, 9)

13. (-1, -5) and (3, -1)

14. (-12, 0) and (5, -19)

In 15–19, use the map at the right, which shows the streets and locations of three buildings in a town. The streets are 1 block apart.

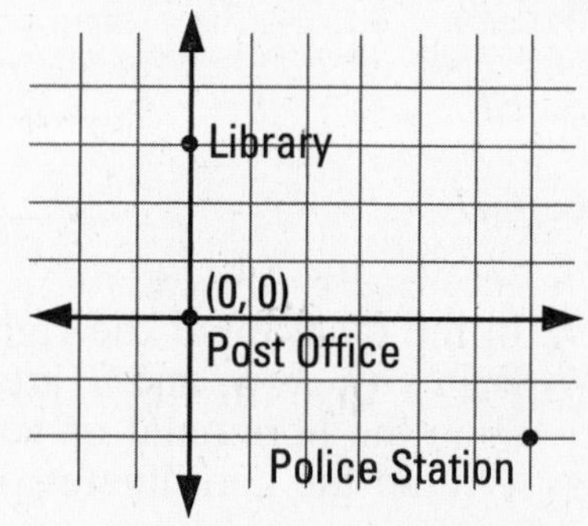

15. If the coordinates of the post office are (0, 0), what are the coordinates of the library and the police station?

16. How far is it from the library to the post office?

17. How far it is from the police station to the post office "as the crow flies"?

18. How far is it from the police station to the library "as the crow flies"?

19. How far is it to drive from the police staton to the library?

Name

LESSON MASTER 10-1 B

Questions on SPUR Objectives

Properties Objective E: Classify polynomials by their degree or number of terms.

In 1–8, tell whether the expression is a *monomial* (M), *binomial* (B), *trinomial* (T), *polynomial* (P), or none of these (N). List all the terms that apply.

1. fgh ______

2. -7.2 ______

3. $3y^{-3}$ ______

4. $\frac{3}{2} + 22ab$ ______

5. $11x^2 - x - 12$ ______

6. $\sqrt{5}$ ______

7. $a^2 + ab - ab^2 + b^3$ ______

8. 100π ______

In 9–12, tell which of these expressions, after being simplified, are binomials. Write *yes* or *no*.

9. $4a + 5a$ ______

10. $2(b^2 + 6)$ ______

11. $5h + 12u - 8h$ ______

12. $77x^2$ ______

13. a. What is the degree of $3m^5$? ______

b. What is the degree of m^3n^7? ______

14. Give an example of a monomial of degree 8 if

a. the only variable is a. ______

b. the monomial has two variables, a and b. ______

In 15–20, give the degree of the polynomial.

15. $3xy + 2x$ ______

16. $3r^5 + 6.9$ ______

17. $5m^8 - m^3$ ______

18. $3e^5 - 2e^5 + 4e^7$ ______

19. $a^4 + a^3 - ab^2 + ab^4$ ______

20. $w^3 + 2w^2v^2 - 6$ ______

Name

Properties Objective F: Write whole numbers as polynomials in base 10.

In 21–24, write as a polynomial in base 10.

21. 3,945 __________

22. 6,500,004 __________

23. 58,257 __________

24. 431,006,090 __________

In 25–28, simplify each polynomial.

25. $2 \cdot 10^4 + 3 \cdot 10^2 + 10^1$ __________

26. $7 \cdot 10^8 + 2 \cdot 10^4 + 10^3 + 5 \cdot 10^2$ __________

27. $4 \cdot 10^6 + 3 \cdot 10^5 + 10^4 + 7 \cdot 10^3$ __________

28. $9 \cdot 10^7 + 6 \cdot 10^6 + 8 \cdot 10^2 + 5 \cdot 10^1$ __________

Representations Objective I: Represent areas of figures in terms of polynomials.

In 29 and 30, give the area of the figure as a polynomial.

29.

____

30.

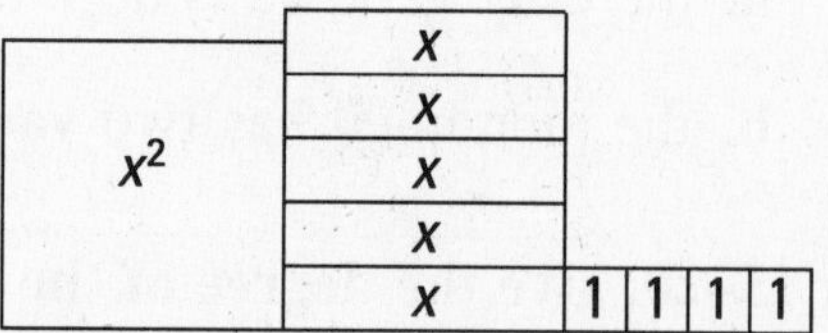

____

In 31 and 32, make a drawing to represent the polynomial using algebra tiles. Arrange the tiles to form a rectangle.

31. $3x + 12$

32. $x^2 + 4x + 3$

Name

LESSON MASTER 

Questions on SPUR Objectives

Skills Objective A: Add and subtract polynomials.

In 1–6, simplify the expression.

1. $(3x^2 - 7x + 1) + (2x^2 + x - 8)$ ________

2. $(9b^2 - 3b - 2) - (b^2 + 4b - 6)$ ________

3. $(16 - 4m^2 + 2m) + (5m^2 - 3m - 10)$ ________

4. $(a^2 - 12) - (a^2 - 4a + 2)$ ________

5. $(2x^2 + 3x - 18) - (4x - 5)$ ________

6. $(p^3 + 2p^2 + 4) + (p^3 + 8p^2 + 7p)$ ________

In 7 and 8, fill in the missing polynomial.

7. $(4x^2 - 7x + 11) + ($________$) = 5x^2 - 5x + 15$

8. $(5e^2 + 12e - 3) - ($________$) = 8e^2 + 1$

Uses Objective G: Translate investment situations into polynomials.

9. Jimmy has enrolled in a retirement plan in which he invests $2,000 at the beginning of each year.

   a. Suppose the money is invested in an account with a yearly scale factor x. Complete the chart to show how much Jimmy would have in his retirement account at the end of each year.

Year	Amount at End of Year
1	$2{,}000x$
2	$2{,}000x^2 + 2{,}000x$
3	
4	
5	

   b. Calculate how much would be in the account after 5 years if the interest rate were 4%. ________

   c. Calculate how much would be in the account after 5 years if the interest rate were 10%. ________

Suppose Jimmy's employer adds $1,000 to Jimmy's retirement account each year.

d. Write a polynomial showing the portion of the account balance after 5 years due to the employer's contributions. Let the yearly scale factor be x.

e. Write a polynomial showing the total amount in the account after 5 years with a yearly scale factor x. Give your answer in simplified form.

In 10–12, Yuko will be ready for college in 6 years. Her mother is examining two plans for college savings. Each plan earns 6.5% interest compounded annually. Here are the plans.

Plan I: Deposit $4,000 at the beginning of the 1st, 2nd, and 3rd years.

Plan II: Wait and deposit $5,000 at the beginning of the 4th, 5th, and 6th years.

10. Fill in the spreadsheet below.

	A	B	C	D	E
1	Year	Plan I Deposit	Plan I End of Year Balance	Plan II Deposit	Plan II End of Year Balance
2	1	4,000		0	
3	2	4,000		0	
4	3	4,000		0	
5	4	0		5,000	
6	5	0		5,000	
7	6	0		5,000	

11. What formula can be used to calculate the value in

a. cell C7?

b. cell E7?

12. Which plan yields more money after 6 years? How much more?

Name

LESSON MASTER 

Questions on SPUR Objectives

Skills Objective C: Multiply a polynomial by a monomial.

In 1–14, simplify.

1. $7(2x)$

2. $8a(6a)$

3. $3m^2(4m^3)$

4. $-r^3(12r^4)$

5. $5(e + 14)$

6. $6(d - 9)$

7. $3y(y^2 - 2y + 1)$

8. $11b^3(2ab^2 + 7a)$

9. $9r(-3r^4 - 8)$

10. $2bc(-4b^2c)$

11. $-7mn(m^2 + 2mn - 3n)$

12. $2(x + 6) + 5(x - 4)$

13. $10(x^2 + 3x + 2) - 4x(x + 8)$

14. $a^2(a^3 + 4a - 7) + a^3(-a^2 - a + 4)$

In 15–20, fill in the blank.

15. $6abc($ __________ $) = -12a^2b^2c^3$

16. $3(x +$ __________ $) = 3x + 21$

17. $5m($ __________ $+ 3) = 15m^2 + 15m$

18. $a^2(a^3 +$ __________ $) = a^5 + 5a^4$

19. (__________)$(4y + 6) = -12y - 18$

20. (__________)$(x^2 - x) = x^3y^2 - x^2y^2$

Name

Representations Objective I: Represent areas of figures in terms of polynomials.

In 21–24, a rectangle is shown.
a. Express the area as length • width.
b. Express the area as the sum of smaller areas.
c. Combine the two expressions from Parts a and b to write an equation for the area of the rectangle.

21. x x 1 1 1; x

a. ______

b. ______

c. ______

22. 1 1 1 1 1 1; x 1

a. ______

b. ______

c. ______

23. x 1 1 1 1 1; x x

a. ______

b. ______

c. ______

24. x x x x; x 1 1 1

a. ______

b. ______

c. ______

25. The length ℓ of a rectangle is 2 more than 3 times its width w.

a. Write an expression for ℓ in terms of w. ______

b. Express the area as length · width in terms of w. ______

c. Multiply to express your answer to Part **b** as a polynomial. ______

d. Check that your answers to Parts **b** and **c** are equal by substituting $\ell = 10$.

______

Name

LESSON MASTER

Questions on SPUR Objectives

Skills Objective B: Multiply polynomials.

In 1–11, multiply and simplify.

1. $(a + 4)(a^2 + 4a - 3)$
2. $(m - 1)(m^2 - 4m + 5)$
3. $(a + b)(2a - 8b)$
4. $(x^2 + 6x + 9)(x^2 - 1)$
5. $(2y^2 + 3y + 4)(y^2 - y + 2)$
6. $(-a^2 + 3a - 2)(a^2 + 3a - 2)$
7. $(2a + 4b - 7)(3a - b + 1)$
8. $(3m + 4)(2m - 2) - (3m)^2$
9. $4(3e^2 + 6e - 9) - (e + 1)(e - 1)$
10. $(p + q + r)(p - q - r) + r(r + q)$
11. $(y + 6)(y + 2)(y - 3)$

Representations Objective I: Represent areas and volumes of figures with polynomials.

12. a. Express the area of the largest rectangle as length • width.

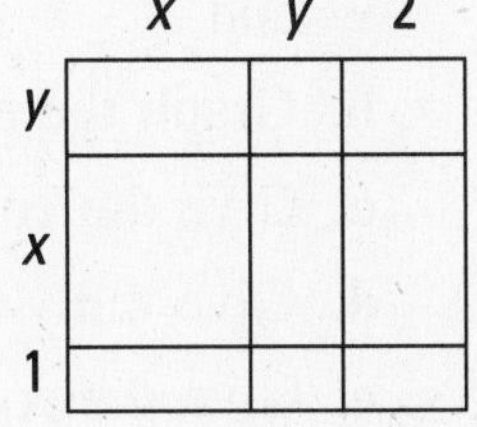

b. Express this area as the sum of nine smaller rectangles.

c. Simplify your answer to Part **b**.

Name

13. A cube has edges of length 8 inches. Suppose a larger cube has edges that are x inches longer.

a. What is the volume of the first cube? ______

b. Write an expression for the volume of the larger cube. ______

c. How much greater is the volume of the larger cube than the volume of the smaller cube? ______

14. a. Write two expressions for the volume of the box at the right.

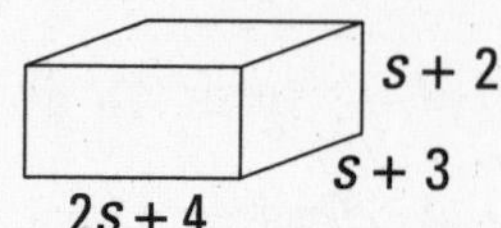

______

______

b. Check your answer by substituting 3 for x.

______

______

Review Objective F, Lesson 9-2

15. Use the equation $y = x^2 - 2x - 8$.

a. Make a table of values using x-values -3, -2, -1, 0, 1, 2, and 3.

b. Graph the equation.

c. Give the coordinates of the vertex.

d. Give the y-intercept.

e. Give the equation of the axis of symmetry.

b.

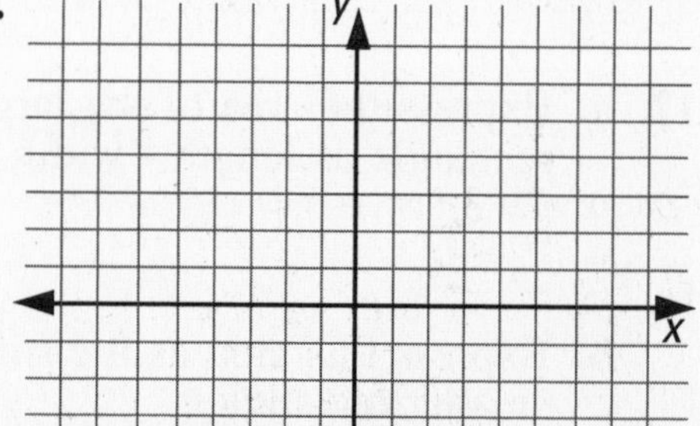

a.

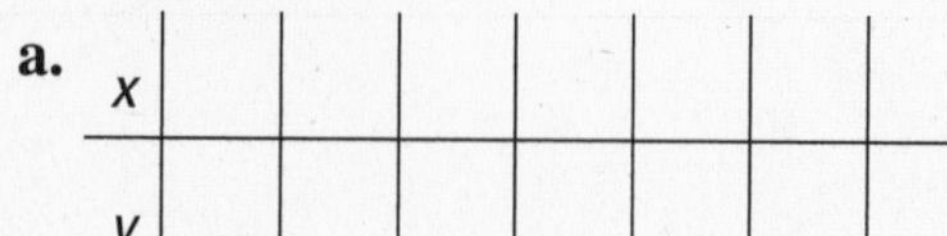

x							
y							

c. ______ **d.** ______ **e.** ______

Name

LESSON MASTER 

Questions on SPUR Objectives

Vocabulary

1. In the FOIL algorithm, explain what the letters F-O-I-L represent.

____

____

____

____

Skills Objective C: Multiply two binomials.

In 2–14, multiply and simplify.

2. $(u + 3)(u + 10)$ ______________

3. $(x - 4)(x - 5)$ ______________

4. $(e - 2)(e + 1)$ ______________

5. $(y + 6)(y - 4)$ ______________

6. $(2a + 1)(a - 7)$ ______________

7. $(3b + 6)(4b + 2)$ ______________

8. $(x - 7)(x + 7)$ ______________

9. $(r^2 + 3r)(r + 4)$ ______________

10. $(4m + 7)(4m - 7)$ ______________

11. $(3a + b)(2a - 8b)$ ______________

12. $(2u^2 - 3uv)(6u - 2v)$ ______________

13. $(p + 3q)^2$ ______________

14. $(2 + \sqrt{3})(8 - \sqrt{3})$ ______________

In 15 and 16, fill in the blanks.

15. $(x + 5)(x +$ ________ $) = x^2 + 8x + 15$

16. $(y -$ ________ $)(y + 4) = y^2 + 3y - 4$

Name ____________________

▶ **LESSON MASTER 10-5 B** *page 2*

17. Complete the table for each equation, and graph the points for both equations on the grid at the right.

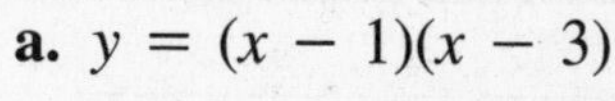

a. $y = (x - 1)(x - 3)$

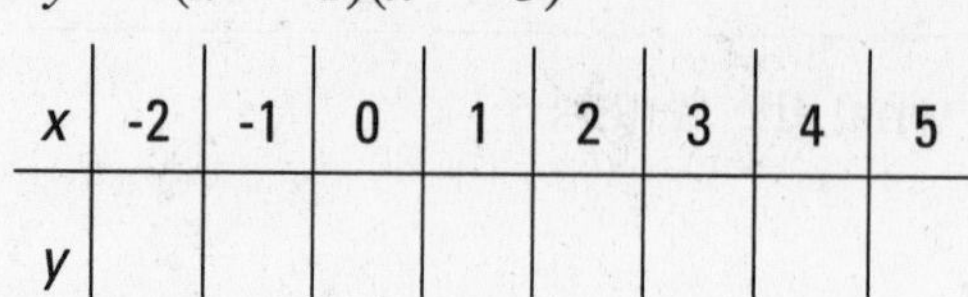

x	-2	-1	0	1	2	3	4	5
y								

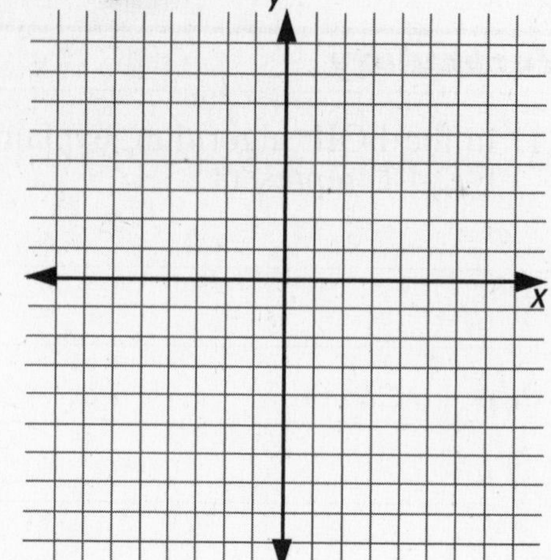

b. $y = x^2 - 4x + 3$

x	-2	-1	0	1	2	3	4	5
y								

18. What is true of the points you graphed for the equations above? Explain why this relationship exists.

____

____

Representations Objective I: Represent the product of two binomials as an area.

In 19 and 20, an area representation is shown. a. Express the area as length · width. b. Multiply and simplify the expression you wrote for Part a.

19.

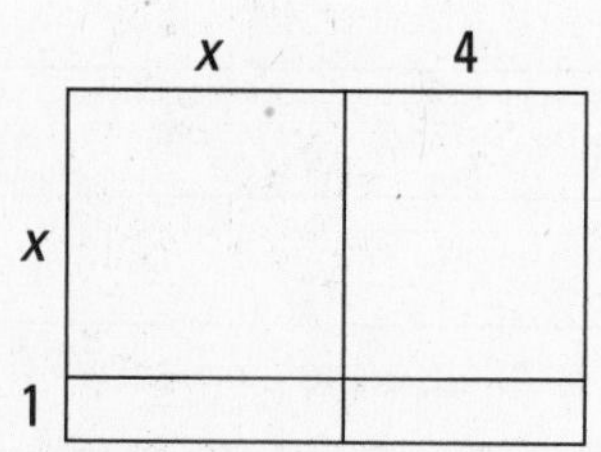

a. ____________________

b. ____________________

20.

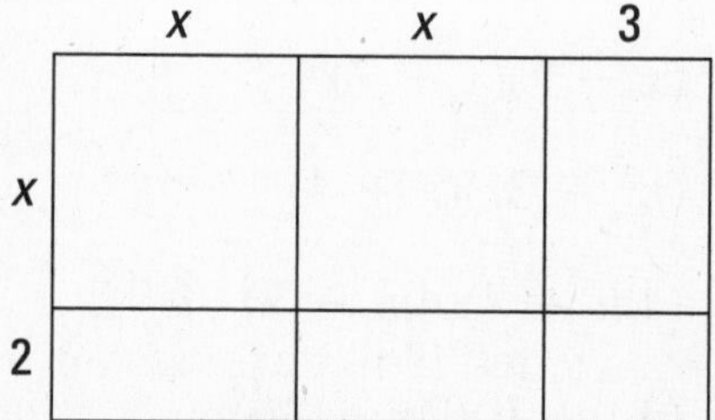

a. ____________________

b. ____________________

21. **a.** Multiply $(x + 3)(2x + 1)$.

____

b. At the right, draw an area diagram to represent the multiplication.

22. An oil painting that measures 14 in. by 20 in. is surrounded by a frame f in. wide. Write a polynomial for the total area of the painting and frame. ____________________

Name

LESSON MASTER

Questions on SPUR Objectives

Skills Objective C: Multiply two binomials.
Objective D: Expand squares of binomials.

In 1–4, match equivalent expressions.

1. $a^2 + 2ab + b^2$ ________ **a.** $(a - b)^2$

2. $a^2 + b^2$ ________ **b.** $(a + b)(a - b)$

3. $a^2 - 2ab + b^2$ ________ **c.** $(a + b)^2$

4. $a^2 - b^2$ ________ **d.** none of these

5. Expand $(m + 8)^2$ by

a. using the FOIL algorithm.

____

b. using the Perfect Square Patterns.

____

In 6–10, expand.

6. $(d + 5)^2$ ________

7. $(b - 6)^2$ ________

8. $(2x - 7)^2$ ________

9. $(3e + 1)^2$ ________

10. $(4a + 7)^2$ ________

In 11–15, tell if the expression is the difference of two squares. Write *yes* or *no*. If you write *no*, explain your answer.

11. $d^2 - 17$ ________________

12. $m^2 - 25$ ________________

13. $r^2 + 36$ ________________

14. $4x^2y^2 - 81$ ________________

15. $(u - 4)^2$ ________________

Name ______________________________

In 16–22, multiply and simplify.

16. $(b + 7)(b - 7)$ ____________

17. $(3m + 2)(3m - 2)$ ____________

18. $(4b - 5)^2$ ____________

19. $(8a + 2e)(8a - 2e)$ ____________

20. $(x - y)^2 - (x + y)(x - y)$ ____________

21. $(2 + \sqrt{5})(2 - \sqrt{5})$ ____________

22. $(2 + \sqrt{5})^2$ ____________

23. Explain how you could use the Difference of Two Squares Pattern to calculate $21 \cdot 19$ mentally.

____

Representations Objective I: Represent the square of a binomial as an area.

24. a. Express the area of the figure at the right as the square of a binomial.

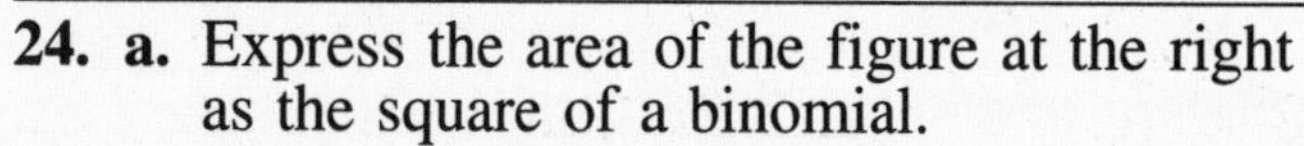

____

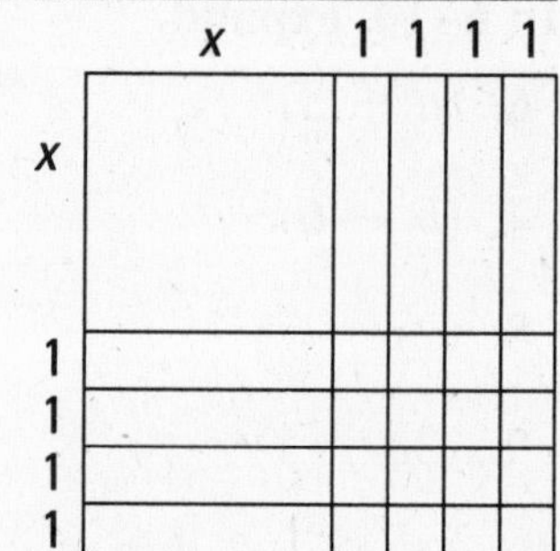

b. Express the area as the sum of smaller areas.

____

In 25 and 26, an expression is given. a. Make an algebra-tile drawing to illustrate the expression. b. Write the expanded polynomial expression represented by your drawing.

25. $(x + 2)^2$

b. ____________

26. $(2x + 3)^2$

b. ____________

Name ______________________________

LESSON MASTER  **Questions on SPUR Objectives**

Uses Objective H: Use the chi-square statistic to determine whether or not an event is likely.

In 1–3, use the following information and the chi-square critical value table given on page 180.

A market researcher wanted to know if a new cereal, Oat-Toasties, would be more appealing to people than the four leading sellers in a particular city. A taste test in a local shopping center gave the following results.

Cereal	Percent of People Choosing Cereal
Oat-Toasties	26%
Munch Mates	21%
Sun-Risers	20%
Wheat Cracklers	18%
A.M. Crispies	15%

1. Suppose 200 people had been asked their choices.

a. Find the number of people choosing each cereal.

Oat-Toasties __________ Munch Mates __________

Sun-Risers __________ Wheat Cracklers __________

A.M. Crispies __________

b. Before recommending that Oat-Toasties be manufactured for national distribution, the market researcher must decide whether the test results show a special support for Oat-Toasties. To do this, he first considers the situation in which it is equally likely that a person would choose any of the five cereals. In such a case, how many people would be expected to choose each cereal?

Oat-Toasties __________ Munch Mates __________

Sun-Risers __________ Wheat Cracklers __________

A.M. Crispies __________

c. Find the chi-square statistic for this experiment using the actual test results and the expected values from Part **b**.

____

Name ______

▶ **LESSON MASTER 10-7 B** *page 2*

Critical Chi-Square Values

$n - 1$	.10	.05	.01	.001
1	2.71	3.84	6.63	10.8
2	4.61	5.99	9.21	13.8
3	6.25	7.81	11.34	16.3
4	7.78	9.49	13.28	18.5
5	9.24	11.07	15.09	20.5
6	10.6	12.6	16.8	22.5
7	12.0	14.1	18.5	24.3
8	13.4	15.5	20.1	26.1
9	14.7	16.9	21.7	27.9
10	16.0	18.3	23.2	29.6

d. Refer to the Critical Chi-Square Values Table above. Using your answer to Part **c**, do you think the researcher should recommend that the cereal be manufactured for national distribution? Explain your thinking.

______

______

______

2. Suppose 1,000 people had been asked their opinion, and their percents were those given in the table on page 179.

a. Calculate the chi-square statistic for these test results. (Follow the steps suggested by Parts **a** and **b** in Question 1.) ______

b. Refer to the Critical Chi-Square Values Table above. Using your answer to Part **a**, do you think the researcher should recommend that the cereal be manufactured for national distribution? Explain your thinking.

______

______

______

3. From your answers to Questions 1 and 2, what can you say about the relationship between sample size and the conclusions reached by the market researcher?

______

______

______

Name

LESSON MASTER **Questions on SPUR Objectives**

Representations Objective H: Find solutions to systems of equations by graphing.

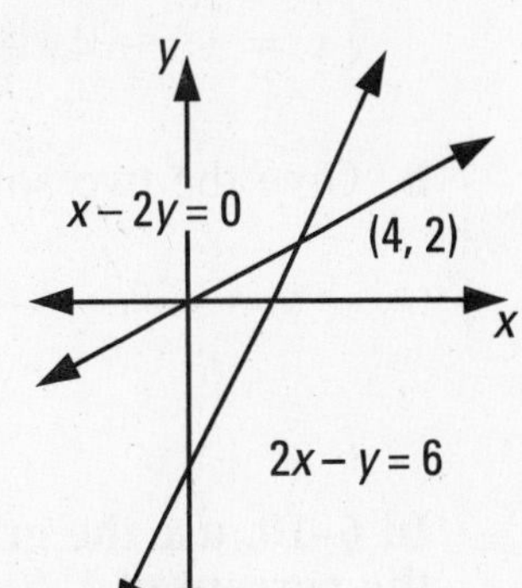

1. a. Use a brace { to write the system shown on this graph.

b. What is the solution to the system? ________

c. Write a check to show that your answer to Part **b** is a solution to the system from Part **a**.

____

In 2–4, a system of equations is given. a. Graph the equations. b. Give the solution. c. If there is a solution, check it.

2. $\begin{cases} y = x - 1 \\ y = 2x + 3 \end{cases}$

a.

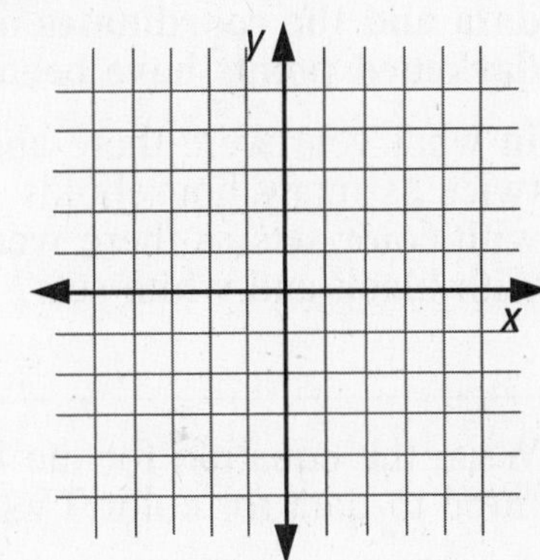

b. ________

c. ________

____

3. $\begin{cases} x - 2y = 5 \\ 4x - y = -1 \end{cases}$

a.

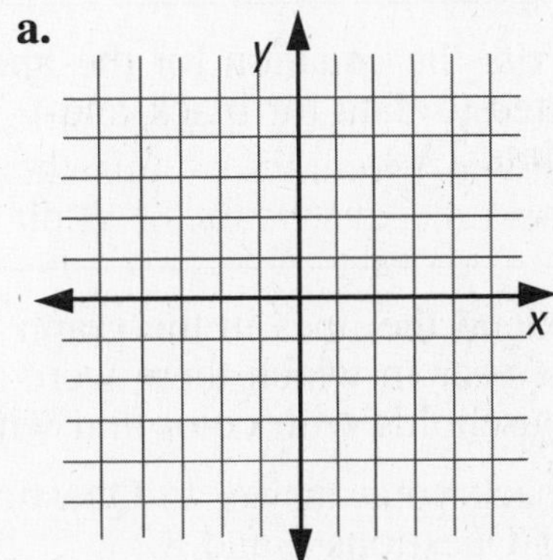

b. ________

c. ________

____

4. $\begin{cases} y = 3x - 2 \\ 6x - 2y = 6 \end{cases}$

a.

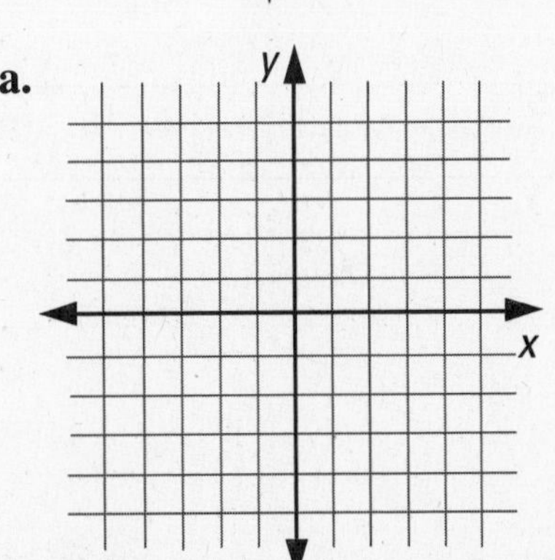

b. ________

c. ________

____

Name

5. a. Graph the system below for $-5 \le x \le 5$.

$$\begin{cases} y = 2x - 5 \\ y = x^2 - 4x + 3 \end{cases}$$

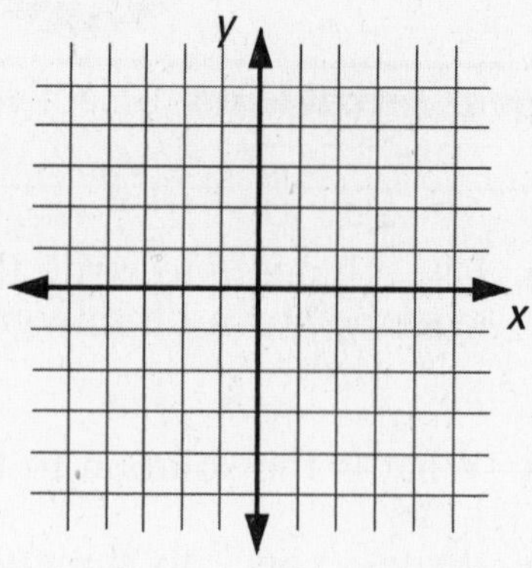

b. Give the two solutions.

____

In 6–10, use the graph which shows the percent of U.S. households that had color or black-and-white television sets in various years. A line has been fitted to each set of data and the coordinates of the darkened points have been given.

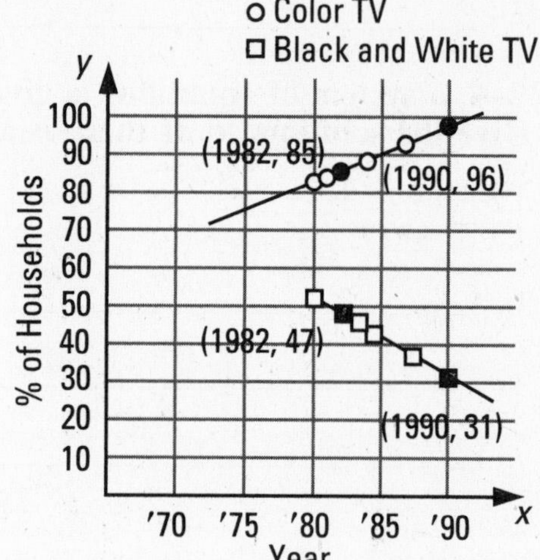

6. In what year were there about twice as many households with color sets as there were with black-and-white sets?

____

7. Write the equation for the line fitted to data for color TVs.

____

8. Write the equation for the line fitted to data for black-and-white TVs.

____

9. Extend the lines in the graph to find an estimate of the year in which there were an equal number of households with color and with black-and-white TVs. ______________

10. Check your answer to Question 9 in the equations for Questions 7 and 8.

____

____

Name

LESSON MASTER 11-2 B

Questions on SPUR Objectives

Skills Objective A: Solve systems of linear equations using substitution.

In 1 and 2, tell if the given point is the solution of the system.

1. (3, 8) $\begin{cases} y = 4x - 4 \\ y = \frac{2}{3}x + 6 \end{cases}$

2. (-2, 12) $\begin{cases} y = -5x + 2 \\ y = 2x - 8 \end{cases}$

In 3–10, solve the system using substitution and check your results.

3. $\begin{cases} a = b - 5 \\ a = -2b + 7 \end{cases}$

4. $\begin{cases} y = 3x + 23 \\ y = x + 11 \end{cases}$

5. $\begin{cases} y = \frac{3}{2}x + 12 \\ y = x + 8 \end{cases}$

6. $\begin{cases} m = 8n - 3 \\ m = -4n + 6 \end{cases}$

7. $\begin{cases} d = 2e + 1 \\ d = 5e - 8 \end{cases}$

8. $\begin{cases} y = 6x - 7 \\ y = -2x - 9 \end{cases}$

9. $\begin{cases} y = x \\ y = 3x - 20 \end{cases}$

10. $\begin{cases} r = \frac{1}{2}s + 1 \\ r = -\frac{2}{3}s + 15 \end{cases}$

Name

▶ **LESSON MASTER 11-2 B** *page 2*

Uses Objective F: Use systems of linear equations to solve real-world problems.

11. A cellular telephone company offers two plans to customers who use their mobile phone service. The monthly charges are given below.

Basic Plan: $20 service fee plus $.30 per minute of use
Frequent-Caller Plan: $45 service fee plus $.20 per minute of use

Let x = minutes of phone use and y = cost.

a. Write an equation describing the basic plan. __________

b. Write an equation describing the frequent-caller plan. __________

c. Solve a system of equations to find the number of minutes of phone use that would cost the same under the two plans. __________

d. If you estimate that you will use a cellular telephone for 100 minutes per month, which plan is better? Explain your reasoning.

____

____

____

12. CD Showcase Club charges a membership fee of $15 and then $10.50 for each CD purchased. CD Budget Club charges a membership fee of $5 and then $11.75 for each CD.

a. Describe these charges with a system of equations. __________

b. Solve the system to find the number of CDs purchased for which the total charges at each club are the same. __________

c. If you think you will be buying many, many CDs, which club is less expensive? Explain your reasoning.

____

____

____

Name

LESSON MASTER

Questions on SPUR Objectives

Skills Objective A: Solve systems of linear equations using substitution.

In 1–8, solve and check the system of equations.

1. $\begin{cases} y = x + 5 \\ 3x + y = 17 \end{cases}$

2. $\begin{cases} y = 3x \\ 3x - 2y = 12 \end{cases}$

3. $\begin{cases} m = 10n - 2 \\ m - 2n = 2 \end{cases}$

4. $\begin{cases} x = y - 6 \\ 2x + 10y = 0 \end{cases}$

5. $\begin{cases} x = \frac{1}{2}y \\ 4x + y = 30 \end{cases}$

6. $\begin{cases} a = 3b - 3 \\ 7a - 2b = 17 \end{cases}$

7. $\begin{cases} x + y = 8 \\ x - y = 4 \end{cases}$

8. $\begin{cases} x - y = 3 \\ 4x - 3y = 19 \end{cases}$

In 9 and 10, two lines have the given equations. Find the point of intersection.

9. Line ℓ: $y = -2x - 6$
Line m: $y = 5x + 15$

____

10. Line p: $y = -x + 3$
Line q: $y = -5x - 2$

____

Name

11. Solve the system below.

$$\begin{cases} A = B + 2 \\ B = 2C + 9 \\ A + C = -1 \end{cases}$$

Uses Objective F: Use systems of linear equations to solve real-world problems.

12. A concession stand sells hot dogs for \$2 and hamburgers for \$3. One day 486 sandwiches worth \$1,218 were sold. How many hot dogs and how many hamburgers were sold?

13. One newspaper reported that the mayor received a salary increase of 5%. Another paper reported that the mayor's salary went up \$2000. What was the mayor's salary before the increase?

14. A garden with a perimeter of 75 meters is to be 1.5 times as long as it is wide. What will be the dimensions of the garden?

Review Objective A, Lesson 10-2

In 15–17, simplify the expression.

15. $(5x^2 - 12x + 3) + (2x^2 + x - 10) - (x^2 + 3)$

16. $(3c^2 - 5c - 8) - (c^2 + 4c - 7)$

17. $(22 - 5a^2 + 4a) + (2a^2 - 4a - 15)$

Name

LESSON MASTER 11-4 B

Questions on SPUR Objectives

Skills Objective B: Solve systems of linear equations by addition.

In 1 and 2, write the equation that results when you add the left and right sides of the two equations.

1. $\begin{cases} 3x + 5y = 13 \\ x - 5y = 3 \end{cases}$

2. $\begin{cases} -4x + 2y = 15 \\ 4x - 8y = 10 \end{cases}$

In 3–10, solve the system. Check your solution.

3. $\begin{cases} c + d = 1 \\ c - d = -11 \end{cases}$

4. $\begin{cases} -8x + 2y = 2 \\ 8x + 5y = -23 \end{cases}$

5. $\begin{cases} -6x + 4y = 28 \\ 6x + 10y = 28 \end{cases}$

6. $\begin{cases} 5r + 3s = 24 \\ 5r + 8s = 39 \end{cases}$

7. $\begin{cases} 2u + 3w = 26 \\ 5w - 2u = 22 \end{cases}$

8. $\begin{cases} 2m + n = 9 \\ -2m - 3n = -21 \end{cases}$

9. $\begin{cases} \frac{3}{4}x + y = 8 \\ \frac{1}{4}x - y = 0 \end{cases}$

10. $\begin{cases} 5e - 2f = 30 \\ 9e - 2f = 54 \end{cases}$

Name

Uses Objective F: Use systems of linear equations to solve real-world problems.

11. In the school bookstore, four pencils and an eraser cost 65¢. Two pencils and an eraser cost 45¢. Find the cost of each item. ______________

12. Joanie weighs 8 pounds more than Jennie does. Together they weigh 212 pounds. Find the weight of each girl. ______________

13. When Brad flew from Indianapolis to St. Louis, he had the wind with him and was traveling at 260 mph. However, on the return trip, he was going against the wind and traveled only 170 mph. What was the plane's speed (without wind)? What was the average speed of the wind? ______________

14. Mark has one less than twice the number of tapes as Felipe has. Together they have 65 tapes. How many tapes does each boy have? ______________

15. On Saturday, Katie earned $51 for mowing 3 lawns and weeding 3 gardens. On Sunday, she earned $25 for mowing 1 lawn and weeding 3 gardens. How much does she earn for each lawn she mows and for each garden she weeds? ______________

16. At the university dormitory, two plans are offered.

Plan 1: Room and board and 13 meals per week for $5,110
Plan 2: Room and board and 19 meals per week for $5,146

At these rates what is the cost for room and board alone? What is the cost per meal? ______________

17. A sandwich with 2 slices of bread and 4 slices of ham has 350 calories. A sandwich with 2 slices of bread and 2 slices of ham has 240 calories. How many calories are in each slice of bread and in each slice of ham? ______________

Name

LESSON MASTER 11-5 B

Questions on SPUR Objectives

Skills Objective C: Solve systems of linear equations by multiplying.

1. Consider the system $\begin{cases} 9x - y = -4 \\ 3x + 5y = 10 \end{cases}$.

a. What is the result if the two equations are added? __________

b. What is the result if the first equation is multiplied by five and then the two equations are added? __________

c. What is the result if the second equation is multiplied by -3 and then the two equations are added? __________

2. Solve the system $\begin{cases} a - 3b = 7 \\ 5a + b = 19 \end{cases}$

a. by multiplying and adding to eliminate b. __________

b. by multiplying and adding to eliminate a. __________

3. Consider the system $\begin{cases} 4x + 5y = 2 \\ 2x - 3y = 34 \end{cases}$.

a. Would you plan to eliminate x or y to solve the system? Explain your choice.

____

____

b. Solve the system. __________

c. Check your solution to Part **c**.

____

____

Name

In 4–9, solve the system. Check your solution.

4. $\begin{cases} 3t + 2u = -1 \\ 6t - u = 8 \end{cases}$

5. $\begin{cases} -y + 4x = 12 \\ 5y + 5x = 40 \end{cases}$

6. $\begin{cases} 5x + 2y = -19 \\ 2x - 10y = 14 \end{cases}$

7. $\begin{cases} 10x + 3y = 34 \\ 5x + 4y = 37 \end{cases}$

8. $\begin{cases} 2c - 9d = 15 \\ \frac{1}{4}c - 2d = 1 \end{cases}$

9. $\begin{cases} -6x - 9y = 42 \\ 8x + 42y = -36 \end{cases}$

Uses Objective F: Use systems of linear equations to solve real-world problems.

10. At Clucker's Chicken, a bucket of 4 pieces of dark meat and 5 pieces of white meat costs $7.05. A bucket of 3 pieces of dark meat and 8 pieces of white meat costs $8.90. Find the cost of a piece of dark meat and of a piece of white meat. ______________

11. At Curly's Copies, Chad made 56 copies costing $16. Color copies cost $.75 each and black-and-white copies cost $.10 each. How many copies of each type did Chad make? ______________

12. Ann has 30 straws of length *a* and 24 straws of length *b*. How many triangles of each type drawn at the right can she make using all the straws?

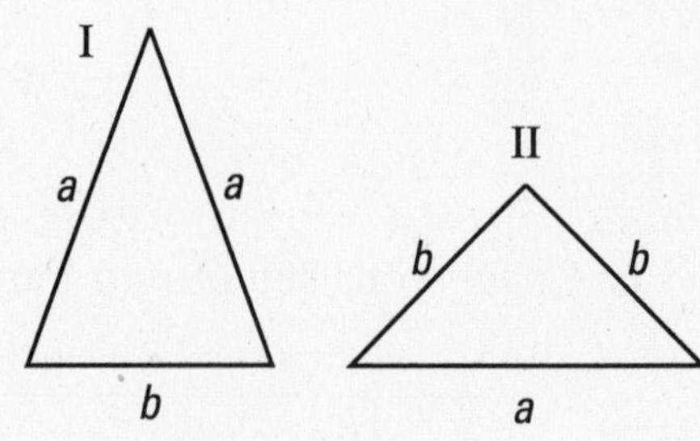

I ______________ II ______________

Name

LESSON MASTER

Questions on SPUR Objectives

Properties Objective E: Determine whether a system has no solutions, one solution, or infinitely many solutions.

In 1–4, match equations whose graphs are parallel lines.

1. $y = 2x + 7$ ________ **a.** $y = 3x - 6$

2. $y = -3x - 9$ ________ **b.** $3x + y = 40$

3. $4x + 3y = 18$ ________ **c.** $y = 2x + 12$

4. $6x - 2y = 12$ ________ **d.** $8x + 6y = 22$

5. Consider the system $\begin{cases} y = 5x + 1 \\ 10x - 2y = -2 \end{cases}$.

a. Find three ordered pairs that are solutions to $y = 5x + 1$.

____

b. Show that each ordered pair from Part **a** is also a solution to $10x - 2y = -2$.

____

____

c. How many solutions does this system have? ________________

In 6–9, tell if the system has *no solutions*, *one solution*, or *infinitely many solutions*.

6. $\begin{cases} 3x + 2y = -4 \\ 6x + 4y = 7 \end{cases}$

____

7. $\begin{cases} 5a + b = 18 \\ 10a + b = 36 \end{cases}$

____

8. $\begin{cases} 8r + 2s = -18 \\ s = -4r - 9 \end{cases}$

____

9. $\begin{cases} 2(x + 3) = y \\ 5x - y = 1 \end{cases}$

____

Name ______________________________

▶ **LESSON MASTER 11-6 B** *page 2*

Uses Objective F: Use systems of linear equations to solve real-world problems.

10. At a movie theater, the Ohira family bought 2 adult tickets and 4 children's tickets for \$26. The Teasdale family bought 3 adult tickets and 6 children's tickets for \$42. How much does an adult ticket cost?

a. Write a system of equations to answer the question. ______________

b. How many solutions does this system have? ______________

c. What does your answer to Part **b** suggest about the situation?

____

____

Representations Objective H: Find solutions to systems of equations by graphing.

11. Describe the graph of a system of linear equations that has

a. no solutions. ______________________

b. one solution. ______________________

c. infinitely many solutions. ______________________

In 12 and 13, a system of equations is given.
a. Graph each system. b. Give the solution.

12. $\begin{cases} 4x + 2y = -8 \\ 6x + 3y = 4 \end{cases}$

13. 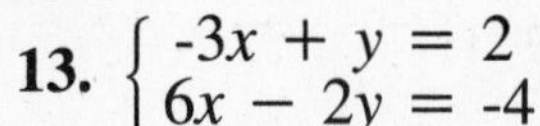 $\begin{cases} -3x + y = 2 \\ 6x - 2y = -4 \end{cases}$

a.

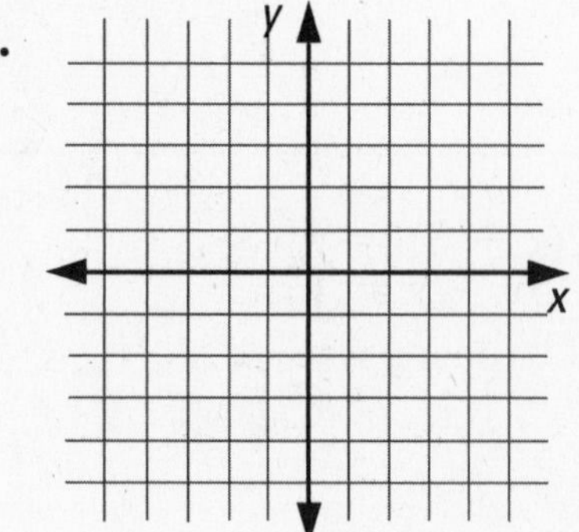

a.

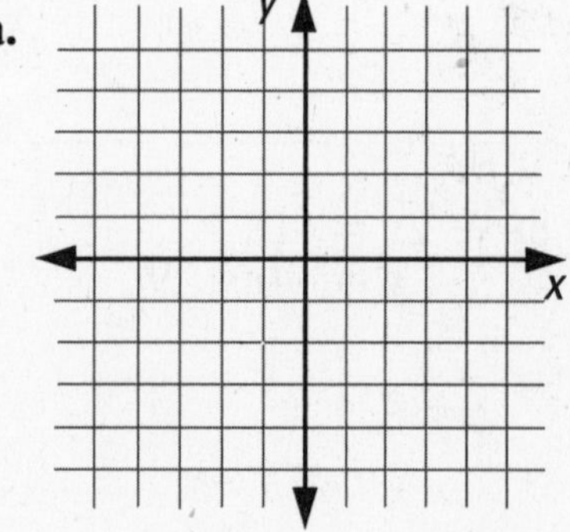

b. ______________________

b. ______________________

Name

Questions on SPUR Objectives

Properties Objective D: Recognize sentences with no solutions, one solution, or all real numbers as solutions.

1. a. Add $6x$ to both sides of $10 - 6(x + 1) = 4 - 6x$. What sentence results?

b. Describe the solutions to $10 - 6(x + 1) = 4 - 6x$.

2. a. Add $-7x$ to both sides of $7x + 9 < 7 + 7x$. What sentence results?

b. Describe the solutions to $7x + 9 < 7 + 7x$.

In 3–12, *multiple choice*. Tell if the sentence is

(a) ***sometimes true.*** **(b)** ***always true.*** **(c)** ***never true.***

3. $h + 4 > h + 1$

4. $2x + 8 = 2(x + 8)$

5. $-7a = 6 - 7a$

6. $2x + 9 + 7x \geq 9(1 + x)$

7. $m + 17 = -m - 1$

8. $-3u + 12 < 8u - 10$

9. $2(b + 7) = 6b + 14$

10. $-4(x + 8) + 20 = 3x - (12 + 7x)$

11. $-12a + 19 < 4a - 16a + 15$

12. $7n + 16 \leq 3(n + 5) + 1$

In 13–15, write an inequality that

13. has no solutions.

14. has $x > 0$ as its solution.

15. is true for all real numbers.

Name

In 16–19, solve.

16. $8 + 13m = 8 + 10m$

17. $5(x - 2) = 2x + 10 + 3x$

18. $7y + 14 \geq 7(y + 2)$

19. $\frac{2}{3}(x - 9) < x - \frac{1}{3}x$

Uses Objective F: Use systems of linear equations to solve real-world problems.

20. The printing charges for business cards at four different companies are given below.

Company A: \$20 plus \$.02 per card
Company B: \$15 plus \$.03 per card
Company C: \$20 plus \$.03 per card
Company D: \$16 plus \$.02 per card plus \$4 delivery (already included in the charges at the other companies)

a. Let x = number of cards. Write an expression for the cost of x business cards from each company.

A __________ B __________

C __________ D __________

b. When does Company A charge more than Company B?

c. When does Company B charge more than Company C?

d. When are the charges at Company A and Company D the same?

Name

LESSON MASTER

Questions on SPUR Objectives

Uses Objective G: Use systems of linear inequalities to solve real-world problems.

1. A craft company sells kits for sewing banners and wind socks. They fill boxes with either 15 banner kits or 10 wind sock kits. They want to bring between 200 and 300 items to sell at an upcoming flea market. Let b = the number of boxes containing banner kits and w = the number of boxes containing wind sock kits.

a. Find two different combinations of boxes of banner kits and boxes of wind sock kits that satisfy the company's plans.

____

____

b. Describe this situation with a system of four inequalities.

____

____

____

____

c. Graph the system.

c.

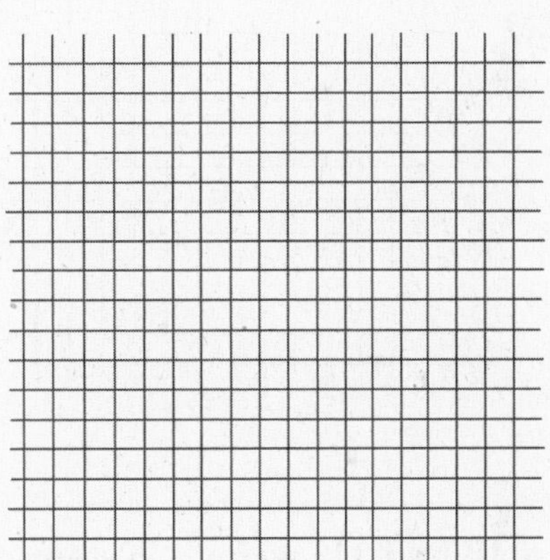

Representations Objective I: Graphically represent solutions to systems of linear inequalities.

2. *Multiple choice.* Which point is a solution to $\begin{cases} y < 3x + 1 \\ y > x - 3 \end{cases}$? ________

(a) (2, 7) (b) (-2, -5) (c) (2, 0) (d) (5, 1)

3. Write a system of inequalities to describe the points in Quadrant IV. ________

4. Describe the graph of $x = 0$, $y > 0$.

____

Name

In 5–7, consider the system $\begin{cases} x > 0 \\ y > -x \\ y < x - 4 \end{cases}$.

**Tell if each point below is a solution of the system.
If not, tell which inequality it fails to satisfy.**

5. (6, 1) ________ **6.** (1, 1) ________ **7.** (2, -5) ________

In 8 and 9, graph the system of inequalities.

8. $\begin{cases} x > 0 \\ y > 0 \\ 3x + y < 7 \end{cases}$

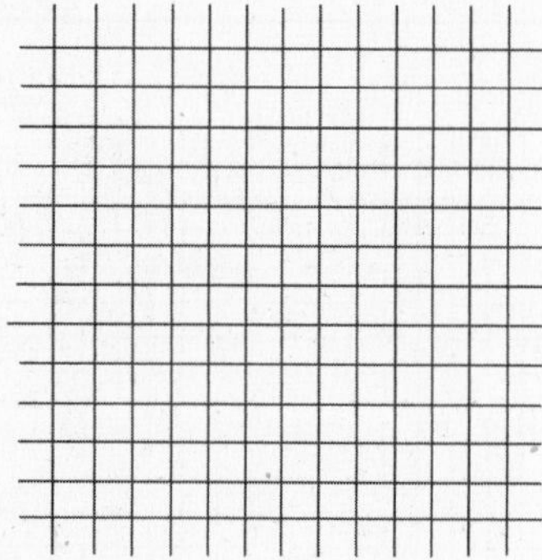

9. $\begin{cases} x \leq 0 \\ y \geq 0 \\ y \geq 2x + 5 \end{cases}$

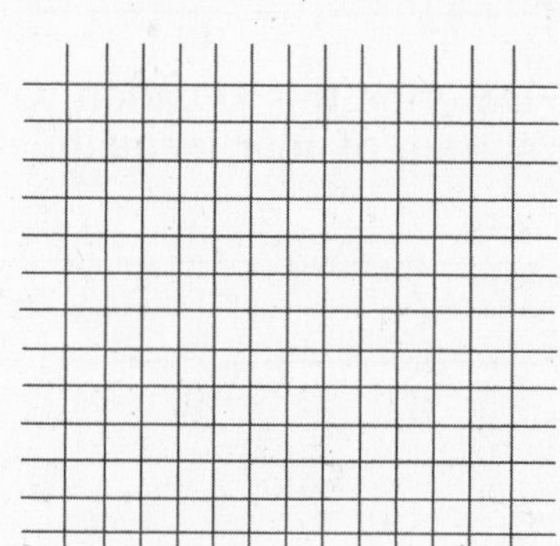

In 10 and 11, write a system of inequalities to describe the graph.

10.

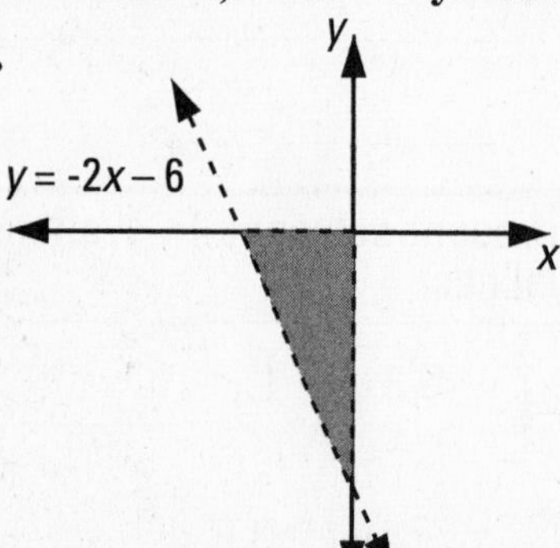

____

11.

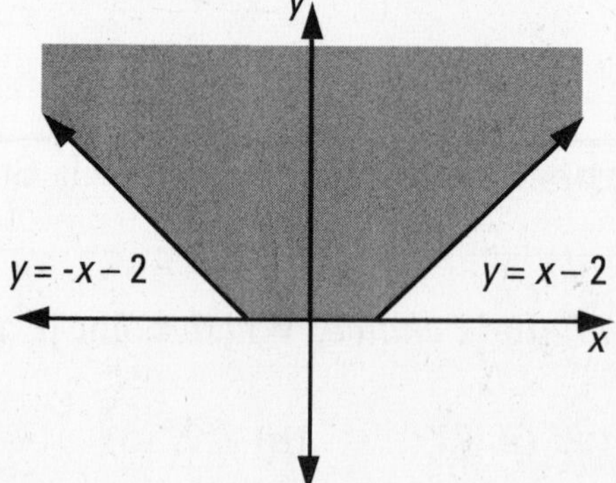

____

Name ______________________________

LESSON MASTER 12-1 B

Questions on SPUR Objectives

Skills Objective A: Factor positive integers into primes.

In 1–4, list all the pairs of integers whose product is the given integer.

1. 42 ______________________________

2. 67 ______________________________

3. -32 ______________________________

4. -55 ______________________________

In 5–7, list all the common factors of the given pair of integers.

5. 12 and 20 ______________________________

6. 6 and 27 ______________________________

7. 8 and 25 ______________________________

In 8–12, write the prime factorization of the given integer in standard form.

8. 72 ______________________________

9. 177 ______________________________

10. 540 ______________________________

11. 4653 ______________________________

12. 5775 ______________________________

In 13–18, determine if the given number is prime.

13. 71 ______________ **14.** 91 ______________

15. 131 ______________ **16.** 1149 ______________

17. 2001 ______________ **18.** 5537 ______________

19. Show with an array that 30 is a composite number.

Name ____________________

In 20–23, the product and sum of a pair of integers is given. Find the numbers.

20. product = 12, sum = 8 ____________________

21. product = 36, sum = 37 ____________________

22. product = -16, sum = 6 ____________________

23. product = -24, sum = -2 ____________________

In 24–27, rewrite the fraction in lowest terms.

24. $\frac{168}{196}$ ____________________

25. $\frac{484}{1331}$ ____________________

26. $\frac{3528}{140}$ ____________________

27. $\frac{4455}{189}$ ____________________

Properties Objective E: Apply the definitions and properties of primes and factors.

In 28–30, give the number of factors in the prime factorization.

28. 5^3 ________

29. 27^4 ________

30. $2^3 \cdot 25^2$ ________

31. Explain why the number $11^4 + 11^{15} + 11^{23}$ could not be prime.

____

____

Review Objective B, Lesson 8-5

In 32–39, simplify.

32. $y^2 \cdot y^5$ ________

33. $x^7 \cdot x^7$ ________

34. $(m^5)^3$ ________

35. $(e^5)^5$ ________

36. $a^2 \cdot a^4 \cdot a^4$ ________

37. $c \cdot c^5$ ________

38. $(m^2 \cdot m^6)^3$ ________

39. $x^4 \cdot y \cdot x^3 \cdot y^3$ ________

Name ______

LESSON MASTER 12-2 B **Questions on SPUR Objectives**

Skills Objective B: Find common monomial factors of polynomials.

In 1 and 2, list all the factors of the given monomial.

1. $5x^2$ ______

2. $49ax^2$ ______

In 3–8, tell if the polynomial is prime.

3. $4x + 8$ ______

4. $3n + 10$ ______

5. $x^2 + 7x$ ______

6. $pq + 2y$ ______

7. $2m + 3mn$ ______

8. $2x^2y + bx^2$ ______

In 9–14, find the greatest common factor of the given monomials.

9. $20x$ and 5 ______

10. $12x^2$ and $18x^3$ ______

11. y^5 and y^3 ______

12. $5t$ and 32 ______

13. $5x^3$, $12x^2$, and $20x^2y$ ______

14. $15ab^2$, $21a^2b^2$, and $6a^2b$ ______

In 15–19, fill in the blanks.

15. $16x + 24 = 8($______ $+$ ______$)$

16. $7b^5 - 12b^2 = b^2($______ $-$ ______$)$

17. $20uv^2 + 28u^2v = 4uv($______ $+$ ______$)$

18. $12x^4 + 18x^3 - 30x^2 = 6x^2($______ $+$ ______ $-$ ______$)$

19. $3m^2n + 6m^2n^2 =$ ______$(1 + 2n)$

Name ______________________________

In 20–25, factor the polynomial completely.

20. $45x + 50$ ______________________

21. $32x^2 - 16x$ ______________________

22. $10ax^2 - 2a^2x$ ______________________

23. $9r^2 - 3r$ ______________________

24. $11 + 4x + 1$ ______________________

25. $30m^4 + 11m^3y - 5m^2$ ______________________

In 26 and 27, a fraction is given. a. Factor the numerator. b. Simplify the fraction.

26. $\frac{2x^3 + 5x}{x}$, $(x \neq 0)$

a. ______________________

b. ______________________

27. $\frac{24r - 16}{80}$

a. ______________________

b. ______________________

Representations Objective J: Represent quadratic expressions and their factorization with areas.

In 28 and 29, make a drawing of algebra tiles showing a rectangle that has the given area.

28. $x^2 + 5x$

29. $4x + 2$

30. a. Use algebra-tile diagrams to show two different rectangles each with area $4x^2 + 8x$.

b. What is the complete factorization of $4x^2 + 8x$? ______________________

Name

LESSON MASTER 12-3 B

Questions on SPUR Objectives

Skills Objective C: Factor quadratic expressions.

In 1–16, factor the expression.

1. $b^2 + 7b + 12$

2. $a^2 - 2a - 15$

3. $h^2 + 10h - 24$

4. $x^2 - 12x + 27$

5. $y^2 - 16y + 64$

6. $12 + 13w + w^2$

7. $8 + n^2 + 6n$

8. $x^2 - 81$

9. $y^2 + 17 + 18y$

10. $2x^2 - 14x$

11. $10a^2 + 50a + 60$

12. $x^3 - 10x^2 + 9x$

13. $m^3 - 16m$

14. $6y^2 + 18y - 60$

15. $2a^2 - 20a + 50$

16. $-140 + 4x^2 - 8x$

Properties Objective G: Determine whether a quadratic polynomial can be factored over the integers.

In 17–21, tell whether the expression is factorable over the integers. If so, give the factorization.

17. $a^2 + 17a + 12$

18. $c^2 - 144$

19. $x^2 + 9x - 10$

20. $y^2 + 15y + 56$

21. $b^2 + 8b + 20$

Name ______________________________

Representations Objective J: Represent quadratic expressions and their factorization with areas.

22. An algebra-tile diagram is shown at the right.

   a. Give the area of the figure as a polynomial.

   ____

   b. Give the area in factored form.

   ____

	x	x	x	1
x				
1				
1				
1				
1				

In 23 and 24, show that the polynomial can be factored by drawing a rectangular algebra-tile diagram.

23. $x^2 + 6x + 8$

24. $x^2 + 5x + 4$

Review Objective A, Lesson 9-5

In 25–28, an equation in standard form is given. a. Use the quadratic formula to give the values of *a*, *b*, and *c*. b. Give the solutions rounded to the nearest hundredth.

25. $x^2 - 12x + 20 = 0$

a. $a =$ ____ $b =$ ____ $c =$ ____

b. ______________________

26. $x^2 + 8x + 10 = 0$

a. $a =$ ____ $b =$ ____ $c =$ ____

b. ______________________

27. $2x^2 + 6x - 1 = 0$

a. $a =$ ____ $b =$ ____ $c =$ ____

b. ______________________

28. $-x^2 + 9x = 0$

a. $a =$ ____ $b =$ ____ $c =$ ____

b. ______________________

Name

LESSON MASTER 12-4 B

Questions on SPUR Objectives

Skills Objective D: Solve quadratic equations by factoring.

In 1–12, solve by factoring.

1. $x^2 + 7x + 6 = 0$

2. $x^2 - 9x + 18 = 0$

3. $x^2 + 5x - 24 = 0$

4. $0 = x^2 - x - 20$

5. $y^2 = 14y - 49$

6. $a^2 + a = 56$

7. $45 + n^2 + 14n = 0$

8. $a^2 - 144 = 0$

9. $3x^2 - 27x = 0$

10. $x^2 + 10x + 25 = 0$

11. $2x^2 = 12x$

12. $\frac{x^2 + 5x}{2} = -2$

Properties Objective F: Recognize and use the Zero Product Property.

In 13 and 14, tell what equations result from applying the Zero Product Property.

13. $(x + 3)(x - 8) = 0$

14. $a(a - 4) = 0$

15. $(n + 5)(n + 6)(n - 4) = 0$

16. a. Give four pairs of numbers whose product is 12. ____________

b. Give four pairs of numbers whose product is 0. ____________

c. Explain why there is a Zero Product Property but there is no Twelve Product Property.

____

____

____

In 17–20, if the polynomial is factorable over the integers, factor and solve the equation using the Zero Product Property. If it is not factorable, use the Quadratic Formula.

17. $x^2 + 9x + 12 = 0$

18. $x^2 - 8x - 20 = 0$

19. $t^2 + 9t + 14 = 0$

20. $x^2 - 12x = 0$

Uses Objective I: Solve quadratic equations in real situations.

21. A rectangular park is 3 blocks longer than it is wide. Its area is 40 square blocks. Let w = width.

a. Write an expression for the length of the rectangle. ____________

b. Write an equation of the form length · width = area. ____________

c. Find the length and width of the park. ____________

22. At a party with n guests, every guest shook hands with every other guest once, for $\frac{n^2 - n}{2}$ handshakes. If there were 66 handshakes, how many guests were there? ____________

Name

Questions on SPUR Objectives

Skills Objective C: Factor quadratic expressions.

1. Consider factoring the polynomial $4x^2 + 4x - 3$ into two binomials $(ax + b)(cx + d)$.

a. List all the possible pairs of numbers for a and c.

b. List all the possible pairs of numbers for b and d.

c. List all the possible binomials $(ax + b)(cx + d)$.

d. Factor $4x^2 + 4x - 3$.

In 2–15, factor.

2. $2x^2 + 9x + 9$

3. $3x^2 - 14x - 5$

4. $5x^2 + 6 - 17x$

5. $6x^2 + 5x + 1$

6. $6x^2 + 13x + 2$

7. $4n^2 - 3n - 7$

8. $10a^2 + 11a - 6$

9. $20x + 4 + 9x^2$

10. $3x^2 + 14x - 49$

11. $4y^2 + 4y + 1$

12. $4a^2 + 10a + 4$

13. $3x^3 - 7x^2 + 4x$

14. $27m^2 - 36m + 12$

15. $30y^3 - 2y^2 - 4y$

Skills Objective D: Solve quadratic equations by factoring.

In 16–21, solve the equation.

16. $(2z - 1)(z + 4) = 0$

17. $t(3t - 7) = 0$

18. $3s(2s + 5) = 0$

19. $2m^2 + m - 3 = 0$

20. $-12y = -4 - 5y^2$

21. $0 = 9x^2 - 12x + 4$

Name

LESSON MASTER **12-6 B**

Questions on SPUR Objectives

Uses Objective I: Solve quadratic equations in real situations.

In 1 and 2, use this information: The area of a rectangular parking lot is 9,600 square meters and its perimeter is 400 meters.

1. Use the Babylonian method to find the dimensions of the parking lot. Show your work.

____

2. Use a modern method to find the dimensions of the parking lot. Show your work.

____

In 3 and 4, use this information: The serving area of a restaurant is 4000 square feet, while its perimeter is 260 feet.

3. Use the Babylonian method to find the dimensions of the restaurant. Show your work.

____

▶ **LESSON MASTER 12-6 B** *page 2*

4. Use a modern method to find the dimensions of the restaurant. Show your work.

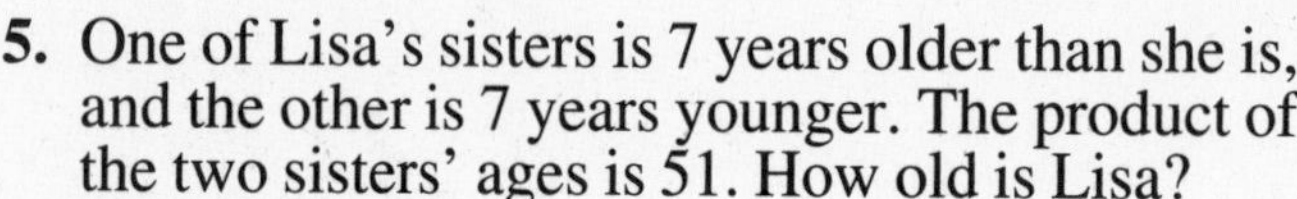

5. One of Lisa's sisters is 7 years older than she is, and the other is 7 years younger. The product of the two sisters' ages is 51. How old is Lisa?

6. The square and rectangle pictured at the right have the same area.

a. What is the area of each figure?

36

b. What are the dimensions of the rectangle?

$x + 15$

$x - 15$

Review Objective E, Lesson 1-2

In 7–20, tell if the number is a *whole number* (W), an *integer* (I), or a *real number* (R). List all terms that apply.

7. 17 ______ **8.** 23.9 ______

9. $\sqrt{121}$ ______ **10.** $\frac{3}{2}$ ______

11. $\sqrt{10}$ ______ **12.** $\frac{1}{3}$ ______

13. $-\pi$ ______ **14.** $-\frac{40}{20}$ ______

15. -.5% ______ **16.** -443 ______

17. $2.\overline{88}$ ______ **18.** $-\sqrt{32}$ ______

19. 0 ______ **20.** 0.001 ______

Name ________________

LESSON MASTER  **Questions on SPUR Objectives**

Vocabulary

1. a. Explain what a *simple fraction* is.

____

____

b. List any three simple fractions. ________________

c. List any three fractions that are *not* simple fractions. ________________

2. a. Explain what a *rational number* is.

____

____

b. List any three rational numbers. ________________

c. List any three numbers that are *not* rational numbers. ________________

Properties Objective H: Apply the definitions and properties of rational and irrational numbers.

In 3–14, tell whether the number is *rational* or *irrational*.

3. $\frac{4}{5}$ ________	4. $\sqrt{3}$ ________	5. 8.7 ________
6. $6\frac{1}{2}$ ________	7. $2.\overline{6}$ ________	8. -0.4 ________
9. $\frac{8}{9}$ ________	10. 0 ________	11. $-\sqrt{81}$ ________
12. $\sqrt{50}$ ________	13. $\sqrt{36}$ ________	14. $9.\overline{83}$ ________

Name ______________________

In 15–22, find a simple fraction for the number.

15. $8\frac{1}{3}$ ________ **16.** 1.025 ________

17. $16\frac{12}{31}$ ________ **18.** $.\overline{7}$ ________

19. 56% ________ **20.** $9.\overline{45}$ ________

21. $.\overline{541}$ ________ **22.** $6.84\overline{8}$ ________

In 23 and 24, determine whether the solutions are *rational* or *irrational*.

23. $4x^2 - 9 = 0$ ________

24. $x^2 - 4x - 1 = 0$ ________

25. A tire has a diameter of 24 inches. Find its circumference and tell if the circumference is *rational* or *irrational*.

____

26. A square window has a side of length of 18. Find the length of a diagonal and tell if the length is *rational* or *irrational*.

____

27. A square picture has a side of length $12\sqrt{2}$. Find the length of a diagonal and tell if the length is *rational* or *irrational*.

____

Name ______________________________

LESSON MASTER 12-8 B

Questions on SPUR Objectives

Properties Objective G: Determine whether a quadratic polynomial can be factored over the integers.

In 1 and 2, consider the polynomial $ax^2 + bx + c$.

1. Suppose $b^2 - 4ac$ is a perfect square.

   a. What must be true about the solutions to $ax^2 + bx + c = 0$? ______________________________

   b. Is $ax^2 + bx + c$ factorable over the set of polynomials with integer coefficients? ______________________________

2. Suppose $b^2 - 4ac$ is not a perfect square.

   a. What must be true about the solutions to $ax^2 + bx + c = 0$? ______________________________

   b. Is $ax^2 + bx + c$ factorable over the set of polynomials with integer coefficients? ______________________________

In 3–10, a polynomial is given. a. Calculate the discriminant of the polynomial. b. Use the discriminant to determine whether the expression can be factored over the integers. c. If possible, factor the polynomial.

3. $x^2 + 3x + 1$

   a. ____________________

   b. ____________________

   c. ____________________

4. $3x^2 + 8x + 4$

   a. ____________________

   b. ____________________

   c. ____________________

5. $2w^2 - 10w + 8$

   a. ____________________

   b. ____________________

   c. ____________________

6. $5y^2 + 4y - 3$

   a. ____________________

   b. ____________________

   c. ____________________

Name ______________________________

7. $6x^2 + 12x - 5$

a. ______________

b. ______________

c. ______________

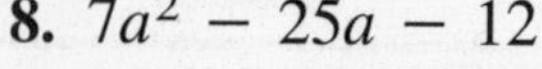

8. $7a^2 - 25a - 12$

a. ______________

b. ______________

c. ______________

9. $8x^2 - 15$

a. ______________

b. ______________

c. ______________

10. $2 + 9x^2 - 16x$

a. ______________

b. ______________

c. ______________

11. The equation $y = 2x^2 - 20x + 41$ is graphed at the right. Are the x-intercepts rational? Explain your thinking.

____

____

____

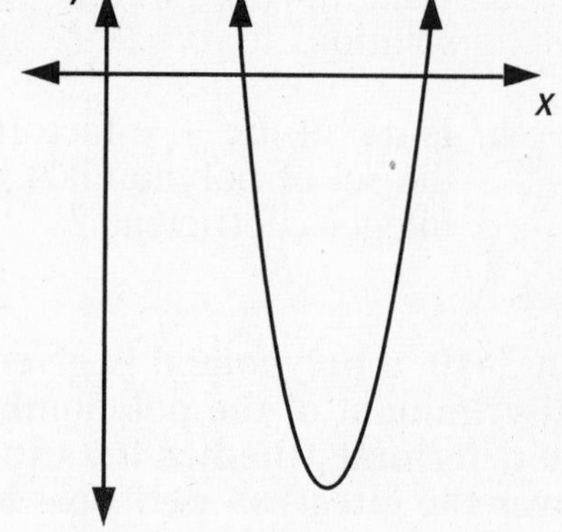

12. Consider the polynomial $ax^2 + 12x + 5$. For what value(s) of a from 1 to 7 is the polynomial factorable?

____

13. The polynomial $x^2 - 6$ can be factored into $(x + \sqrt{6})(x - \sqrt{6})$.

a. Show that $(x + \sqrt{6})(x - \sqrt{6}) = x^2 - 6$.

____

b. Calculate the discriminant of $x^2 - 6$. ______________

c. Does the situation in Parts **a** and **b** violate the Discriminant Theorem? Explain your answer.

____

____

____

Name ______________________________

LESSON MASTER

Questions on SPUR Objectives

Vocabulary

1. Give a definition for *function*.

____

____

____

____

Properties Objective C: Determine whether a set of ordered pairs is a function.

In 2–11, decide if the equation, inequality, or set of points represents a function. If it is *not* a function, give two ordered pairs that show why a function is not described.

2. $\{(4, 3), (5, 4), (6, 5), (7, 6), (8, 7)\}$

____

3. $y = 7x$

____

4. $\{(9, 3), (6, -3), (8, 10), (4, -3), (9, 18)\}$

____

5. $y = \pm\sqrt{x}$

____

6. $\{(9, 5), (6, 5), (12, 5), (2, 5), (-17, 5), (0, 5)\}$

____

7. $y < x + 4$

____

8. $3x + 5y = 16$

____

9. $y = |x + 1|$

____

Name

10. $y = 2x^2$

11. $x = 2y^2$

12. Give an example of a relation that is *not* a function.

Representations Objective H: Determine whether or not a graph represents a function.

In 13–15, tell if the graph represents a function.

13.

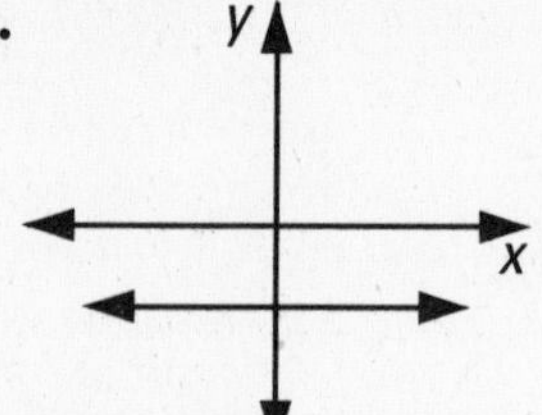

14.

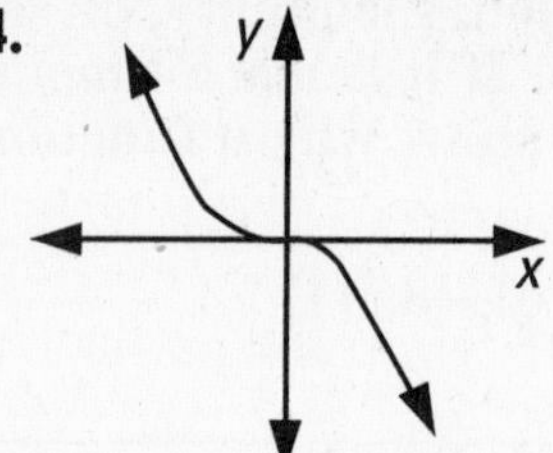

15.

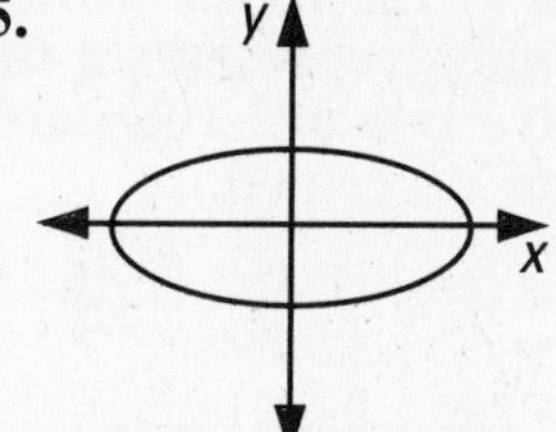

Representations Objective I: Graph functions.

In 16 and 17, a. graph the equation, and b. tell if the equation describes a function.

16. $x + y = 7$

a.

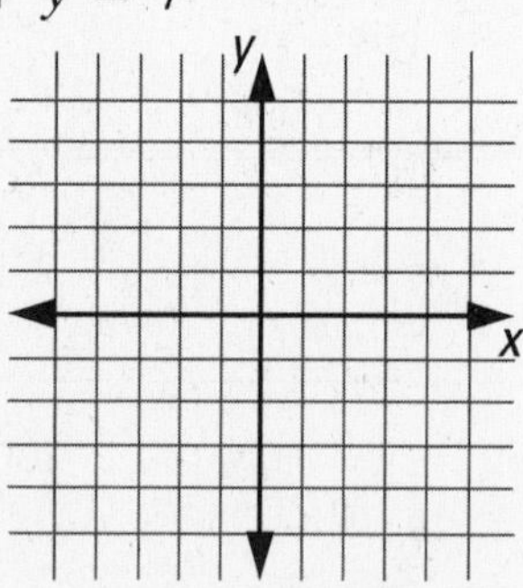

b.

17. $x = -4$

a.

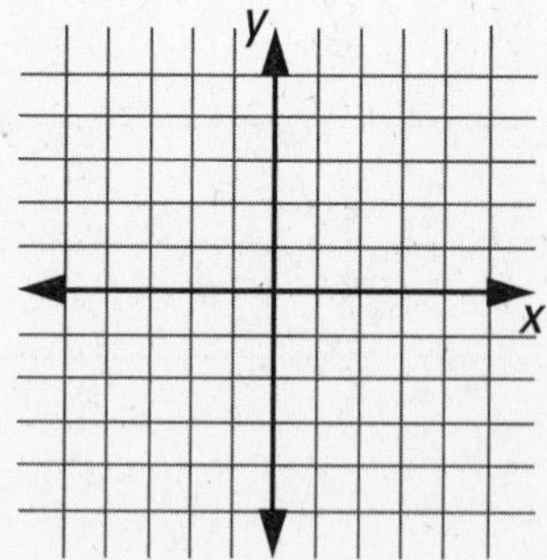

b.

Name ______________________________

LESSON MASTER

Questions on SPUR Objectives

Skills Objective A: Evaluate functions and solve equations involving function notation.

In 1–3, tell how the expression or equation should be read.

1. SQR(8) ______________________________

2. $f(x) = 6x$ ______________________________

3. ABS(-1) ______________________________

In 4–9, evaluate.

4. SQR(121) ______________

5. $f(8)$ if $f(x) = 7x$ ______________

6. ABS(13) ______________

7. SQR(25) + 14 ______________

8. $g(10)$ if $g(x) = x + 13.8$ ______________

9. $f(-3)$ if $f(x) = x^2 + 2x + 1$ ______________

In 10–13, an equation for a function is given. Find *f*(-5).

10. $f(x) = -x$ ______________

11. $f(t) = t^3$ ______________

12. $f(x) = 2^x$ ______________

13. $f(x) = \frac{x}{10} + \frac{4x}{5}$ ______________

14. Let $f(x) = -4x + 2$. Calculate.

   a. $f(3)$ ______________

   b. $f(6)$ ______________

   c. $\frac{f(3) - f(6)}{3(6)}$ ______________

15. Suppose $f(x) = 6x + 14$. For what value of x is $f(x) = -34$? ______________

Uses Objective E: Use function notation and language in real situations.

16. Let $c(x)$ = the number of children in classroom x.
Let $a(x)$ = the number of adults in classroom x.

a. If your classroom is classroom x, find $c(x)$ and $a(x)$.

b. Find $c(x) + a(x)$ and tell what it represents.

17. During the first 6 decades of the 1900s, Crestview's population during decade d could be approximated by $p(d) = 2{,}500 \cdot (1.15)^d$.

a. Evaluate $p(5) - p(4)$.

b. What does $p(5) - p(4)$ stand for?

Representations Objective I: Graph functions.

In 18 and 19, the equation of a function is given.
a. Graph the function. b. Give the y-intercept.

18. $f(x) = 3x - 5$

a.

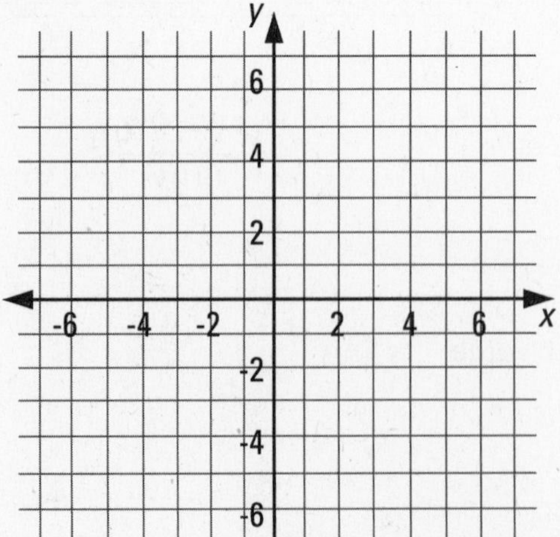
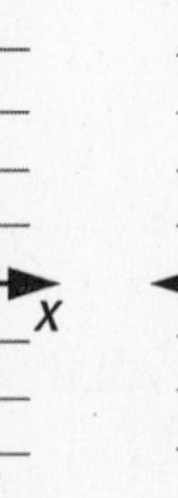

b.

19. $g(x) = x^2 + 3$

a.

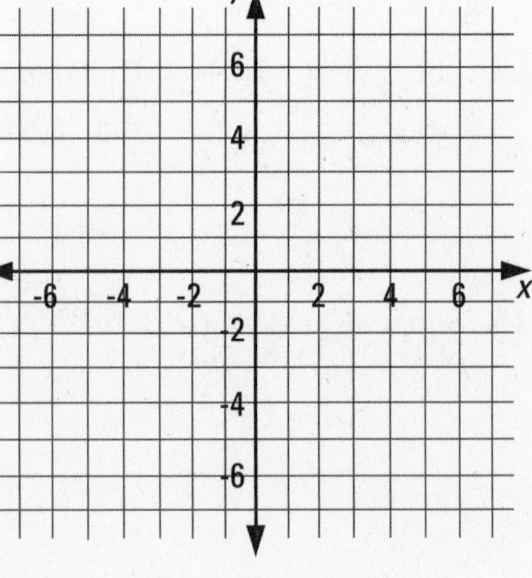

b.

Name ______________________________

LESSON MASTER **13-3 B**

Questions on SPUR Objectives

Skills Objective A: Evaluate functions and solve equations involving absolute-value notation.

In 1–4, let $A(x) = |x|$. Calculate.

1. $A(-12)$ ____________ **2.** $A(8)$ ____________

3. $A(-5.9)$ ____________ **4.** $A\left(\frac{6}{5}\right)$ ____________

In 5–8, let $g(x) = |3x - 4|$. Calculate.

5. $g(6)$ ____________ **6.** $g(1)$ ____________

7. $g\left(\frac{4}{3}\right)$ ____________ **8.** $g(-5)$ ____________

In 9–12, let $f(x) = -|2x|$. Calculate.

9. $f(-4)$ ____________ **10.** $f\left(\frac{1}{2}\right)$ ____________

11. $f(-11)$ ____________ **12.** $f(-0.05)$ ____________

In 13–16, solve.

13. $|x + 3| = 5$ ____________ **14.** $|y - 4| + 1 = 3$ ____________

15. $3|2z| = 30$ ____________ **16.** $-4|5a + 2| = -28$ ____________

Uses Objective E: Use function notation and language in real situations.

17. *Multiple choice.* When 2-inch nails are manufactured, the actual length is usually slightly more or less than 2 inches. Let $f(x)$ = the error in a nail with length x. Which equation relates $f(x)$ and x? ____________

(a) $f(x) = \frac{|2 + x|}{2}$ (b) $f(x) = |2 - x|$

(c) $f(x) = |x|$ (d) $f(x) = -|x + 2|$

Name

18. *Multiple choice.* Suppose you start at home and walk along Kinzer Street to the library. Let $f(b)$ = the distance from home to the school after you have walked b blocks. Which equation relates $f(b)$ and b? ________

(a) $f(b) = |b|$ (b) $f(b) = |10 - b|$

(c) $f(b) = |6 - b|$ (d) $f(b) = |b - 10|$

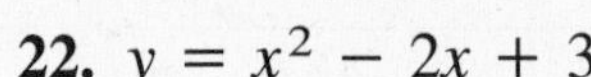

Representations Objective I: Graph absolute-value functions.

In 19 and 20, graph the function.

19. $f(x) = \left|\frac{1}{2}x\right|$

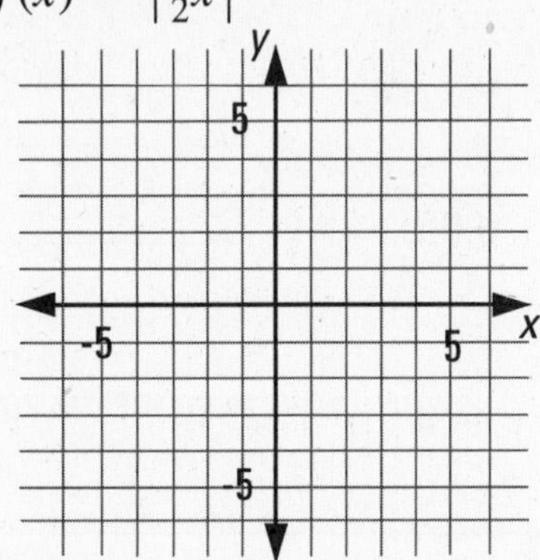

20. $f(x) = -|x - 4| + 1$

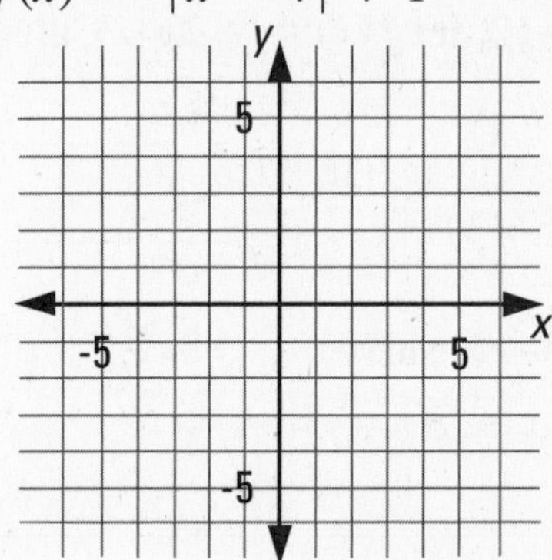

Review Objective F, Lesson 9-2

In 21 and 22, an equation is given. a. Graph the equation. b. Give the coordinates of the vertex. c. Give the y-intercept.

21. $y = -\frac{1}{2}x^2 + 5$

a.

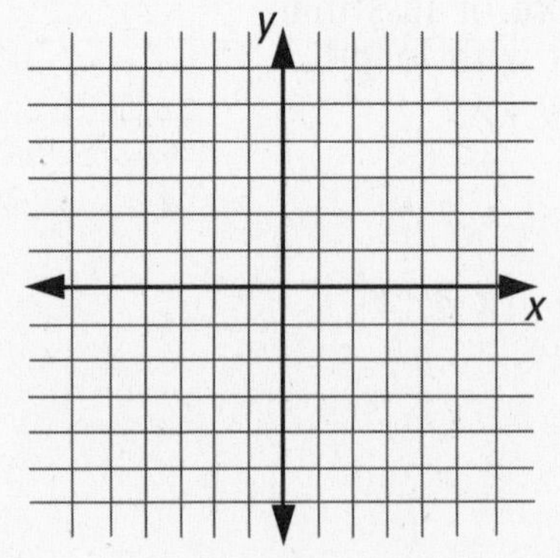

b. ________ **c.** ________

22. $y = x^2 - 2x + 3$

a.

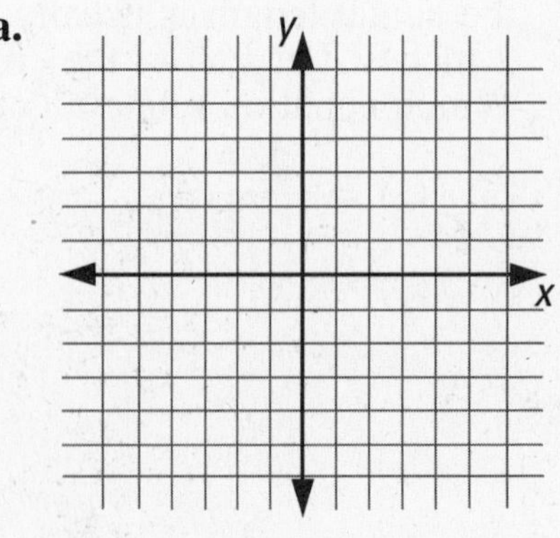

b. ________ **c.** ________

Name ___

LESSON MASTER 

Questions on SPUR Objectives

Properties Objective D: Find the domain and the range of a function from its formula, graph, or rule.

1. Explain how to find the range of f when $f(x) = 2x^2 + 1$.

___

___

2. a. Give the domain of f when $f(x) = \frac{3}{9 - x}$. ___

b. Give the domain of g when $g(x) = \frac{x + 2}{5 + x}$. ___

c. Give an example of a function whose domain is the set of all real numbers but 7. ___

In 3–12, a function is described. a. Give its domain. b. Give its range.

3. $\{(-4, 9), (7, 7), (0, 3), (2, -8), (5, 3)\}$

a. ___

b. ___

4. $\{(-9, 3), (6, 3), (0, 3), (11, 3)\}$

a. ___

b. ___

5. $g(x) = \sqrt{x} + 4$

a. ___

b. ___

6. $f(x) = -|x| - 3$

a. ___

b. ___

7. $f(x) = \frac{2x}{x}$

a. ___

b. ___

8. $g(x) = 5x^2$

a. ___

b. ___

9.

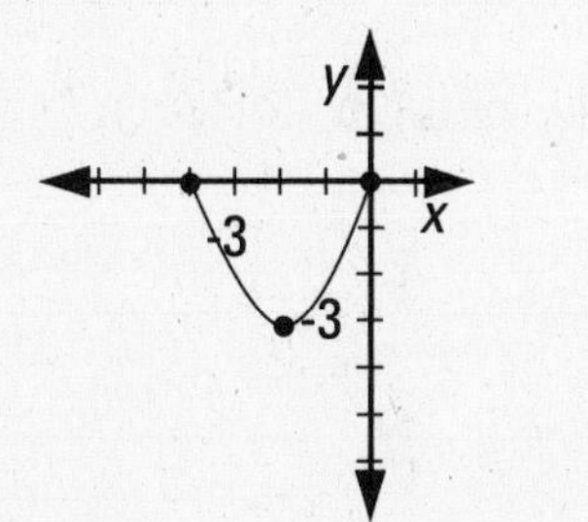

a. ___

b. ___

10.

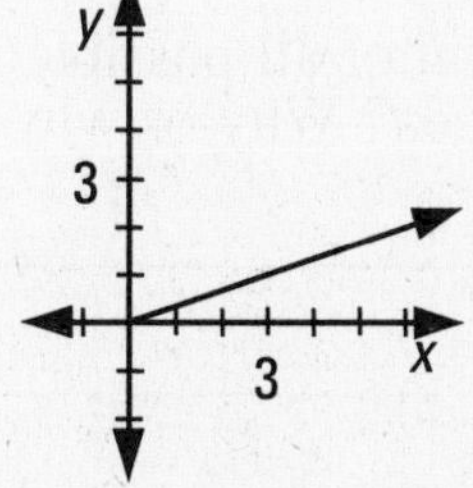

a. ___

b. ___

Name ____

► **LESSON MASTER 13-4 B** *page 2*

11.

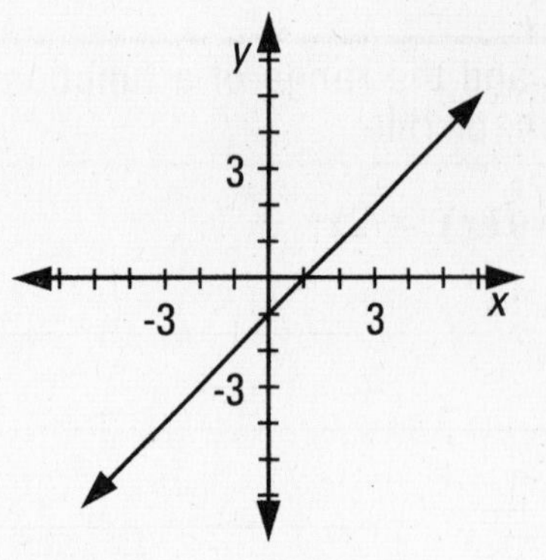

12.

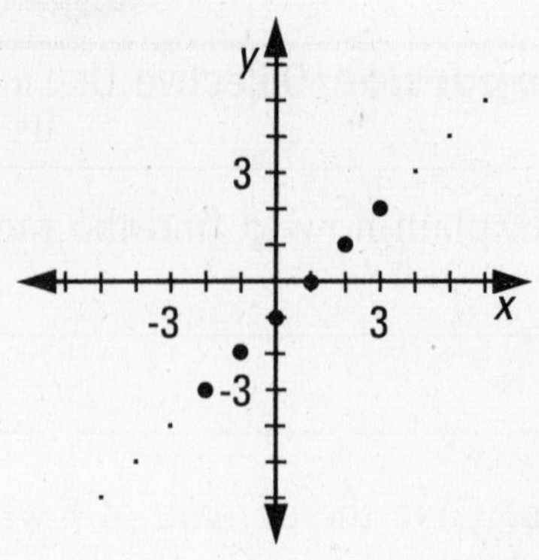

a. ____________________ **a.** ____________________

b. ____________________ **b.** ____________________

Uses Objective E: Use function notation and language in real situations.

13. The set of ordered pairs below associates a year with the population of New York City (rounded to the nearest million) in that year.

{(1860, 1.2), (1880, 1.9), (1900, 2.4), (1920, 5.6)}

a. Give the domain. ____________________

b. Give the range. ____________________

14. Let $s(x)$ = a student's test grade when the percent of correct answers is x. The chart at the right gives the values of this function.

Percent Correct	Grade
88–100	5
75–87	4
62–74	3
50–61	2
0–49	1

a. Give the domain. ____________________

b. Give the range. ____________________

c. Is the set of all possible ordered pairs (grade, percent correct) a function? Why or why not?

____

____

Name

LESSON MASTER

Questions on SPUR Objectives

Uses Objective F: Determine values of probability functions.

1. *Multiple choice*. Let x be a value in the range of a probability function. Tell which inequality must be true. ________

   (a) $x \geq 0$ (b) $0 < x < 1$ (c) $0 \leq x \leq 1$ (d) $x < 1$

2. A bag contains cherry, lemon, and grape candies. $P(\text{cherry}) = \frac{2}{5}$, and $P(\text{lemon}) = \frac{1}{5}$, where $P(\text{flavor})$ means the probability that a candy drawn at random is flavor x.

   a. Find $P(\text{grape})$. ________

   b. What is the range of this function? ________

3. During the holiday season, the student council has a lottery to give away gift certificates to the school store. This year, $P(\text{freshman}) = \frac{3}{16}$, $P(\text{sophomore}) = \frac{1}{4}$, and $P(\text{junior}) = \frac{3}{16}$, where $P(\text{class})$ means the probability that the name drawn is a member of class x.

   a. Find $P(\text{senior})$. ________

   b. What is the range of this function? ________

4. Let $P(n)$ = the probability of getting a *product* of n when two fair dice are thrown.

   a. Find $P(6)$. ________

   b. List 3 numbers that *cannot* be values for n. ________

   c. If $P(n) = \frac{1}{36}$, give a possible value for n. ________

   d. Could $P(n)$ ever be equal to $\frac{1}{10}$? Explain your reasoning.

   ____

   ____

   ____

Representations Objective I: Graph probability functions.

5. This fair spinner is divided into 8 congruent parts. The point value of each region is labeled. Let $P(n)$ = the probability of getting n points on a spin.

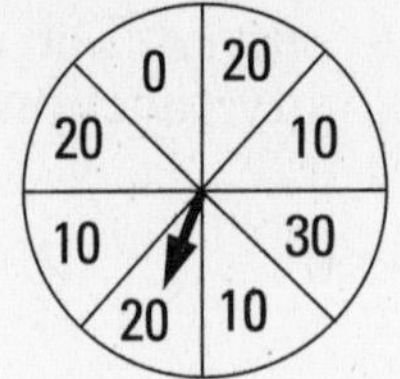

   a. Find $P(0)$, $P(10)$, $P(20)$, and $P(30)$.

   ____

   ____

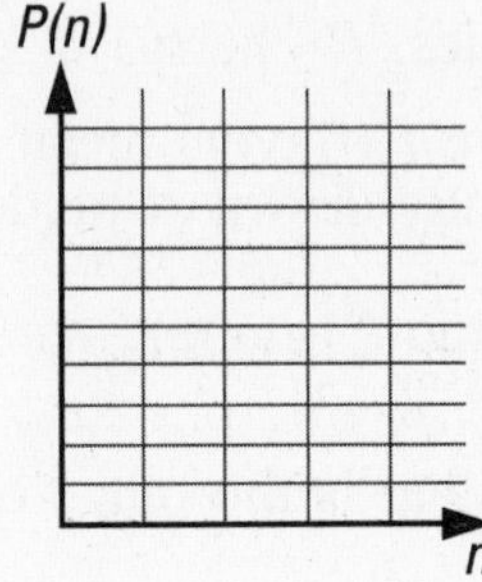

   b. At the right, graph $P(n)$.

6. A cooler contains 20 cans of soft drinks: 4 lemon-lime (LL), 6 cola (C), and 10 root beer (RB). You reach in and choose a can at random. Let $P(n)$ = the probability that you will choose flavor n.

   a. Find $P(\text{LL})$.

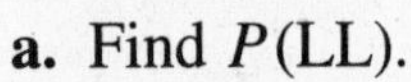

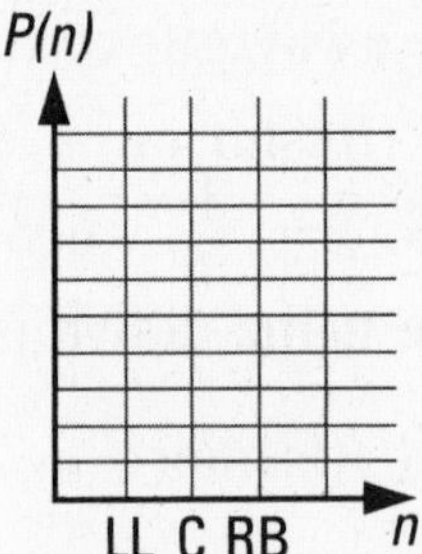

   b. At the right, graph the probability function $P(n)$.

7. A mail carrier delivered four letters. Let $P(n)$ = the probability that exactly n of these letters will be bills.

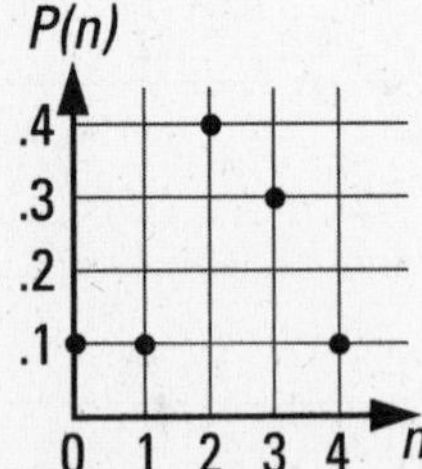

   a. What is the probability that there will be fewer than 3 bills?

   ____

   b. Find $P(0) + P(1) + P(2) + P(3) + P(4)$.

   ____

Name

LESSON MASTER 13-6 B

Questions on SPUR Objectives

Representations Objective J: Graph polynomial functions.

In 1 and 2, an equation is given. a. Complete the table of x- and y-values. b. Plot the points in the table and connect them with a smooth curve. c. Describe the graph.

1. $y = x^3 + x^2 - 3x - 2$

a.

x	y
-3	
-2	
-1	
0	
1	
2	
3	

b.

c. ______________________________

____

2. $y = x^4 - 3x^3 - 6x^2 + 8x$

a.

x	y
-3	
-2	
-1	
0	
1	
2	
3	

b.

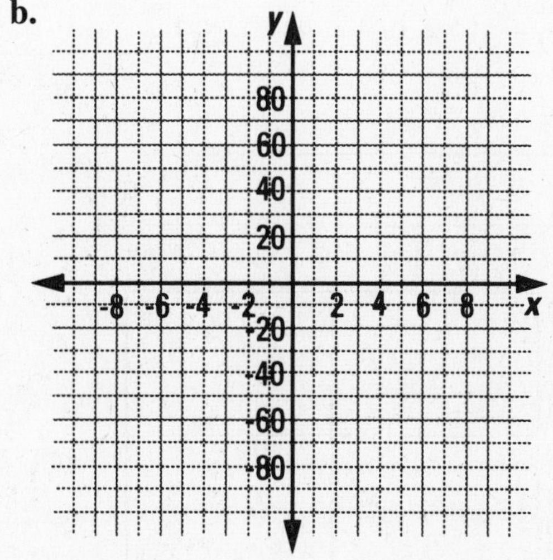

c. ______________________________

____

Name ______________________________

3. Consider the polynomial function $f(x) = 3x^4 + 2x^3 - x - 7$.

a. Give the number of x-intercepts. ____________

b. Give the number of y-intercepts. ____________

In 4–7, use an automatic grapher. A function is given.
a. Find a window which shows all of the x- and y-intercepts.
b. Draw the graph as it appears on your automatic grapher.

4. $f(x) = -x^3 + 4x$

a. ____________________

____

b.

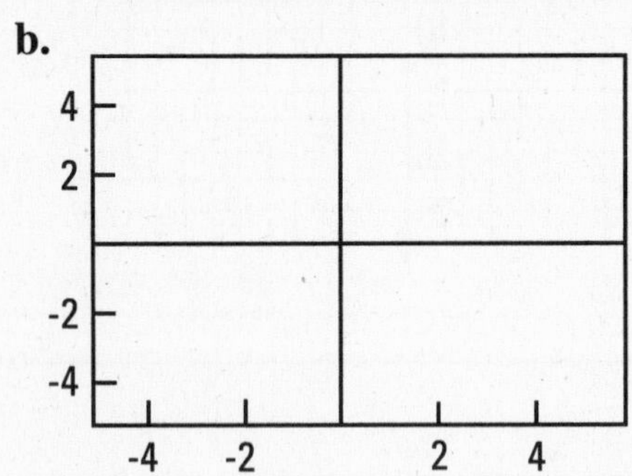

5. $y = x^4 - 2x^2 - 10$

a. ____________________

____

b.

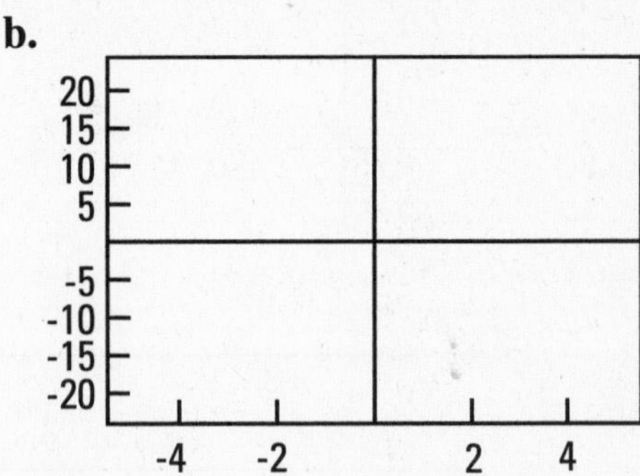

6. $g(x) = 3x^5 - 9x^4 - 8x^3 + 2x^2 + 10x + 30$

a. ____________________

____

b.

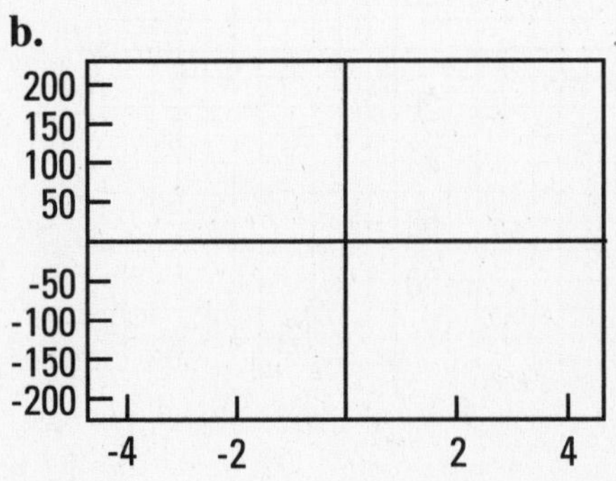

7. $h(x) = .5x^3 + 2x^2 - 5x + 20$

a. 

____

b.

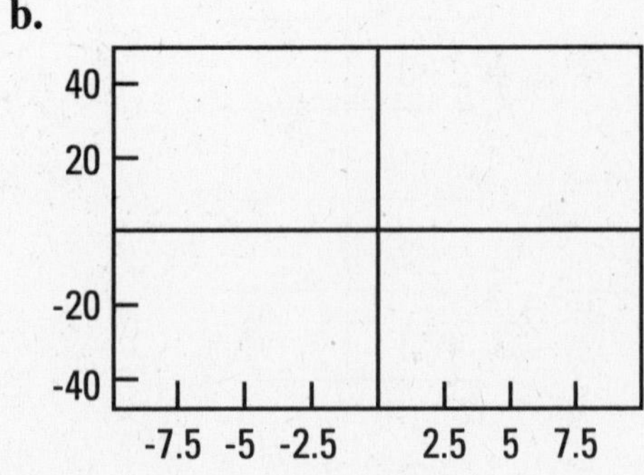

Name ______________________________

LESSON MASTER

Questions on SPUR Objectives

Vocabulary

1. Use right triangle *RST* at the right.

a. Name the leg adjacent to $\angle T$. __________

b. Name the leg opposite $\angle T$. __________

c. What ratio equals tan *T*? __________

d. Name the leg adjacent to $\angle R$. __________

e. Name the leg opposite $\angle R$. __________

f. What ratio equals tan *R*? __________

2. Write a key sequence to find tan 72° on your calculator.

____

Skills Objective B: Use the tangent key on a calculator.

In 3–6, round to the nearest hundredth.

3. tan 18° __________ **4.** tan 84° __________

5. tan 58° __________ **6.** tan 22.5° __________

Uses Objective G: Find lengths of sides or tangents of angles in right triangles using the tangent function.

7. Use right triangle *XYZ* at the right.

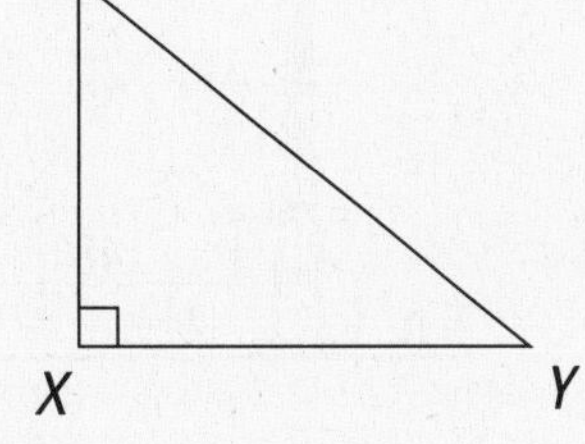

a. Measure $\angle Y$. __________

b. Measure the legs.

____

____

c. Compute tan *Y* by dividing the lengths given in Part **b**. Round to the nearest hundredth. __________

d. On your calculator find tan *Y* to the nearest hundredth. __________

e. How close are the values you found in Parts **c** and **d**? __________

Name ______________________________

8. 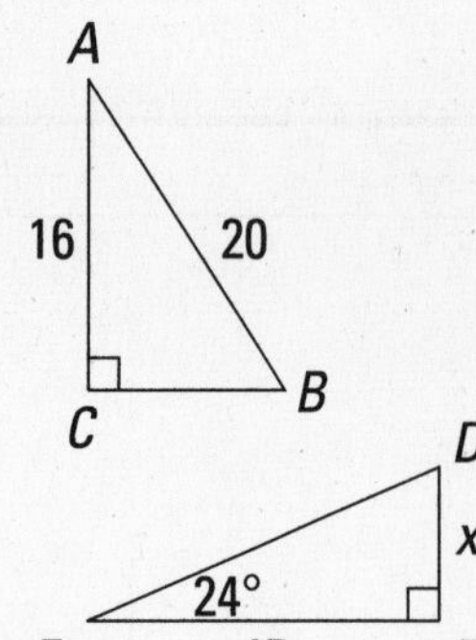

Use right triangle ABC at the left.

a. Find the length of $\overline{BC}$. ________

b. Find the tangent of $\angle B$. ________

9. 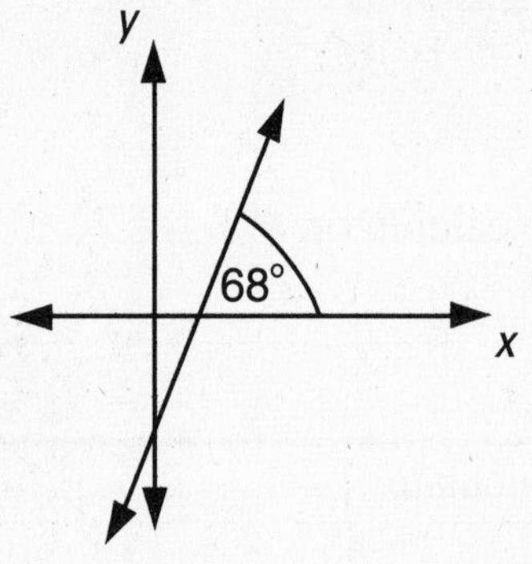

Use right triangle DEF at the left.

a. Find tan 24° to the nearest hundredth. ________

b. Find x. ________

In 10 and 11, find the slope of the line.

10. 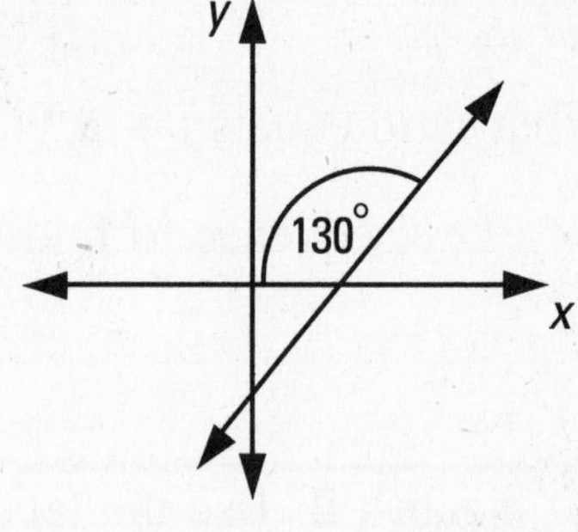

____

11. 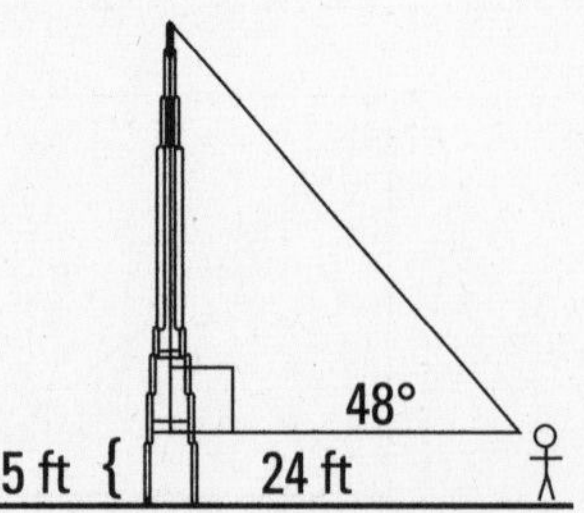

____

In 12 and 13, find the tangent of the angle formed by the positive ray of the x-axis and the line whose equation is given.

12. $y = \frac{3}{4}x - 5$ ________

13. $2x - y = 8$ ________

14.

When Juan stands 24 feet away from a tower, he has to look up 48° to see the top. His eyes are 5 ft above the ground. How high is the tower?

____

Name

LESSON MASTER 13-8 B

Questions on SPUR Objectives

Vocabulary

1. Use right triangle *RST* at the right.

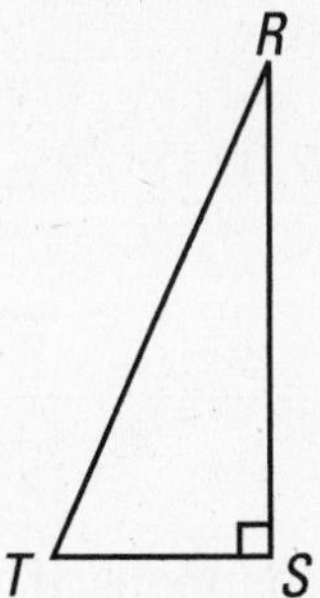

a. What ratio equals sin *T*? ____________

b. What ratio equals cos *T*? ____________

Skills Objective B: Use function keys on a calculator.

In 2–9, a. write a key sequence to find each value. b. Write what is shown in the display.

2. sin 16°

a. ____________________

b. ____________________

3. cos 8°

a. ____________________

b. ____________________

4. $(-2.088)^2$

a. ____________________

b. ____________________

5. $\sqrt{0.008}$

a. ____________________

b. ____________________

6. log(43)

a. ____________________

b. ____________________

7. log (10^6)

a. ____________________

b. ____________________

8. 8!

a. ____________________

b. ____________________

9. $\frac{1}{3.44}$

a. ____________________

b. ____________________

Name ______

In 10–17, give a decimal approximation rounded to the nearest hundredth.

10. cos 33° ______ **11.** sin 15° ______

12. log(77,024) ______ **13.** $\frac{1}{.0073}$ ______

14. 11! ______ **15.** $(62.1)^2$ ______

16. $\sqrt{5008}$ ______ **17.** tan 70° ______

18. What happens if you use a function key on your calculator with a value of x that is not in the domain of the function?

______

In 19–24, a calculator key with a given function is shown. Give an example of a real number x that is *not* in the domain of the function. If all real numbers are in the domain, write *all*.

19. [!] ______ **20.** [tan] ______ **21.** [$1/x$] ______

22. [x^2] ______ **23.** [sin] ______ **24.** [$\sqrt{\ }$] ______

25. Many calculators have an inverse function key [INV]. Try the following.

a. On your calculator, find sin 30°. ______

b. On your calculator, press .5 [INV] [sin]. What does the display show? ______

c. Study Parts **a** and **b**. For a number x in the display, what do you think pressing [INV] [sin] finds?

______

______

d. On your calculator, find log(10,000). ______

e. On your calculator, press 4 [INV] [log]. What does the display show? ______

f. Study Parts **d** and **e**. For a number x in the display, what do you think pressing [INV] [log] finds?

______

Name

LESSON MASTER 1-1 B

Questions on SPUR Objectives

Vocabulary

1. Explain what a *variable* is.
Sample: a letter or other symbol that can be replaced by a number or object from a set

In 2–8, write the correct symbol for each mathematical verb.

2. is less than $<$
3. is approximately equal to $\approx$
4. is greater than or equal to $\geq$
5. is equal to $=$
6. is less than or equal to $\leq$
7. is not equal to $\neq$
8. is greater than $>$
9. Tell whether or not the given sentence is an open sentence. Write *yes* or *no*.
   a. $2.5g$ no b. $6\frac{1}{2} < 6\frac{5}{8}$ no c. $m^2 = 81$ yes
   d. $24 < 8A$ yes e. $y \geq 14$ yes f. $0.1855 - w$ no
10. Write an inequality comparing $\frac{6}{11}$ and $\frac{1}{2}$
    a. using the symbol ">." $\frac{6}{11} > \frac{1}{2}$
    b. using the symbol "<." $\frac{1}{2} < \frac{6}{11}$
11. Write an inequality comparing $\frac{3}{4}$ and $\frac{5}{6}$
    a. using the symbol "≥." $\frac{5}{6} \geq \frac{3}{4}$
    b. using the symbol "≤." $\frac{3}{4} \leq \frac{5}{6}$

Name

In 12–14, let r = Ruth's math test score. Write a sentence in words for each algebraic sentence. Samples are given.

12. $r \geq 84$ Ruth got at least 84 on the test.
13. $r \neq 84$ Ruth did not get 84 on the test.
14. $r < 100$ Ruth got less than 100 on the test.
15. Give a number that is a solution to the sentence in Question 15. Sample: 91
16. Let A = the land area of Rhode Island in square miles. Write in inequality to describe the following statement:
    The land area of Rhode Island is less than 2,000 square miles. $A < 2{,}000$

Skills Objective A: Find solutions to open sentences using trial and error.

17. Which of the numbers 3, 6, and 10 are solutions of $4 + n = 10$? 6
18. Which of the numbers 4, 5, and 8 are solutions of $9 - b = 4 \cdot b - 11$? 4
19. Which of the numbers 1, 4, and 7 are solutions of $2 \cdot m \geq 8$? 4, 7
20. Which of the numbers 8, 15, and 20 are solutions of $\frac{h}{4} < 8$? 8, 15, 20

In 21 and 22, give three solutions to each open sentence. Samples are given.

21. $u > 4.8$ 5 6 7.5
22. $v \leq 13.5$ 0 5.5 13.5

In 23 and 24, give both solutions to the equation.

23. $a^2 = 64$ $a = 8$ $a = -8$
24. $d^2 = 1$ $d = 1$ $d = -1$
25. Give an example of an inequality for which 6 is a solution. Sample: $n > 4$

Name

LESSON MASTER 1-2 B

Questions on SPUR Objectives

Vocabulary

1. A *set* is a collection of objects called members or elements.

In 2–7, write *W* if the number is a whole number, *I* if the number is an integer, and *R* if the number is a real number. List all terms that apply.

2. -4 I, R 3. 17.3 R 4. $\sqrt{15}$ R
5. $\frac{2}{3}$ R 6. 266 W, I, R 7. -7.886 R
8. Suppose you are asked to find the whole numbers that are in the solution set of the inequality $x < 7.6$.
   a. What is the domain of x? set of whole numbers
   b. What is the solution set for the inequality? {0, 1, 2, 3, 4, 5, 6, 7}

In 9–14, tell if the interval is open, closed, or neither.

9. 

neither
10. $9 > s > -7$ open
11. 

open
12. $4 \leq d \leq 14.6$ closed
13. 

closed
14. $3 \geq u > -3$ neither

Properties Objective E: Read and interpret set language and notation.

In 15–18, name two elements in each set. Samples are given.

15. set of planets Pluto, Mars
16. set of integers 7, -11
17. {-4, 10, 13, -8.9} 10, -8.9
18. {cat, rat, sat} cat, rat
19. Which of the following sets are equal?
    A = {6, 9.4} B = {9.4, 6, 7}
    C = {6, 9.4, 7, 5} D = {7, 6, 9.4} B and D

Name

Uses Objective I: In real situations, choose a reasonable domain for a variable.

In 20–23, *multiple choice*. Which is the most reasonable domain for the variable?

(a) set of whole numbers (b) set of integers
(c) set of positive real numbers (d) set of real numbers

20. v = the number of registered voters in an election a
21. t = the temperature at noon in Toronto b
22. g = the amount of gas in a car's gas tank c
23. a = altitude with respect to sea level d

Representations Objective L: Draw and interpret graphs of solution sets to inequalities.

24. Explain how the graph of $n < 3$ differs from the graph of $n \leq 3$.
Sample: for $n < 3$, an open circle at 3; for $n \leq 3$, a closed circle at 3

In 25–27, graph the solution set on a number line.

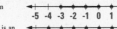

25. $y > -4$ when y is an integer.
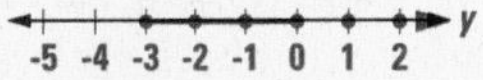

26. $-2 < j < 5$ when j is an integer.
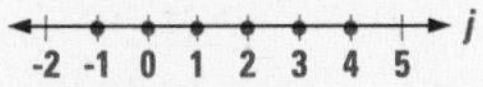

27. $1.6 \geq k > 1.1$ when k is a real number.
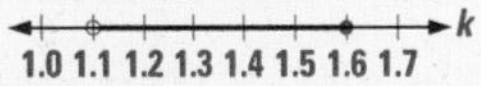

In 28–31, *multiple choice*. Select from the four choices in 20–23 above. Which domain was used in each graph of $y \geq -4$?

28. 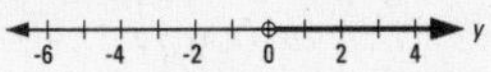

c
29. 

b
30. 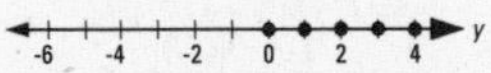

a
31. 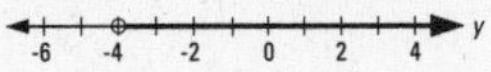

d

Name

LESSON MASTER 1-3 B

Questions on SPUR Objectives

Skills Objective B: Find unions and intersections.

1. For the Venn diagram at the left, list the elements of
   V: 3, -4, 9, -6 W: 0, 12, 8 V and W: 5, -2

   a. V ∪ W. {-6, -4, -2, 0, 3, 5, 8, 9, 12}

   b. V ∩ W. {-2, 5}

2. Let R = {0, -2, -4, -6} and S = {-2, -1, 0, 1, 2}. Draw a Venn diagram to illustrate

   a. R ∩ S.

   R: -4, -6 R and S: 0, -2 S: -1, 1, 2

   b. R ∪ S.

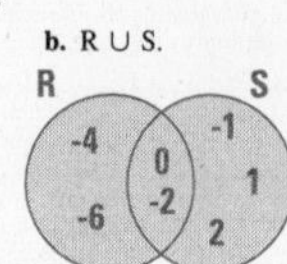

3. Let A = {1, 4, 9, 16, 25} and B = {2, 4, 8, 16}.

   a. Give the union of A and B. {1, 2, 4, 8, 9, 16, 25}

   b. Give the intersection of A and B. {4, 16}

4. Let G = the set of divisors of 18 and H = the set of divisors of 27. List the elements of G ∩ H.
   {1, 3, 9}

Properties Objective E: Read and interpret set language and notation.

5. When is the intersection of two sets equal to the null set? Sample: when the sets have no elements in common

6. Suppose M ∩ N = {0, 8} and M ∪ N = {0, 2, 4, 6, 8}. Draw a Venn diagram to show sets M and N that fit this description. There are several possible answers.
   Samples:

   M: 2 M and N: 0, 8 N: 4, 6

Name

Representations Objective L: Draw and interpret graphs of solution sets to inequalities.

7. Graph the solution sets. Let the domain be the set of real numbers.

   a. $x < 18$ b. $x > 12$

   c. $x > 12$ and $x < 18$ d. $x > 12$ or $x < 18$

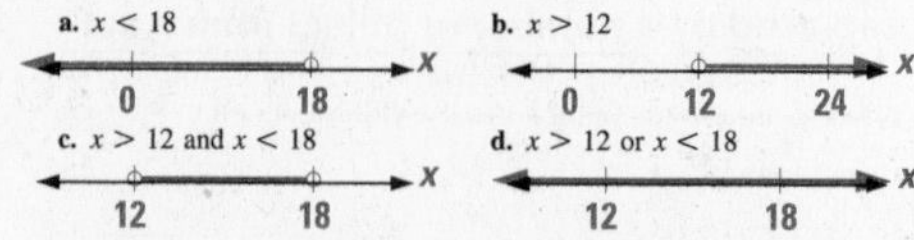

8. The heights, in inches, of the members of the drill team satisfy the inequality $64 \le h < 72$.

   a. Graph this interval.

   h
   64 66 68 70 72

   b. Describe the interval with two inequalities linked by the word "and."
   $h \ge 64$ and $h < 72$ or $64 \le h$ and $72 > h$

9. A meteorologist graphed the temperatures for Monday, Tuesday, and Wednesday.

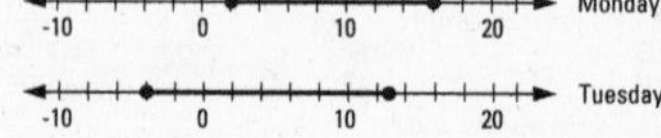

   Tuesday: -10 0 10 20

   Wednesday: -10 0 10 20

   a. Graph the temperatures during the three-day period.

   x
   -10 0 10 20

   b. Is your answer to Part a the union or the intersection of the three graphs? union

   c. To describe the interval from Part a, fill in the blanks:
   -4 $\le x \le$ 16

Name

LESSON MASTER 1-4 B

Questions on SPUR Objectives

Vocabulary

In 1–9, tell if each is a numerical expression, an algebraic expression, or neither.

1. $42ab$ algebraic expression
2. $7x = 21$ neither
3. $3^2 + 9(7 - 1)$ numerical expression
4. $\frac{4m}{20}$ algebraic expression
5. g algebraic expression
6. $24.7 + 6(y^2 + 31)$ algebraic expression
7. $22 \ge u$ neither
8. $16 = 4^2$ neither
9. Finding the numerical value of an expression is called evaluating the expression.

Skills Objective C: Evaluate numerical and algebraic expressions.

In 10–21, evaluate each expression when e = 5, f = 3.2, and g = 0.

10. $4e$ 20
11. $e + f$ 8.2
12. $7^2 + 22$ 71
13. $3(33 - 3^3)$ 18
14. $\frac{8e}{2}$ 20
15. $e - fg$ 5
16. $9 + \frac{5}{3}$ $10\frac{2}{3}$
17. $\frac{2e + f}{1.1} - 3eg$ 12
18. $e^2 + f^2 + g^2$ 35.24
19. $(8 + 7)(8 - 7)$ 15
20. $2(3 + 7)^2 - 6 \cdot 9$ 146
21. $6.1e + 2.9g$ 30.5

22.

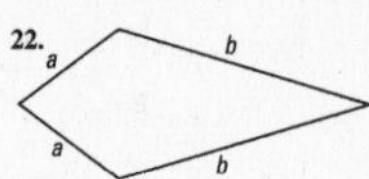

The perimeter of the quadrilateral at the left is $2a + 2b$. Find the perimeter when $a = 6.75$ and $b = 14.4$.
42.3

Name

23. What is the value of the BASIC expression (4 * 3 + 9)/(40 − 38)? 10.5

In 24 and 25, write each expression in BASIC.

24. $7(2.2 + 9)$ 7 * (2.2 + 9)
25. $(5 \cdot 6 - 3.07)^5$ (5 * 6 − 3.07)^5

In 26 and 27, tell what you would input on a computer to evaluate each expression when u = 7 and v = 5.5.

26. $\frac{3u + 9}{v - 4}$ (3 * 7 + 9)/(5.5 − 4)
27. $5(u + v)^2$ 5 * (7 + 5.5)^2

28. Which expression, A or B, has the greater value? Explain your answer.

    A = 50 − 25 − 10 − 5 B = 50 − (25 − (10 − 5))

    B; the value of expression A is 10, and the value of expression B = 30.

29. a. Evaluate $4m^2$ when $m = 3$. 36

    b. Evaluate $(4m)^2$ when $m = 3$. 144

    c. Find a value of m so that the value of $4m^2$ is the same as the value of $(4m)^2$. $m = 0$

Review Objective A, Lesson 1-1

30. Which of the numbers 1, 2, and 7 are solutions of $11 + n = 18$? 7
31. Which of the numbers 3, 6, and 9 are solutions of $6 \cdot u - 11 = 19 + u$? 6
32. Which of the numbers 5, 9, and 18 are solutions of $7 \cdot e \le 80$? 5, 9
33. Which of the numbers 12, 17, and 24 are solutions of $\frac{h}{3} > 7$? 24

Name

LESSON MASTER 1-5 B

Questions on SPUR Objectives

Vocabulary

1. a. *Multiple Choice.* Which of the equations below is a formula for y in terms of other variables? **b**

   (a) $b = y - mx$ (b) $y = mx + b$ (c) $x = \frac{y - b}{m}$

   b. What are the other variables? **m, x, b**

Uses Objective J: Evaluate formulas in real situations

2. A sports concession sells T-shirts and caps. The price P of a purchase, including sales tax, is given by the formula

$$P = 1.07(9.75C + 12T)$$

where C = the number of caps purchased and T = the number of T-shirts purchased. Find the cost of each order. If rounding is necessary, round up to the next cent.

   a. 3 caps and 2 T-shirts **\$56.98**

   b. 4 T-shirts **\$51.36**

   c. 1 cap **\$10.44**

3. Use the formula $S = 4\pi r^2$ for the surface area of a sphere. Find the surface area of a basketball with radius 4.8 inches. **$\approx$ 289.5 in.^{2}**

4. The formula $M = 0.38E$ gives the weight on Mars M of a person who weighs E pounds on Earth. If a person weighs 120 pounds on Earth, how much does that person weigh on Mars? **45.6 pounds**

5. The formula $t = 0.15b$ can be used to find the amount of a tip t on a restaurant bill of b dollars. What would the tip be on a restaurant bill of \$18.49? **\$2.77**

6. Mrs. Day wants to invest in stocks that are expected to pay 6.5% interest and bonds that should pay 5%. For an investment of S dollars in stocks and B dollars in bonds, the amount of yearly income I is given by this formula: $I = 0.065S + 0.05B$

   How much money will Mrs. Day earn each year if

   a. she invests \$1,000 in stocks and \$2,000 in bonds? **\$165**

   b. she invests \$1,500 in stocks and \$1,500 in bonds? **\$172.50**

Name

7. Carpet often comes in rolls 12 feet wide. The number of square yards Y in a piece of carpet L feet long is given by the formula

$$Y = \tfrac{4}{3}L.$$

   Find the number of square yards in a piece of carpet that is

   a. 15 feet long. **20 yd^2**

   b. 22 feet long. **29$\frac{1}{3}$ yd^2**

8. When Jeff calls his uncle, the cost C of a call for m minutes is given by the formula

$$C = 0.55 + 0.15m.$$

   Find the cost of a 7-minute call. **\$1.60**

9. The formula $C = \frac{5}{9}(F - 32)$ converts the temperature from degrees Fahrenheit to degrees Celsius.

   Find the Celsius temperature to the nearest degree for

   a. 77°F. **25°C**

   b. 54°F. **12°C**

   c. 98.6°F. **37°C**

   d. 32°F. **0°C**

10. a. Recall the formula $d = rt$. Fill in the blank to complete this BASIC program which computes distances traveled.

```
10 PRINT "DISTANCE TRAVELED"
20 INPUT "RATE"; R
30 INPUT "TIME"; T
40 LET D = R * T
50 PRINT "DISTANCE"
60 PRINT D
70 END
```

   b. What will the computer find for the distance when R = 55 and T = 4.5? **247.5**

Name

LESSON MASTER 1-6 B

Questions on SPUR Objectives

Vocabulary

1. Since $4^2 = 16$, we say that 4 is the **square root** of 16.

2. Write the radical symbol. **$\sqrt{\ }$**

3. For each number below write *perfect square* or *not perfect square.*

   a. 21 **not perfect square**

   b. 36 **perfect square**

   c. 8000 **not perfect square**

   d. 810 **not perfect square**

Skills Objective C: Evaluate numerical and algebraic expressions.

In 4–9, evaluate each expression when $a = 25$, $b = 7$, and $c = 9$.

4. $\sqrt{a}$ **5**
5. $\sqrt{b + c}$ **4**
6. $b\sqrt{a}$ **35**
7. $\sqrt{ac}$ **15**
8. $-\sqrt{a}$ **-5**
9. $-\sqrt{a - c}$ **-4**

Skills Objective D: Evaluate square roots with and without a calculator.

In 10–13, give a. the exact square roots of the given number and b. the approximate square roots, rounded to the nearest hundredth.

10. 37 a. **$\sqrt{37}$, $-\sqrt{37}$** b. **6.08, -6.08**

11. 418 a. **$\sqrt{418}$, $-\sqrt{418}$** b. **20.45, -20.45**

12. 5 a. **$\sqrt{5}$, $-\sqrt{5}$** b. **2.24, -2.24**

13. 60 a. **$\sqrt{60}$, $-\sqrt{60}$** b. **7.75, -7.75**

In 14 and 15, the area of a square is given.
a. Give the exact length of a side of the square.
b. Give the length of a side rounded to the nearest hundredth.

14. 876 sq ft a. **$\sqrt{876}$ ft** b. **29.60 ft**

15. 10 sq mi a. **$\sqrt{10}$ mi** b. **3.16 mi**

Name

In 16–25, evaluate without a calculator.

16. $\sqrt{81}$ **9**
17. $-\sqrt{16}$ **-4**
18. $3\sqrt{49}$ **21**
19. $10\sqrt{64}$ **80**
20. $\sqrt{9} + \sqrt{16}$ **7**
21. $\sqrt{9 + 16}$ **5**
22. $\sqrt{7^2}$ **7**
23. $(\sqrt{7})^2$ **7**
24. $\sqrt{9} \cdot \sqrt{9}$ **9**
25. $8 \cdot \sqrt{9} \cdot \sqrt{9}$ **72**

In 26–29, evaluate and give the answer to the nearest thousandth.

26. $\sqrt{5} + \sqrt{2}$ **3.650**
27. $\sqrt{7} + \sqrt{0}$ **2.646**
28. $\sqrt{0.8} \cdot \sqrt{0.9}$ **0.849**
29. $5 \cdot \sqrt{4.1} \cdot \sqrt{3.8}$ **19.736**

In 30 and 31, an equation is given.
a. Describe each solution using the radical symbol.
b. Write each solution as a decimal rounded to the nearest hundredth.

30. $x^2 = 144$

   a. **$x = \sqrt{144}$ or $-\sqrt{144}$** b. **x = 12 or -12**

31. $211 = h^2$

   a. **$h = \sqrt{211}$ or $-\sqrt{211}$** b. **h = 14.53 or -14.53**

32. If an object is dropped, it falls d feet in t seconds. Then $t = \sqrt{\frac{d}{16}}$.

   If an object were dropped from the top of the Sears Tower, which is 1454 feet tall, how long would it take the object to hit the ground? Round your answer to the nearest tenth of a second. **9.5 seconds**

Properties Objective F: Use the Square of the Square Root Property.

33. According to the Square of the Square Root Property, if a is not negative, $\sqrt{a} \cdot \sqrt{a}$ = **a**.

34. *Multiple choice.* Which of the following is equal to $\sqrt{x^2} \cdot \sqrt{x^2}$? **b**

   (a) x (b) x^2 (c) x^4

Name

LESSON MASTER 1-7 B Questions on SPUR Objectives

Vocabulary

1. An example of a pattern is called a(n) **instance**.

2. What is a *counterexample* to a pattern?
Sample: an example that shows that the pattern is not always true

Properties Objective G: Give instances or counterexamples of patterns.

In 3–7, give two instances of the pattern. **Samples are given.**

3. $m + m + m + m = 4m$
$3+3+3+3=4\cdot3$ (12) $8+8+8+8=4\cdot8$ (32)

4. $\frac{xy}{x} = y$
$\frac{9\cdot2}{9} = 2$ (2) $\frac{6\cdot4}{6} = 4$ (4)

5. $a(4 + 6) = 4a + 6a$
$7(4+6)=4\cdot7+6\cdot7$ (70) $100(4+6)=100\cdot4+100\cdot6$ (1000)

6. $w \cdot w^2 = w^3$
$4\cdot4^2 = 4^3$ (64) $12\cdot12^2=12^3$ (1728)

7. d dimes is equal to $0.1d$ dollars
15 dimes = 1.5 dollars 2 dimes = 0.2 dollars

In 8–11, give a counterexample to the pattern. **Samples are given.**

8. $\frac{a+b}{a} = b$ $a = 2, b = 8; \frac{2+8}{2} \neq 8$

9. $v + v + v = v\cdot v\cdot v$ $v = 5; 5 + 5 + 5 \neq 5\cdot5\cdot5$

10. $b < bc$ $b = 6, c = .5; 6 \not< 6(.5)$

11. $n^2 > n$ $n = 0; n^2 \not> n$

Name

Properties Objective H: Use variables to describe patterns in instances.

12. 

A panel of cedar fencing has 2 posts. Describe the following pattern using one variable.

1 panel has 1 + 1 posts.
2 panels have 2 + 1 posts.
3 panels have 3 + 1 posts.

***p* panels have *p* + 1 posts.**

13. a. Describe this pattern with one variable.
$3 + 12 > 3$
$3 + 2\frac{1}{2} > 3$
$3 + 44.2 > 3$
$3 + a > 3$

b. Find a number other than 3 that is an instance of this pattern. Sample: $a = 4; 3 + 4 > 3$

c. Find a number that is a counterexample to the pattern. Sample: $a = 0; 3 + 0 \not> 3$

14. a. Describe this pattern with one variable.
$4^3 > 4^2$
$\left(\frac{5}{2}\right)^3 > \left(\frac{5}{2}\right)^2$
$8.3^3 > 8.3^2$
$m^3 > m^2$

b. Find another integer that is an instance of this pattern. Sample: $m = 5; 5^3 > 5^2$

c. Find an integer that is a counterexample to the pattern. Sample: $m = 0; 0^3 \not> 0^2$

d. Find a non-integer that is a counterexample to the pattern. Sample: $m = \frac{1}{2}; \left(\frac{1}{2}\right)^3 \not> \left(\frac{1}{2}\right)^2$

15. Describe this pattern with two variables.
$6 + 6 + 6 + 5 + 5 = 3\cdot6 + 2\cdot5$
$41 + 41 + 41 + 9 + 9 = 3\cdot41 + 2\cdot9$
$2.8 + 2.8 + 2.8 + .31 + .31 = 3\cdot2.8 + 2\cdot.31$
$x + x + x + y + y = 3x + 2y$

Name

LESSON MASTER 1-8 B Questions on SPUR Objectives

Vocabulary

In 1–3, name a. the hypotenuse and b. the legs.

1. 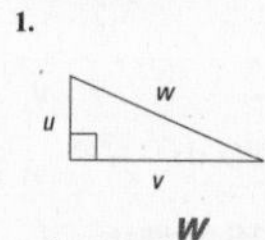 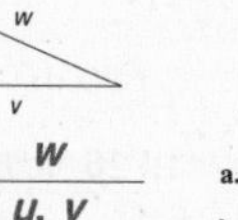

a. **w**
b. **u, v**

2. 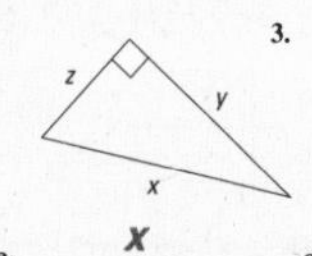

a. **x**
b. **y, z**

3. 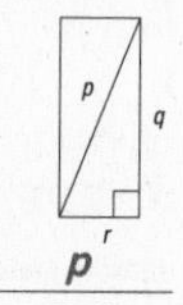

a. **p**
b. **q, r**

2. What is *theorem*?
an important property that has been proved to be true

Uses Objective K: Apply the Pythagorean Theorem to solve problems in real situations.

3. The diagram at the right shows three square offices built around a lobby. Square tiles cover the floors of the two smaller offices.

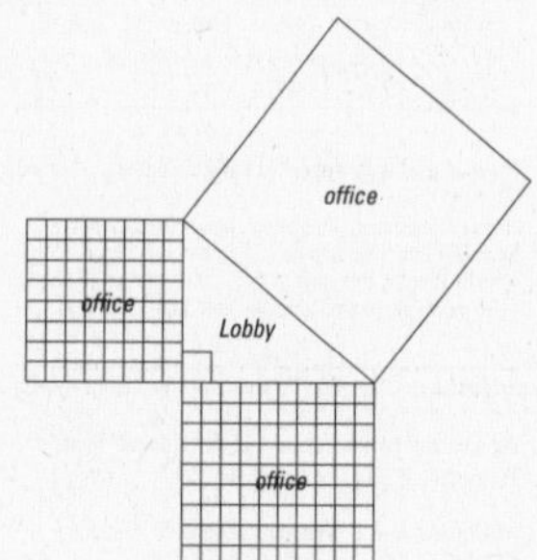

a. How many tiles would be needed for the floor of the largest office? **164 tiles**

b. If each tile measures 1 foot on a side, what is the length of a wall of the largest office to the nearest tenth? **12.8 ft**

Name

4. Rodolfo lives at point R and Steve lives at S. When Rodolfo walks to Steve's house, he can walk 2 blocks along Dee Road and 6 blocks along Hawkins Lane.

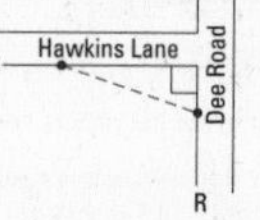

a. How long is Rodolfo's walk along Dee Road and Hawkins lane? **8 blocks**

b. Rodolfo can take a shortcut shown by the dotted line. To the nearest tenth of a block, how long is the shortcut? **6.3 blocks**

c. How much shorter is it for Rodolfo to take the shortcut than to walk along the roads? **≈ 1.7 blocks**

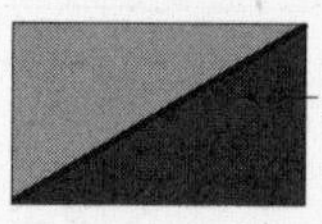

5. The student council is designing a new school flag which will measure 3 feet by 5 feet. A piece of gold cord will be sewn along one diagonal. To the nearest inch, how much cord is needed? **70 inches**

6. The size of a television screen is determined by the length of a diagonal. A 25-inch screen measures 25 inches along the diagonal. What is the size of a screen that is 16 inches wide and 12 inches high? **20-inch screen**

7. A major league baseball diamond, the infield, is actually a square that measures 90 feet on a side.

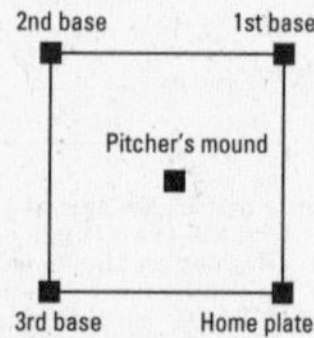

a. What is the distance, to the nearest foot, from 1st base to 3rd base? **127 feet**

b. The pitcher's mound is 60.5 feet from Home plate. Is this the center of the infield? Explain your answer.
Sample: no; the center would be about 63.6 feet from Home plate.

Name

LESSON MASTER 1-9 B Questions on SPUR Objectives

Properties Objective G: Give instances or counterexamples of patterns.

1.

5 squares 6 squares 7 squares **8 squares** **9 squares**

a. In the space above, sketch the next two instances in the pattern.

b. Fill in the chart below.

Number of Squares	5	6	7	8	9	...	n
Perimeter	**12**	**14**	**16**	**18**	**20**		**$2n + 2$**

2. Shown below is a pattern made with square and triangular blocks.

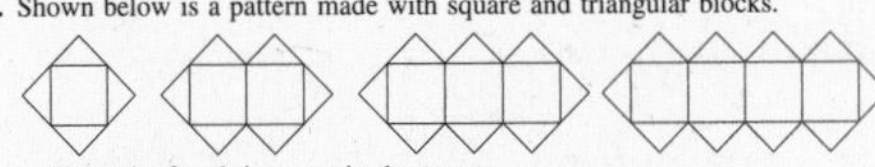

a. Draw the fourth instance in the pattern.

b. How many blocks will be needed to make the 20th instance? How many of these blocks will be triangular? Explain how you got your answers.

62 blocks; 42 triangles; sample: The number of squares is 20, and the number of triangles is $20 \cdot 2 + 2$, or 42; the total is 62.

Properties Objective H: Use variables to describe patterns in tables.

For 3 and 4, use the chart at the right.

e	f
1	3
2	6
3	9
4	12

3. Does the equation $f = e + 2$ describe the numbers in the table? Explain why or why not.

No; sample: If $e = 2$, $e + 2 = 4$, not 6.

4. Does the equation $f = 3e$ describe the numbers in the table? Explain why or why not.

Yes; sample: For each e value in the table, the f value agrees with the equation.

Name

▶ LESSON MASTER 1-9 B *page 2*

7.

1 panel 1 square 6 triangles — 2 panels 2 squares 12 triangles — 3 panels 3 squares 18 triangles

The diagram above shows windows made from square and triangular pieces of glass. Let p = the number of panels, s = the number of square pieces, and t = the number of triangular pieces.

a. Write a formula that describes the relationship between p and s. **$p = s$**

b. Write a formula that describes the relationship between p and t. **$p = \frac{t}{6}$ or $t = 6p$**

In 8–10, use the pattern below.

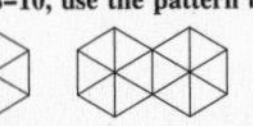

1 hexagon 6 triangles perimeter = 6 — 2 hexagons 12 triangles perimeter = 10 — 3 hexagons 18 triangles perimeter = 14 — 4 hexagons 24 triangles perimeter = 18

8. Let h = the number of hexagons and t = the number of triangles. Describe the relationship between h and t. **$h = \frac{t}{6}$ or $t = 6h$**

9. Explain why the formula $p = h + 10$ does not relate the perimeter p of the figure to the number of hexagons.

Sample: When $h = 1$, $h + 10 = 11$. But for $h = 1$, the perimeter is 6.

10. A correct formula giving the perimeter in terms of the number of hexagons is $p = 4h + 2$. Show that the formula works for a figure with 6 hexagons by drawing the figure and finding the perimeter.

$p = 4 \cdot 6 + 2 = 26$

6 hexagons
36 triangles
perimeter = 26

Name

LESSON MASTER 2-1 B Questions on SPUR Objectives

Skills Objective F: Identify and apply the Commutative and Associative Properties of Multiplication.

In 1–5, tell whether the statement illustrates the Commutative Property of Multiplication or the Associative Property of Multiplication.

1. $4m = m \cdot 4$ **Commut. Prop. of Mult.**

2. $7(x^3y) = 7(yx^3)$ **Commut. Prop. of Mult.**

3. $5(\frac{1}{3}r) = (5 \cdot \frac{1}{3})r$ **Assoc. Prop. of Mult.**

4. Five 2-foot-long boards have the same total length as two 5-foot-long boards. **Commut. Prop. of Mult.**

5. The amount of discount on two 40-dollar speakers at 10% off is the same as twice the discount on one 40-dollar speaker at 10% off. **Assoc. Prop. of Mult.**

In 6–13, simplify.

6. $3t \cdot 10u$ **$30tu$**

7. $6g^3 \cdot 2 \cdot 25$ **$300g^3$**

8. $\frac{1}{8}d \cdot 16e$ **$2de$**

9. $\frac{2}{5} \cdot 18 \cdot 5$ **36**

10. $10a \cdot 5a \cdot 12a$ **$600a^3$**

11. $15y^2 \cdot 5y$ **$75y^3$**

12. $100w \cdot 23 \cdot 0.5$ **$1{,}150w$**

13. $20ab \cdot 4a \cdot 2bc$ **$160a^2b^2c$**

Uses Objective G: Apply the Area Model for Multiplication in real situations.

In 14-16, find the area of the shaded region.

14. 15. 16.

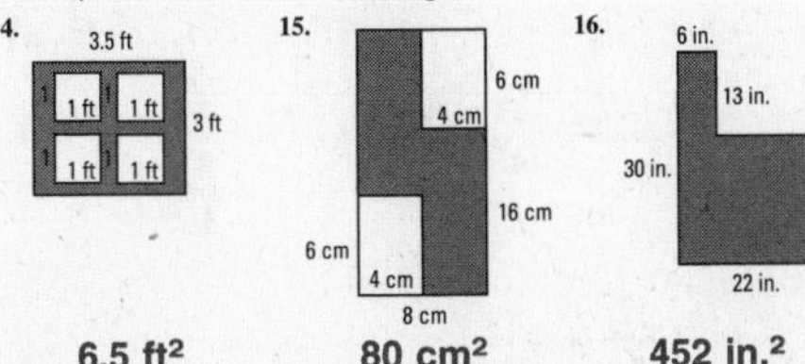

14. **6.5 ft²** 15. **80 cm²** 16. **452 in.²**

Name

▶ LESSON MASTER 2-1 B *page 2*

17. A building code requires that a garage have a floor area no greater than 8% of the area of the lot. Mr. Koo is planning to build a 21-ft-by-24-ft garage on a 50-ft-by-130-ft rectangular lot. Is the garage within the code requirements? Why or why not?

Sample: yes; the area of the garage is 504 ft², about 7.8% of the area of the lot, 6,500 ft².

18. Find the volume of a storage crate that measures 2 m by 2.5 m by 4 m. **20 m³**

19. How many boxes 2″ × 2″ × 1″ can be packed in a carton 2 ft by 2 ft × 1 ft? **1,728 boxes**

Representations Objective J: Use rectangles, rectangular solids, or rectangular arrays to picture multiplication.

21.

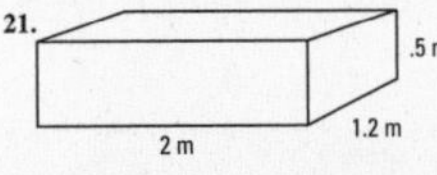

A box has the dimensions shown. What is its volume? **1.2 m³**

22. ♠♠♠♠♠♠♠♠♠♠♠♠♠♠♠♠ (6 rows of 16)

Write a multiplication sentence suggested by the array at the left. **6×16=96 or 16×6=96**

23. At the right, each of the smallest rectangles has length y and width x.

a. Express the area of the largest rectangle as length times width. **$5x \cdot 4y$**

b. Simplify your answer to Part a. **$20xy$**

c. How many of the smallest rectangles make up the largest rectangle? Find the area of each. **20** **xy**

Explain how these answers are related to your answer in Part b.

Sample: The total area of the smallest rectangle is $20xy$, which is the answer to Part B, the area of the largest rectangle.

Name

LESSON MASTER 2-2 B Questions on SPUR Objectives

Vocabulary

1. What number is called the *multiplicative identity*? 1
2. What is another name for *reciprocal*? mult. inverse

Properties Objective F: Identify and apply the following properties: Multiplication Property of 1; Property of Reciprocals; Multiplication Property of Zero.

In 3–11, give the reciprocal.

3. $\frac{4}{5}$ $\frac{5}{4}$ 4. $3\frac{1}{4}$ $\frac{4}{13}$ 5. $-\frac{9}{7}$ $-\frac{7}{9}$

6. $\frac{1}{8}$ 8 7. $\frac{e}{f}$ $\frac{f}{e}$ 8. $\frac{w}{-2}$ $\frac{-2}{w}$

9. 0.4 2.5 10. -1.6 -.625 11. $\frac{a}{m+n}$ $\frac{m+n}{a}$

12. Write a key sequence to find the reciprocal of .385 on a calculator that has no reciprocal key.
Samples: 1 ÷ .385 = or 1000 ÷ 385 =

13. *Multiple choice.* Which equation shows that p and q are reciprocals? c

(a) $p + q = 1$ (b) $\frac{p}{q} = 1$ (c) $pq = 1$ (d) $1p = q$ (e) $\frac{p}{q} = \frac{q}{p}$

In 14–19, a. tell whether the two numbers are reciprocals, and b. briefly explain why or why not.

14. $\frac{3}{4}$ and .75 a. no b. $\frac{3}{4}(.75) = .5625$
15. 6 and $\frac{1}{6}$ a. yes b. $6\left(\frac{1}{6}\right) = 1$
16. $\frac{1}{8}$ and -8 a. no b. $\frac{1}{8}(-8) = -1$
17. 7 and -7 a. no b. $7(-7) = -49$
18. $-\frac{5}{3}$ and $-\frac{3}{5}$ a. yes b. $-\frac{5}{3} \cdot -\frac{3}{5} = 1$
19. 10,000 and 0.00001 a. no b. $10{,}000 \cdot 0.00001 = 0.1$

Name

In 20–23, compute mentally.

20. 5,766(100 − 99) 5,766
21. (94.7)(3.81)(0)(.711) 0
22. $\frac{204}{17} \cdot \frac{17}{204} \cdot \frac{13}{15}$ $\frac{13}{15}$
23. $13.085 \cdot \frac{13}{3} \cdot \frac{3}{13}$ 13.085

In 24–29, simplify. Name the property used to simplify.

24. $\frac{1}{g-h} \cdot (g - h)$ 1 Property of Reciprocals
25. $25(4r - 4r)$ 0 Multiplication Property of Zero
26. $\frac{8y^3}{8y^3} \cdot 12$ 12 Multiplicative Identity Property of 1
27. $(4a + 7)(3a + 90)(2a + 11)(0)$ 0 Multiplication Property of Zero
28. $(35ab)(57 - 56)$ $35ab$ Multiplicative Identity Property of 1
29. $\frac{uv}{x} \cdot \frac{x}{uv}$ 1 Property of Reciprocals

Review Objective L, Lesson 1-2

In 30–32, graph the solution set to the inequality on the number line.

30. $y < -2$ when y is an integer
-5 -4 -3 -2 -1 0 1 y

31. $-3 \le j \le 2$ when j is a real number
-3 -2 -1 0 1 2 3 j

32. $2.5 > k \ge 1.9$ when k is a real number
1.8 1.9 2.0 2.1 2.2 2.3 2.4 2.5 2.6 k

Name

LESSON MASTER 2-3 B Questions on SPUR Objectives

Skills Objective A: Multiply and simplify algebraic fractions.

In 1–12, use the Equal Fractions Property to simplify.

1. $\frac{50}{75}$ $\frac{2}{3}$ 2. $\frac{3t}{7t}$ $\frac{3}{7}$
3. $\frac{10u}{25u}$ $\frac{2}{5}$ 4. $\frac{rs}{3r}$ $\frac{s}{3}$
5. $\frac{220}{1100c}$ $\frac{1}{5c}$ 6. $\frac{45mn}{15m}$ $3n$
7. $\frac{4gh}{12gj}$ $\frac{h}{3j}$ 8. $\frac{1700}{400}$ $\frac{17}{4}$
9. $\frac{28d}{14d}$ 2 10. $\frac{16xy^2}{8x}$ $2y^2$
11. $\frac{19w^2}{12w}$ $\frac{19w}{12}$ 12. $\frac{fg}{g^2}$ $\frac{f}{g}$

13. *Multiple choice.* Choose the fraction which is *not* equal to the others. b

(a) $\frac{7m}{10m}$ (b) $\frac{14}{20y}$ (c) $\frac{35}{50}$ (d) $\frac{70ab}{100ab}$

In 14–27, multiply. Simplify the product where possible.

14. $\frac{2}{5} \cdot \frac{7}{8}$ $\frac{7}{20}$ 15. $\frac{11}{2} \cdot \frac{3}{4}$ $\frac{33}{8}$
16. $\frac{u}{v} \cdot \frac{a}{b}$ $\frac{ua}{bv}$ 17. $\frac{m}{f} \cdot \frac{f}{y}$ $\frac{m}{y}$
18. $20 \cdot \frac{2r}{7}$ $\frac{40r}{7}$ 19. $\frac{4w}{5} \cdot \frac{5}{4w}$ 1
20. $\frac{3a}{2a} \cdot \frac{1}{6}$ $\frac{1}{4}$ 21. $\frac{1}{b} \cdot b$ 1
22. $62k \cdot \frac{1}{62}$ k 23. $\frac{st}{9} \cdot \frac{2}{su}$ $\frac{2t}{9u}$
24. $\frac{110b}{9c} \cdot \frac{3c^2}{44b^2}$ $\frac{5c}{6b}$ 25. $\frac{2.5e}{f^2} \cdot \frac{f^2}{e^2}$ $\frac{2.5}{e}$
26. $\frac{2}{3d} \cdot \frac{h}{8} \cdot \frac{6d}{a}$ $\frac{h}{2a}$ 27. $\frac{85}{100} \cdot \frac{30}{7s} \cdot \frac{10s}{3r}$ $\frac{85}{7r}$

Name

28. Janine's math classroom is $\frac{2}{3}$ as long and $\frac{3}{4}$ as wide as the computer lab. How do the areas of these two room compare?
The area of the classroom is $\frac{2}{3} \cdot \frac{3}{4}$, or $\frac{1}{2}$, the area of the computer lab.

29. A box is $\frac{1}{2}$ as long, $\frac{1}{2}$ as wide, and $\frac{1}{2}$ as high as a crate. How many of these boxes will fit in the crate? Explain how you got your answer.
8 boxes; sample: Since $\frac{1}{2} \cdot \frac{1}{2} \cdot \frac{1}{2} = \frac{1}{8}$, the box has $\frac{1}{8}$ the volume of the crate.

Representations Objective J: Use rectangles to picture multiplication.

30. What multiplication sentence is pictured at the right?
$\frac{5}{8} \cdot \frac{3}{4} = \frac{15}{32}$

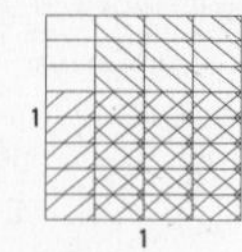

31. Draw a picture at the right to represent the product $\frac{1}{3} \cdot \frac{2}{5}$. Sample:

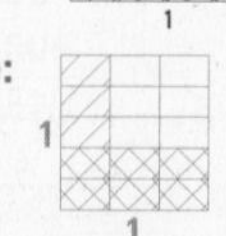

32. The largest rectangle at the right has width x and length y.

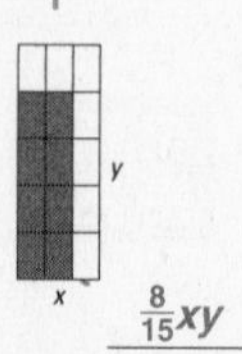

a. If each of the smallest rectangles has the same dimensions, what are these dimensions? What is the area of each of the smallest rectangles?
$\frac{1}{3}x$, $\frac{1}{5}y$ $\frac{1}{15}xy$

b. What is the area of the shaded region? $\frac{8}{15}xy$

c. What product of algebraic fractions is represented by the product of the length and width of the shaded region? $\frac{2}{3}x \cdot \frac{4}{5}y$

Name

LESSON MASTER 2-4 B

Questions on SPUR Objectives

Uses Objective H: Apply the Rate Factor Model for Multiplication in real situations.

1. Mr. Kremers drove at an average speed of 50 miles per hour. How far did he travel in $6\frac{1}{2}$ hours?

   325 mi.

2. Ms. Grabinski drove 450 miles on 15.4 gallons of gas. Compute the mpg (miles per gallon) for her car.

   ≈29.2 mpg

3. If a box of cereal contains 24 servings, how many boxes are needed to serve breakfast to 130 campers?

   6 boxes

4. A box of tile contains 40 pieces. Five boxes will cover 25 square feet. What area can be covered by 400 tiles?

   50 ft²

5. Over a quarter-mile distance, an elephant can run at a speed of 25 miles per hour. How many miles per *minute* is this?

   $\approx .4 \frac{mi}{min}$

6. A 120-gram serving of pudding contains 170 calories in food energy.
   a. What is the number of calories per gram?

   $\approx 1.4 \frac{cal}{g}$

   b. A person burns about 5 calories per minute of walking. How long will it take to burn off the calories from a serving of this pudding?

   ≈ 34 min

Name

7. A cookbook says to cook a beef roast 35 minutes per pound. How many *hours* will it take to cook a $6\frac{1}{2}$-pound roast?

   ≈ 3.8 hr

8. It takes about 1.4 columns to print 100 entries in the North-Metro phone book.
   a. If there are four columns per page, how many entries are on a page?

   ≈ 286 entries

   b. About how many entries are there in the 340-page North-Metro phone book?

   ≈ 97,000 entries

   c. About how many pages would it take to list a quarter million entries?

   ≈ 875 pages

Review Objective C, Lessons 1-4 and 1-6

In 9–24, evaluate each expression when $x = 4$, $y = 5.1$, and $z = 2.8$.

9. $8x$	32	10. $x + y$	9.1
11. $\frac{21x}{7}$	12	12. $xy - z$	17.6
13. $y^2 - 2x$	18.01	14. $6.1x + 2.9z$	32.52
15. $(x + y)^2$	82.81	16. $\sqrt{x}$	2
17. $x^2 + y^2 + z^2$	49.85	18. $\frac{7y + 2z}{14}$	2.95
19. $10(3y - 4z)$	41	20. $-\sqrt{16x}$	-8
21. $-x^2 - y^2$	-42.01	22. $xyz - zxy$	0
23. $\frac{y + z}{y - z}$	≈ 3.4	24. $\frac{3x^2}{4} \cdot \frac{4}{3x}$	4

Name

LESSON MASTER 2-5 B

Questions on SPUR Objectives

Skills Objective B: Multiply positive and negative numbers.

In 1 and 2, write a product as a negative rate, and give the answer.

1. Mr. Ladd is hoping to lose 3 pounds per month on a special diet. What does he expect his change in weight to be after 6 months?

   $6 \text{ mo} \cdot -3 \frac{lb}{mo}$; -18 lb

2. Over the past 8 years, the population of Riverside has dropped about 1,200 people per year. What was the total change for this time period?

   $8 \text{ yr} \cdot -1200 \frac{people}{yr}$; -9,600 people

3. Show that $-\frac{5}{8}$ is the reciprocal of $-\frac{8}{5}$.

   $-\frac{5}{8} \cdot -\frac{8}{5} = -1 \cdot -1 \cdot \frac{5}{8} \cdot \frac{8}{5} = 1 \cdot 1 = 1$

4. Show that -1 is the reciprocal of -1.

   $-1 \cdot -1 = 1$

In 5–24, multiply. Simplify where possible.

5. $-8 \cdot -4$	32	6. $-5 \cdot 9$	-45
7. $6 \cdot 7 \cdot -1$	-42	8. $-3 \cdot -5 \cdot -1 \cdot 8$	-120
9. $10 \cdot 16 \cdot 0 \cdot -4$	0	10. $-26 \cdot -16$	416
11. $-1 \cdot 1 \cdot 1 \cdot -1$	1	12. $-1.18 \cdot -22$	25.96
13. $-c \cdot -d$	cd	14. $-4m \cdot 3$	$-12m$
15. $-11g \cdot -7h$	$77gh$	16. $5a \cdot 2a \cdot -6a$	$-60a^3$
17. $(-9)^2$	81	18. $(-4)^3$	-64
19. $-(3y)^2$	$-9y^2$	20. $(-2p)^3$	$-8p^3$
21. $-\frac{2}{9} \cdot \frac{3}{4}$	$-\frac{1}{6}$	22. $-\frac{u}{5} \cdot \frac{5}{u}$	1
23. $-\frac{5h}{6} \cdot \frac{-h}{3}$	$\frac{5h^2}{18}$	24. $\frac{9x}{4y} \cdot -\frac{y^2}{3x}$	$-\frac{3y}{4}$

In 25 and 26, two expressions are given. Evaluate a and use your answer to help with b.

25. a. $8.5 \cdot 46.2$	392.7	b. $-8.5 \cdot -46.2$	392.7
26. a. $\frac{2h}{3} \cdot \frac{4}{9}$	$\frac{8h}{27}$	b. $\frac{3}{2h} \cdot \frac{9}{4}$	$\frac{27}{8h}$

Name

27. Evaluate $3m + 18$ when $m = -4$. — 6
28. Evaluate $\frac{-6d}{3}$ when $d = -10$. — 20
29. Evaluate $\frac{5r}{12} \cdot r$ when $r = -6$. — 15
30. Evaluate $(-2f)^2$ when $f = 5$. — 100
31. Evaluate $-2x^2 + 7x - 1$ when $x = -3$. — -40

Properties Objective F: Identify and apply the Multiplication Property of -1.

In 32–41, tell whether the expression is positive or negative.

32. $(-9)^3$	negative	33. $(-1)^{15}$	negative
34. $(-8)^2$	positive	35. $(-13)^4$	positive
36. $(-6)^6$	positive	37. -6^6	negative
38. $(-5)(-2)(-1)(-8)$	positive	39. $(-1)(-8)(6.4)(-1)$	negative
40. $5 \cdot 9 \cdot -3 \cdot 8 \cdot 2$	negative	41. $-(-18)$	positive

42. *Multiple choice.* Which of the following is equivalent to the opposite of the opposite of n? — b

    (a) $\frac{1}{n}$ (b) $-1n$ (c) $1n$ (d) $1 - n$

Review Objective J, Lesson 1-5

43. Use the formula $V = e^3$ to find the volume V of a box that measures 80 cm along each edge e. — 512,000 cm³

44. The formula $F = \frac{9}{5}C + 32$ converts the temperature from degrees Celsius to degrees Fahrenheit. Find the Fahrenheit temperature to the nearest degree for
    a. 55°C. — 131°F
    b. 25°C. — 77°F
    c. 0°C. — 32°F
    d. -10°C. — 14°F

Name

LESSON MASTER 2-6 B

Questions on SPUR Objectives

Skills Objective C: Solve and check equations of the form $ax = b$.

In 1–11, solve the equation and check your answer.

1. $\frac{2}{5}y = -44$
   $y = -110$
   $\frac{2}{5} \cdot -110 = -44$

2. $44c = 99$
   $c = \frac{9}{4}$
   $44 \cdot \frac{9}{4} = 99$

3. $-7p = -154$
   $p = 22$
   $-7 \cdot 22 = -154$

4. $\frac{1}{3}d = \frac{7}{6}$
   $d = \frac{7}{2}$
   $\frac{1}{3} \cdot \frac{7}{2} = \frac{7}{6}$

5. $59 = -\frac{1}{8}x$
   $x = -472$
   $59 = -\frac{1}{8} \cdot -472$

6. $3.8s = 475$
   $s = 125$
   $3.8 \cdot 125 = 475$

7. $\frac{h}{12} = 16$
   $h = 192$
   $\frac{192}{12} = 16$

8. $-\frac{7}{12} = -\frac{11}{4}k$
   $k = \frac{7}{33}$
   $-\frac{7}{12} = -\frac{11}{4} \cdot \frac{7}{33}$

9. $\frac{y}{5} = -\frac{7}{10}$
   $y = -\frac{7}{2}$
   $\frac{-\frac{7}{2}}{5} = -\frac{7}{10}$

10. $15(\frac{1}{3})n = 350$
    $n = 70$
    $15(\frac{1}{3})(70) = 350$

11. $-7(1.6)n = 39.2$
    $n = -3.5$
    $-7(1.6)(-3.5) = 39.2$

Properties Objective F: Identify and apply the Multiplication Property of Equality.

12. Large orders of certain items are sometimes sold by the *gross*. A gross is a dozen dozen, or 144. An equation for this relationship is 1 gross = 144 units.

    Tell how you would apply the Multiplicative Property of Equality to this equation to find the number of units in 72 gross.
    Multiply both sides of the equation by 72; 72 gross = 10,368 units

Name

13. For the solution to the equation $60e = 210$, tell which of the properties at the right justifies each step.

    Associative Property of Multiplication
    Multiplicative Identity Property of 1
    Property of Reciprocals
    Multiplication Property of Equality

    $60e = 210$
    $\frac{1}{60} \cdot 60e = \frac{1}{60} \cdot 210$ — **Mult. Prop. of Equality**
    $(\frac{1}{60} \cdot 60)e = \frac{210}{60}$ — **Assoc. Prop. of Mult.**
    $1e = 3.5$ — **Prop. of Reciprocals**
    $e = 3.5$ — **Mult. Ident. Prop. of 1**

Uses Objective H: Apply the Rate Factor Model for Multiplication in real situations.

14. All the sides of a regular polygon have the same length. The formula $p = ns$ gives the perimeter of a regular polygon with n sides of length s.
    a. Use this formula to write an equation that can be used to find the number of sides of a regular polygon with sides of length 8 and a perimeter of 144. **$144 = n \cdot 8$**
    b. Solve the equation from Part a for n. **$n = 18$**
    c. Solve $p = ns$ for n. **$n = \frac{p}{s}$**

15. A plane flies from Chicago to Dallas, a distance of 800 miles, in 1.8 hours.
    a. Write a multiplication equation based on the formula $d = rt$. **$800 = r(1.8)$**
    b. Solve the equation from Part a for r and check. **$r = 444.\bar{4}$**
    check: **$800 = 444.\bar{4}(1.8)$**

16. Jean types 68 words per minute. At this rate, how many words can she type in a half hour? **2,040 words**

17. A marathon is a footrace of 42.2 kilometers. One mile is about 1.6 kilometers. What is the distance of a marathon in miles? **≈ 26.4 mi**

Name

LESSON MASTER 2-7 B

Questions on SPUR Objectives

Skills Objective C: Solve and check equations of the form $ax = b$, when a or b is zero or -1.

In 1–15, solve the equation.

1. $18m = 0$ — **$m = 0$**
2. $0w = 12$ — **no solution**
3. $-d = 67$ — **$d = -67$**
4. $0 = 0p$ — **all real numbers**
5. $-5.2 = -u$ — **$u = 5.2$**
6. $17.5 = 0s$ — **no solution**
7. $0 = -5h$ — **$h = 0$**
8. $(-f) = -81$ — **$f = 81$**
9. $-m = 0$ — **$m = 0$**
10. $-n = \frac{5}{9}$ — **$n = -\frac{5}{9}$**
11. $-3.94y = 0$ — **$y = 0$**
12. $0 = (22 - 22)k$ — **all real numbers**
13. $0.49 = -(-(-x))$ — **$x = -0.49$**
14. $0 = (16 - 11)h$ — **$h = 0$**
15. $(9 - 10)c = 31$ — **$c = -31$**

In 16–22, tell if the equation has no solution, one solution, or an infinite number of solutions. Do not solve.

16. $44g = 210$ **one solution**
17. $783 = 0t$ **no solution**
18. $-u = 54$ **one solution**
19. $0q = 0$ **infinite number of solutions**
20. $\frac{2}{3} = 0a$ **no solution**
21. $\frac{9}{8} = -3d$ **one solution**
22. $0 = 0v$ **infinite number of solutions**

Name

In 23–27, write an equation of the form $ax = b$ that has the given solution. **Samples are given.**

23. Solution: 3 **$8x = 24$**
24. Solution: 0 **$5m = 0$**
25. Solution: All real numbers **$0w = 0$**
26. No solution **$0a = 9$**
27. Solution: -5 **$2q = -10$**

Properties Objective F: Identify and apply the following properties: Multiplication Property of -1; Multiplication Property of Zero; Multiplication Property of Equality.

In 28–30, find all solutions and use properties of multiplication to explain why the answer makes sense. **Sample explanations are given.**

28. $0c = 0$
    all real numbers; The Mult. Prop. of Zero states that any real number times 0 = 0.
29. $0c = 27$
    no solution; The Mult. Prop. of Zero states that any real number times 0 = 0.
30. $-a = 0.459$
    $a = -0.459$; By the Mult. Props. of -1 and Equality, $-1 \cdot -a = -1 \cdot -0.459$ and $a = -0.459$.

Review Objective L, Lesson 1-3

In 31–34, graph the solution set. Consider the domain as the set of real numbers.

31. $x < 13$
32. $y \geq -4$

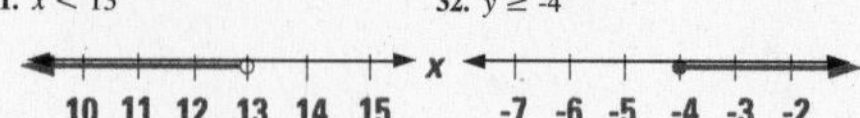

33. $z \leq -\frac{4}{3}$
34. $w > 2.7$

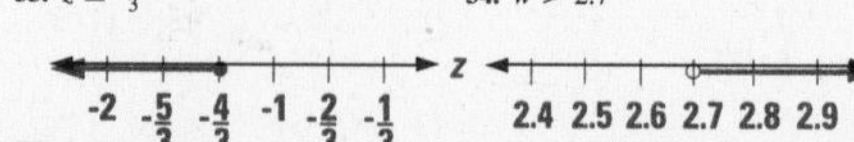

Name

LESSON MASTER 2-8 B

Questions on SPUR Objectives

Skills Objective D: Solve and check inequalities of the form $ax < b$.

In 1–12, solve and check the inequality. Sample checks are given.

1. $7y < 56$

   $y < 8$
   $7 \cdot 8 = 56$
   $7 \cdot 7 < 56?$
   $49 < 56$

2. $99 \geq 11e$

   $e \leq 9$
   $99 = 11 \cdot 9$
   $99 > 11 \cdot 8?$
   $99 > 88$

3. $-5p > 30$

   $p < -6$
   $-5 \cdot -6 = 30$
   $-5 \cdot -7 > 30?$
   $35 > 30$

4. $27 \leq -3m$

   $m \leq -9$
   $27 = -3 \cdot -9$
   $27 < -3 \cdot -10?$
   $27 < 30$

5. $-\frac{7}{8}k > 63$

   $k < -72$
   $-\frac{7}{8}(-72) = 63$
   $-\frac{7}{8}(-80) > 63?$
   $70 > 63$

6. $-1.9s \geq -0.95$

   $s \leq 0.5$
   $-1.9(0.5) = -0.95$
   $-1.9(0.4) > -0.95?$
   $-0.78 > -0.95$

7. $\frac{u}{15} > -7$

   $u > -105$
   $-\frac{105}{15} = -7$
   $-\frac{90}{15} > -7?$
   $-6 > -7$

8. $-\frac{1}{3} \leq -\frac{3}{10}k$

   $k \leq \frac{10}{9}$
   $-\frac{1}{3} = -\frac{3}{10} \cdot \frac{10}{9}$
   $-\frac{1}{3} < -\frac{3}{10} \cdot 0?$
   $-\frac{1}{3} < 0$

9. $-396 < 55f$

   $f > -7.2$
   $-396 = 55 \cdot -7.2$
   $-396 < 55 \cdot -7?$
   $-396 < -385$

10. $-r > 77$

    $r < -77$
    $-(-77) = 77$
    $-(-88) > 77?$
    $88 > 77$

11. $\frac{1}{5} \geq -2x$

    $x \geq -\frac{1}{10}$
    $\frac{1}{5} = -2 \cdot -\frac{1}{10}$
    $\frac{1}{5} > -2 \cdot 0?$
    $\frac{1}{5} > 0$

12. $\frac{5}{6}d \leq 75$

    $d \leq 90$
    $\frac{5}{6} \cdot 90 = 75$
    $\frac{5}{6} \cdot 60 < 75?$
    $50 < 75$

Properties Objective F: Identify and apply the Multiplication Property of Inequality.

13. What inequality results if both sides of $-6 < 10$ are multiplied by -1? $6 > -10$

14. What inequality results if both sides of $-\frac{3}{5}x < -24$ are multiplied by $-\frac{5}{3}$? $x > 40$

Name

15. *Multiple choice.* If $r < s$, then which sentence is true? b

    (a) $s < r$ (b) $-r > -s$ (c) $-r < s$

16. If a number is greater than 1,000, why must its opposite be less than -1,000?

    Sample: If $x > 1{,}000$, then by the Mult. Prop. of Inequality $-1 \cdot x < -1 \cdot 1{,}000$ and $-x < -1{,}000$.

Uses Objective G: Apply the Area Model for Multiplication in real situations.

17. The park board is planning a new rectangular playground. The width will be 75 feet, and its area may not exceed 10,000 square feet. What is the maximum length?

    a. Write an inequality involving the length. $75\ell \leq 10{,}000$

    b. Solve the inequality. $\ell \leq 133\frac{1}{3}$

    c. Answer the question. $133\frac{1}{3}$ ft

Uses Objective H: Apply the Rate Factor for Multiplication in real situations.

18. Mr. Sanchez has a 22-pound turkey in the freezer. If he allows $\frac{3}{4}$ pound per person, how many people can he serve?

    a. Write an inequality describing the number of people he can serve. $n \text{ peo.} \cdot \frac{3 \text{ lb}}{4 \text{ per.}} \leq 22 \text{ lb}$

    b. Solve the inequality. $n \leq 29\frac{1}{3}$

    c. Answer the question. no more than 29 people

19. The gas tank of Dorothy's car holds 12.6 gallons of gas. If she get 18 miles to the gallon, how far can she drive on a full tank?

    a. Write an inequality describing the distance she can drive on a full tank. $m \text{ mi} \leq 12.6 \text{ gal} \cdot 18 \frac{\text{mi}}{\text{gal}}$

    b. Solve the inequality. $m \leq 226.8$

    c. Answer the question. no more than 226.8 mi

Name

LESSON MASTER 2-9 B

Questions on SPUR Objectives

Uses Objective I: Apply the Multiplication Counting Principle.

1. An earring shop offers a certain style of earrings in gold or silver, with garnets, jade, onyx, or pearls, and for pierced or unpierced ears. Use a list or a tree diagram to show all the possibilities for this style.

   A sample list of abbreviations is given. 16 choices are possible.

GGP	GOP	SGP	SOP
GGU	GOU	SGU	SOU
GJP	GPP	SJP	SPP
GJU	GPU	SJU	SPU

2. A bakery offers rye bread in 1-pound or $1\frac{1}{2}$-pound loaves, with seeds or without, and sliced or unsliced. How many choices of rye bread are there? 8 choices

3. Freshmen at Louis Academy must take one course from each of the following:

   English (Literature or Creative Writing)
   Mathematics (Algebra, Geometry, or Advanced Algebra)
   Social Studies (World Cultures or American History)
   Science (Lab Survey, Biology, or Physics)
   Fine Arts (Choir, Band, Orchestra, Freshman Art, Speech, or Drama)
   Foreign Language (French, Spanish, Italian, German, or Russian)
   Gym (Swimming, Wrestling, or Aerobics)

   How many different freshman programs are possible? 3,240 ways

4. Write a problem involving the Multiplication Counting Principle that has as its answer $2 \cdot 4 \cdot 3$.

   Sample: How many outfits are possible with 2 T-shirts, 4 pairs of jeans, and 3 pairs of socks?

5. Write a problem involving the Multiplication Counting Principle that has as its answer 4^3.

   Sample: How many three-digit numbers are possible if each digit is greater than 5?

Name

6. A customer calling Cavalier Savings and Loan on a touch-tone phone is instructed to press 1 for the Savings Department, 2 for the Checking Department, 3 for the Home Loan Department, or 4 for the Commercial Loan Department. After making that selection, the customer is told to press 1 followed by the account number to hear the current balance, 2 followed by the account number to hear information about the last transaction, or 3 to talk to an employee from that department. How many different selections are possible? 12 selections

7. Some license plates contain two letters followed by 4 numbers such as GY 1884.

   a. How many such plates are possible? 6,760,000 plates

   b. How many are possible if you cannot use the letters I or O? 5,760,000 plates

   c. Why do you think the letters I and O might be excluded?

   Sample: I and O look like the numerals for 1 and 0.

8. A science test has six multiple-choice questions each with five options, A, B, C, D, and E. The test also has eight true-false questions.

   a. How many different ways are there for a student to answer the questions on the test? 4,000,000 ways

   b. How many different ways are there for a student to answer the questions on the test if there are p multiple-choice questions and q true-false questions? $(5^p)(2^q)$ ways

9. a. In how many ways can 12 children line up at the drinking fountain? 479,001,600 ways

   b. How many ways are there if this week's "front captain" is first? 39,916,800 ways

10. A bicycle lock uses a combination of 4 digits, each ranging from 1 to 6.

    a. How many different combinations are possible? 1,296 combinations

    b. Frannie forgot her combination but does remember that the middle two digits are 5 and 5. What is the greatest number of possible combinations she would have to try until she finds the right one? 36 combinations

Name

LESSON MASTER 2-10 B

Questions on SPUR Objectives

Vocabulary

1. An arrangement of letters, names, or objects is called a permutation.

2. Explain how to read 18! and tell what it means.
Eighteen factorial; it means the product of the positive integers from 18 to 1.

Skills Objective E: Evaluate expressions containing a factorial symbol.

In 3–5, evaluate.

3. 4! 24 4. 7! 5,040 5. 10! 3,628,800

6. Are 9! and $9 \cdot 8!$ equal? Explain.
yes; both equal $9 \cdot 8 \cdot 7 \cdot 6 \cdot 5 \cdot 4 \cdot 3 \cdot 2 \cdot 1$.

7. Are $3! \cdot 4!$ and $(3 \cdot 4)!$ equal? Explain.
no; $3! \cdot 4! = 3 \cdot 2 \cdot 1 \cdot 4 \cdot 3 \cdot 2 \cdot 1 = 144$; $(3 \cdot 4)! = 12 \cdot 11 \cdot 10 \cdot 9 \cdot 8 \cdot 7 \cdot 6 \cdot 5 \cdot 4 \cdot 3 \cdot 2 \cdot 1 = 479{,}001{,}600$

8. Tell if the following statement is *true* or *false* and justify your answer.
If $n > 1$, n! is even.
true; sample: For $n > 1$, $n!$ includes 2 as a factor.

9. Explain how to evaluate $\frac{100!}{98!}$ without a calculator.
Sample: Use the Equal Fractions Property;
$\frac{100 \cdot 99 \cdot 98 \cdot \ldots \cdot 1}{98 \cdot 97 \cdot 96 \cdot \ldots \cdot 1} = 100 \cdot 99 = 9{,}900$

In 10–12, find *n*.

10. $n! = 24$ $n=4$ 11. $n! = 1$ $n=1$ 12. $n! = 362{,}880$ $n=9$

Name

Uses Objective I: Apply the Permutation Theorem.

In 13–18, tell if the Permutation Theorem can be used to solve the problem. Write *yes* or *no*.

13. In how many ways can 14 books be lined up on a shelf? yes

14. How many different sets of 2-letter initials are there? no

15. How many different ways are there to arrange a trip to 20 cities? yes

16. In how many ways can you choose a sandwich from a choice of 4 breads, 2 fillings, and 2 spreads? no

17. In how many different orders can 11 people get off an elevator one at a time? yes

18. How many different outfits can be made from 3 skirts and 5 blouses? no

19. In the movie *Close Encounters of the Third Kind*, aliens transmit a message that consists of five different tones of music played one at a time.

a. In how many orders can five different tones be played with none repeated? 120 orders

b. In how many orders can six different tones be played with none repeated? 720 orders

c. In how many orders can seven different tones such as DO-RE-MI-FA-SOL-LA-TI, be played with none repeated? 5,040 orders

d. In how many different orders can the 12 black and white keys indicated below be played if no key is played twice? 479,001,600 orders

12 keys

e. Write an expression for the number of different orders there are for playing the 88 black and white keys of a piano if no key is played twice. 88!

Name

LESSON MASTER 3-1 B

Questions on SPUR Objectives

Skills Objective A: Use properties of addition to simplify expressions.

In 1–9, simplify the expression.

1. (10 + -2) + -6 2
2. (-4 + 9) + (-9 + 4) 0
3. 19.99 + 4.95 + 0.05 + 0.01 25
4. 38 + (3*p* + 9) 3*p* + 47
5. -17 + (*x* + -13) *x* + -30
6. (*b* + 22) + -18 *b* + 4
7. (*m* + 11) + (*n* + 44) *m* + *n* + 55
8. (*e* + -26) + (24 + 2*f*) *e* + 2*f* + -2
9. 9 + (*h* + -6.5) + 2.4 *h* + 4.9

10. In a magic square, each row, column, and diagonal has the same sum. Fill in the boxes at the right so each of these sums is -3.
A sample is given.

2	-5	0
-3	-1	1
-2	3	-4

Properties Objective E: Identify the Commutative and Associative Properties of Addition.

In 11–14, tell which property of addition is illustrated.

11. (5 + 7*v*) + -16 = 5 + (7*v* + -16)
Associative Property of Addition

12. (9 + -4*w*) + (8*r* + 33) = (8*r* + 33) + (9 + -4*w*)
Commutative Property of Addition

13. (11 + 2*g*) + 80 = (2*g* + 11) + 80
Commutative Property of Addition

14. (-7 + 8*a*) + (9*a* + 14) = -7 + (8*a* + 9*a*) + 14
Associative Property of Addition

Name

15. Give three instances of the Commutative Property of Addition.
Samples: $8 + 9 = 9 + 8$, $\frac{1}{2} + 10 = 10 + \frac{1}{2}$, $x + 4y = 4y + x$

16. Give three instances of the Associative Property of Addition.
Samples: $4 + (9 + 6) = (4 + 9) + 6$, $(x + y) + z = x + (y + z)$, $\frac{1}{2} + \left(\frac{1}{2} + 9\right) = \left(\frac{1}{2} + \frac{1}{2}\right) + 9$

Uses Objective G: Apply the Putting-Together and Slide Models of Addition to write linear expressions and equations involving addition.

In 17–19, write an addition expression or equation suggested by each situation.

17. Doreen is *Y* years old.

a. 7 years from now, Doreen's age will be $y + 7$.

b. 2 years ago, Doreen's age was $y + -2$.

18. The price of a yard of denim was $4.66. The price rose *d* dollars, then it dropped 49¢, and then rose 18¢. Now the price of denim is $4.66 + d + -.49 + .18$

19. On a vacation, a family spent $750 for hotels, $622 for food, $94 for gas, and *E* dollars for other expenses. Altogether, they spent $1700. $750 + 622 + 94 + E = 1700$

20. Refer to the graphs below.

a. In Week 1, the total number of books checked out is expressed by the sum $10 + 23$.

b. In Week 4, the total number of books, checked out is expressed by the sum $10 + 15$.

c. In Week 5, if *f* fiction books and *n* nonfiction books were checked out, then the total number of books checked out is expressed by the sum $f + n$.

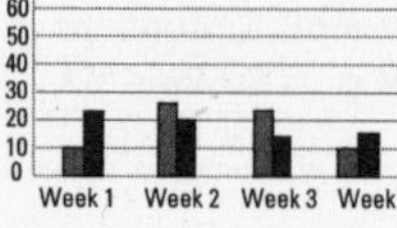

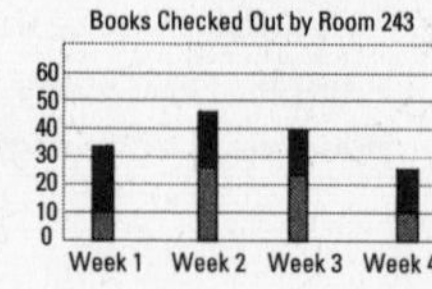

Name

LESSON MASTER 3-2 B **Questions on SPUR Objectives**

Skills Objective A: Use properties of addition to simplify expressions.

In 1–8, simplify the expression.

1. -(-94) **94**
2. -8.66 + 8.66 **0**
3. $-\frac{6}{5} + \frac{6}{5}$ **0**
4. $-4g + 0$ **$-4g$**
5. -(-704) + -704 **0**
6. $(e + -232) + 232$ **e**
7. (-44 + 99) + (-99 + 44) **0**
8. $(9v + -16) + 16$ **$9v$**

Skills Objective B: Solve and check equations of the form $x + a = b$.

9. a. Check whether $x = 6.1$ is the correct solution to the equation $-14.2 + x = 8.1$. **Samples are given.**
Substitute 6.1 for x; $-14.2 + 6.1 = 8.1$? $-8.1 \neq 8.1$

b. Use another method to check whether $x = 6.1$ is the correct solution.
Solve for x; $x = 8.1 + 14.2$; $x = 22.3$; $x \neq 6.1$

In 10–18, solve and check the equation.

10. $u + -13 = 7$
$u = 20$
$20 + -13 = 7$?
$7 = 7$

11. $2e = 852$
$e = 426$
$2 \cdot 426 = 852$?
$852 = 852$

12. $66 = f + 88$
$f = -22$
$66 = -22 + 88$?
$66 = 66$

13. $-21 + r = -37$
$r = -16$
$-21 + -16 = -37$?
$-37 = -37$

14. $45 = -\frac{5}{8}x$
$x = -72$
$45 = -\frac{5}{8} \cdot -72$?
$45 = 45$

15. $2.8 + w = 7.4$
$w = 4.6$
$2.8 + 4.6 = 7.4$?
$7.4 = 7.4$

16. $\frac{7}{12} + d = -\frac{5}{12}$
$d = -1$
$\frac{7}{12} + -1 = -\frac{5}{12}$?
$-\frac{5}{12} = -\frac{5}{12}$

17. $-5.09 = -5.09 + h$
$h = 0$
$-5.09 = -5.09 + 0$?
$-5.09 = -5.09$

18. $-6.15 = -.03k$
$k = 205$
$-6.15 = -.03 \cdot 205$?
$-6.15 = -6.15$

Name

Properties Objective E: Identify and apply the Additive Identity Property, the Property of Opposites, the Opposite of Opposites Property, and the Addition Property of Equality.

In 19–21, a. give another instance of the property illustrated and b. name the property. **Sample instances are given.**

19. $\frac{5}{9} + -\frac{5}{9} = 0$ a. **$3 + -3 = 0$** b. **Prop. of Opposites**
20. $0 + \pi = \pi$ a. **$0 + \frac{1}{2} = \frac{1}{2}$** b. **Addit. Ident. Prop.**
21. $-(-19) = 19$ a. **$-(-43) = 43$** b. **Opp. of Opp. Prop.**

In 22 and 23, give the number that should be added to both sides to solve the equation quickly.

22. $x + -18 = 94$ **18**
23. $5.11 = y + 4.9$ **-4.9**

24. a. If 37 is added to both sides of the equation $m + 22 = -4$, what is the result? **$m + 59 = 33$**

b. Does the equation you wrote for part a have the same solution as the equation $m + 22 = -4$? **yes**

Uses Objective G: Apply models for addition to write and solve equations of the form $x + a = b$.

In 25 and 26, write and solve an equation to answer the question.

25. After receiving orders from the captain, a submarine rose 120 feet to 40 feet below sea level. At what level was the submarine before the captain gave the orders?

$S + 120 = -40$ (equation) **160 ft below sea level** (answer)

26. Mr. Craig received notice that his checking account was overdrawn by \$55. After making a deposit, his new balance was \$480. How much did he deposit?

$-55 + D = 480$ (equation) **\$525** (answer)

Name

LESSON MASTER 3-3 B **Questions on SPUR Objectives**

Representations Objective I: Draw and interpret two-dimensional graphs.

1. The chart below compares different schools, showing the number of computers at the school and the number of minutes students averaged at a school computer per week.

School Computers

School	Computers per 100 Students	Minutes Used per Student per Week
Douglas	21	75
Young	14	55
Lincoln	13	64
West Lloyd	11	40
Fernandez	10	85
Carlisle	8	44
East Lloyd	8	35
Hadley	7	32
Powell	7	27
Thayer	5	18

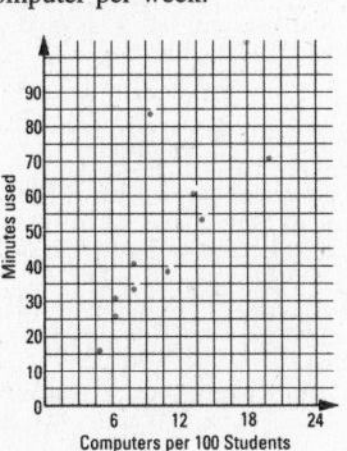

a. Draw a graph of the data on the grid, showing computers per 100 students on the horizontal axis and minutes used per student per week on the vertical axis.

b. Describe any trends you see. Are there any schools that do not follow this trend?
Samples: In general, the more computers per 100 students, the more time students average at the computers; Fernandez

c. If a school has 12 computers per 100 students, give a reasonable prediction for the average number of minutes per week each students uses the computer. **Sample: 45 min**

Name

In 2 and 3, use the graph below, which shows how long the average American had to work, before taxes, to purchase the goods and services shown.

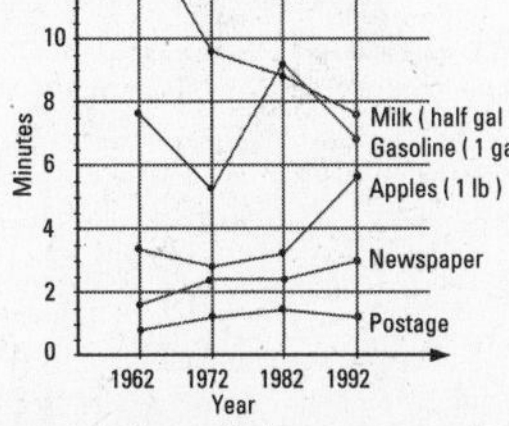

2. On the average, about how long did a worker have to work

a. for a pound of apples in 1982? **≈ 3 min**

b. for a gallon of gasoline in 1972? **≈ 5 min**

3. Does this graph show any general trends? Explain your answer below.
Sample: no; some prices fell, some prices rose, and some prices did both.

4. Use the graph at the right. It has two different vertical scales. To plot a point on this graph, use the student's ACT exam score along the horizontal axis and the student's grade-point and class rank on the two vertical axes. If the point plotted is *on or above* the line graphed, the student is considered for admission to the university. Would a student be considered for admission if the student

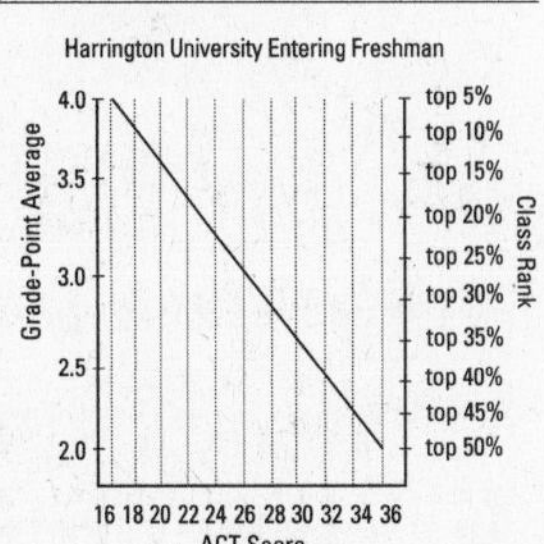

a. scored 26 on the ACT and has a 3.29 grade-point average? **yes**

b. scored 20 on the ACT and is in the top 25% of the class? **no**

Name

LESSON MASTER 3-4 B **Questions on SPUR Objectives**

Representations Objective J: Draw and interpret two-dimensional slides on a coordinate graph.

For 1–5, use the grid at the right. $P'A'R'T'Y'$ is the image of sliding pentagon $PARTY$ 4 units right and 3 units up. $P''A''R''T''Y''$ is the image of $P'A'R'T'Y'$ under the slide 6 units left and 3 units up.

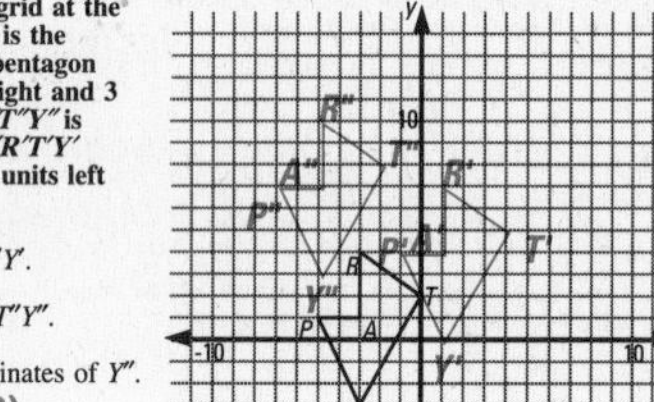

1. Graph $P'A'R'T'Y'$.
2. Graph $P''A''R''T''Y''$.
3. Give the coordinates of Y''. (-5, 3)
4. The coordinates of P are (-5, 1). Explain how to find the coordinates of P' without graphing.
Sample: Add 4 to the x-coordinate and 3 to the y-coordinate; $P' = (-1, 4)$
5. The coordinates of A are (-3, 1). Explain how to find the coordinates of A'' without graphing.
Sample: Add $(4 + -6)$, or -2, to the x-coordinate and $(3 + 3)$, or 6, to the y-coordinate; $A'' = (-5, 7)$
6. Give the coordinates of the point $N = (-5, 9)$ under a slide
   a. 1 unit right and 3 units down. (-4, 6)
   b. 6 units left and 10 units down. (-11, -1)
   c. 5 units right and 4 units up. (0, 13)
   d. 7 units up. (-5, 16)
   e. 2 units left. (-7, 9)
   f. h units right and k units up. $(-5 + h, 9 + k)$

Name

7. Give the coordinates of the point $Q = (x, y)$ under a slide
   a. 4 units left and 8 units up. $(x + -4, y + 8)$
   b. 5 units right and 4 units up. $(x + 5, y + 4)$
   c. 5 units down. $(x, y + -5)$
   d. 9 units right. $(x + 9, y)$
8. Give a formula for a slide for which the image of the point (3, -2) is — Samples are given.
   a. in Quadrant I. 1 unit right, 3 units up
   b. in Quadrant II. 4 units left, 3 units up
   c. in Quadrant III. 5 units left
   d. in Quadrant IV. 2 units right
   e. on the x-axis. 2 units up
   f. on the y-axis. 3 units left

In 9–12, use the graph at the right which shows M and its image, M', after a slide.

9. Describe the slide. 3 units left, 6 units up
10. Point H is shown on the graph. Plot H', its image under the same slide that was used to go from M to M'.
11. Fill in the blanks to describe the slide algebraically:
The image of (x, y) is $(x + \underline{-3}, y + \underline{6})$
12. a. Give a formula for the slide that would move M' onto M. $(x + 3, y + -6)$
    b. Compare your answer in Part a to your answer to Question 9 and explain what you notice.
    Sample: They are slides in the opposite directions.

Name

LESSON MASTER 3-5 B **Questions on SPUR Objectives**

Skills Objective B: Solve and check equations of the form $ax + b = c$.

1. Write a check to determine if $m = -18$ is the correct solution of $21 + -3m = 75$.
$21 + (-3 \cdot -18) = 75?$ $75 = 75$; $m = 18$

In 2–13, solve and check the equation.

2. $3d + 81 = 117$
$d = 12$
$3 \cdot 12 + 81 = 117?$
$117 = 117$

3. $-2g + -16 = 4$
$g = -10$
$-2 \cdot -10 + -16 = 4?$
$4 = 4$

4. $-7 = 9f + 20$
$f = -3$
$-7 = 9 \cdot -3 + 20?$
$-7 = -7$

5. $-75 = 4y$
$y = -18.75$
$-75 = 4 \cdot -18.75?$
$-75 = -75$

6. $\frac{2}{3}t + 16 = 62$
$t = 69$
$\frac{2}{3} \cdot 69 + 16 = 62?$
$62 = 62$

7. $-33 = f + -14$
$f = -19$
$-33 = -19 + -14?$
$-33 = -33$

8. $20 = 30 + -\frac{x}{4}$
$x = 40$
$20 = 30 + -\frac{40}{4}?$
$20 = 20$

9. $8.22 = 1.6h + .22$
$h = 5$
$8.22 = 1.6 \cdot 5 + .22?$
$8.22 = 8.22$

10. $-\frac{7}{9}a = 77$
$a = -99$
$-\frac{7}{9} \cdot -99 = 77?$
$77 = 77$

11. $2.7 + 6s + 1.8 = 6.5$
$s = \frac{1}{3}$
$2.7 + 6 \cdot \frac{1}{3} + 1.8 = 6.5?$
$6.5 = 6.5$

12. $2\frac{1}{2} + 2n = 2\frac{3}{4}$
$n = \frac{1}{8}$
$2\frac{1}{2} + 2 \cdot \frac{1}{8} = 2\frac{3}{4}?$
$2\frac{3}{4} = 2\frac{3}{4}$

13. $9 + -7k = 2 + -77$
$k = 12$
$9 + -7 \cdot 12 = 2 + -77?$
$-75 = -75$

14. If -6 is added to each side of $6x - 8 = 40$, what is the resulting equation? $6x - 14 = 34$
15. Does your answer to Question 14 have the same solution as $6x - 8 = 40$? Explain why or why not.
Sample: yes; the Addition Property of Equality states that the same number can be added to both sides of an equation and the resulting equation is equivalent.

Name

Uses Objective G: Apply models for addition to write and solve equations of the form $ax + b = c$.

In 16–19, write an equation to describe the situation, solve the equation, and answer the question.

16. Ellen bought buttons and $2\frac{1}{2}$ yd of fabric. The buttons cost \$1.95, and the total bill without tax was \$19.40. What was the cost per yard of the fabric?

$2\frac{1}{2}f + 1.95 = 19.40$	$f = 6.98$	\$6.98
equation	solution	answer

17. Jake's phone service is \$21 per month plus 25¢ for each local call, with long-distance calls extra. Last month, with \$6.14 in long-distance charges, his bill was \$36.64. How many local calls did he make?

$21 + .25l + 6.14 = 36.64$	$l = 38$	38 local calls
equation	solution	answer

18. Cindy has saved \$57 and wants to buy a shirt and two pairs of jeans at \$25 a pair. Without tax, how much can she spend on a shirt?

$s + 2 \cdot 25 = 57$	$s = 7$	\$7
equation	solution	answer

19. The Andersons wish to fence in the back and the two sides of their yard. Their lot is 50 feet wide. If they purchase 140 feet of fencing, how long can the fence be along each side?

$50 + 2s = 140$	$s = 45$	45 ft long
equation	solution	answer

Representations Objective K: Use balance scales to represent equations.

20. a. What equation is represented by the diagram at the right?
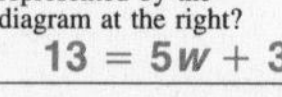
$13 = 5w + 3$
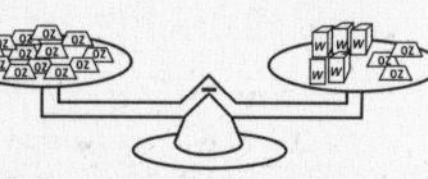
    b. What two steps can be done with the objects on the scale to find the weight of a box?
    Sample: Remove 3 oz from each side; leave $\frac{1}{5}$ of objects on each side.
21. a. Sketch a balance-scale diagram for $3w + 4 = 10$.
    b. What is the value of w? $w = 2$
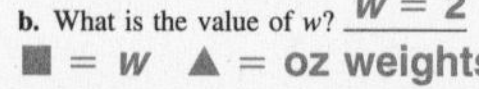
■ = w ▲ = oz weights
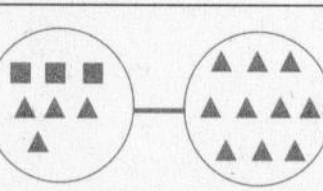

Name

LESSON MASTER 3-6 B **Questions on SPUR Objectives**

Vocabulary

In 1–6, tell if the terms are *like* or *unlike*.

1. $7v \quad 9v^2$ unlike
2. $a \quad 8a$ like
3. $5c^2 \quad -3c^2$ like
4. $-y \quad 44y$ like
5. $88g \quad 88$ unlike
6. $-r^2 \quad r^2$ like

Skills Objective A: Use the Distributive Property to simplify expressions.

In 7–18, simplify the expression.

7. $3u + 11u$ — $14u$
8. $s + 13s$ — $14s$
9. $9m + 3m + -5m$ — $7m$
10. $3d + 17 + -8d$ — $-5d + 17$
11. $15 + -7f + -21 + -2f$ — $-9f + -6$
12. $h + h + h + h$ — $4h$
13. $12g^2 + 18g^2$ — $30g^2$
14. $-5y^2 + 7y + 6y^2$ — $y^2 + 7y$
15. $7 - u^2 + 4u + 9u + u^2$ — $7 + 13u$
16. $\left(\frac{3}{4}t + 16\right) + \left(-\frac{1}{2}t + 4\right)$ — $\frac{1}{4}t + 20$
17. $(14x^2 + 7x) + (-x + 19)$ — $14x^2 + 6x + 19$
18. $6(4j) + 13 + -23j$ — $j + 13$

In 19 and 20, simplify. Check your answer by substituting 10 for *x* in both the original expression and your answer.

19. $2x + 7x^2 + -3x + x^2$ $8x^2 + -x$
$2\cdot10 + 7\cdot10^2 + -3\cdot10 + 10^2 = 790$
$8\cdot10^2 + -10 = 790$

20. $9.4x + 3x$ $12.4x$
$9.4\cdot10 + 3\cdot10 = 124$
$12.4\cdot10 = 124$

Name

Skills Objective B: Solve and check equations of the form $ax + b = c$.

In 21 and 22, solve and check the equation.

21. $10q + -4q = -72$
$q = -12$
$10\cdot-12 + -4\cdot-12 = -72?$
$-72 = -72$

22. $21d + 16 + 13d = 67$
$d = 1.5$
$21\cdot1.5 + 16 + 13\cdot1.5 = 67?$
$67 = 67$

Properties Objective E: Identify and apply the Distributive Property.

In 23–25, tell whether or not the Distributive Property is involved. Write *yes* or *no*.

23. $-(-9) = 9$ no
24. $-9a + 3a = -6a$ yes
25. $\frac{2}{3}b + \frac{1}{3}b = b$ yes

Uses Objective G: Apply models for addition to write and solve equations involving like terms.

In 26 and 27, write an equation to describe the situation, solve the equation, and answer the question.

26. Helen bought a blouse, jeans, and a pair of shoes for $72. The blouse and jeans cost the same amount, and the shoes cost $6 more than the blouse. How much did the jeans cost?

$c + c + (c + 6) = 72$ (equation) $c = 22$ (solution) $22 (answer)

27. The area of Ms. Whitecloud's property is 7,800 square feet. Her house occupies one fourth the area of land as the rest of the property. How many square feet of land does the house cover?

$\frac{1}{4}x + x = 7{,}800$ (equation) $x = 6{,}240$ (solution) $1{,}560 \text{ ft}^2$ (answer)

Representations Objective K: Use area models to represent the Distributive Property.

28. a. What is the area of the top rectangle? $13x$
b. What is the area of the bottom rectangle? $5x$
c. What is the area of the largest rectangle? Give your answer in simplified form. $18x$

x
13
5

Name

LESSON MASTER 3-7 B **Questions on SPUR Objectives**

Skills Objective A: Use the Distributive Property to simplify expressions.

In 1–12, simplify the expression.

1. $6(8m + 7)$ — $48m + 42$
2. $-9(y + 5)$ — $-9y + -45$
3. $u(7u + 10)$ — $7u^2 + 10u$
4. $w(w - 12)$ — $w^2 - 12w$
5. $12(3 - 2y)$ — $36 - 24y$
6. $h + 5(h + 8)$ — $6h + 40$
7. $4g(g + 3) + 2g^2 + -g$ — $6g^2 + 11g$
8. $-4(r + 8) + 9(r + 8)$ — $5r + 40$
9. $15a + 7 + -25a$ — $-10a + 7$
10. $2.5(5f - 3)$ — $12.5f - 7.5$
11. $\frac{1}{2}(s + 17)$ — $\frac{1}{2}s + \frac{17}{2}$
12. $4k + -3(j + k + 8) + 2(3j + -8k)$ — $3j + -15k + -24$

Skills Objective B: Solve and check equations of the form $ax + b = c$.

In 13–16, solve and check the equation.

13. $2(3x + 18) = 102$
$x = 11$
$2(3\cdot11 + 18) = 102?$
$2(51) = 102?$
$102 = 102$

14. $7(j + -4) + j = 4$
$j = 4$
$7(4 + -4) + 4 = 4?$
$7(0) + 4 = 4?$
$4 = 4$

15. $24 = 20(6 + -5y) + 4$
$y = 1$
$24 = 20(6 + -5\cdot1) + 4?$
$24 = 20(1) + 4?$
$24 = 24$

16. $3.1d(2d + 7) + -6.2d^2 = 19.53$
$d = 0.9$
$3.1\cdot0.9(2\cdot0.9 + 7) + -6.2\cdot0.9^2 = 19.53?$
$24.552 + -5.022 = 19.53?$
$19.53 = 19.53$

Name

Properties Objective E: Identify and apply the Distributive Property.

In 17–20, tell if the equation involves the Distributive Property.

17. $6a + (7 + 3a) = 6a + (3a + 7)$ no
18. $5n + 13n + -16 = 18n + -16$ yes
19. $7(2a + 6b + c) = 14a + 42b + 7c$ yes
20. $15t + (7u + -v) = (15t + 7u) + -v$ no

Properties Objective F: Use the Distributive Property to perform calculations mentally.

21. If a recipe makes 60 cookies, how many does a recipe and a half make? Explain how you can mentally compute your answer.

90 cookies; $60\left(1\frac{1}{2}\right) = 60(1) + 60\left(\frac{1}{2}\right) = 60 + 30 = 90$

22. There are 19 students in Room 216. Mentally compute the cost if the entire class buys

a. juice at $.75 each. $14.25
$20(.75) - 1(.75) = 15 - .75$

b. caps at $12 each. $228
$20(12) - 1(12) = 240 - 12$

Representations Objective K: Use area models to represent the Distributive Property.

In 23 and 24 express the area of each largest rectangle as a. length times width and b. the sum of the areas of the smaller rectangles.

23. 6, b, 8
a. $6(b + 8)$
b. $6b + 48$

24. e f g, 3
a. $3(e + f + g)$
b. $3e + 3f + 3g$

Name

LESSON MASTER 3-8 B Questions on SPUR Objectives

Uses Objective H: Write expressions and solve problems involving linear patterns with two variables.

In 1–9, use the sequence of designs shown below.

1st 2nd 3rd

1. Draw the next design in the sequence.

4th

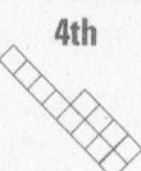

2. Complete the chart below to show the perimeters of the first through fifth designs.

Design Number	Perimeter
1	8
2	12
3	16
4	20
5	24

3. If the perimeter of a design is 40, what would the perimeter of the next design be? 44

4. If n = the design number and p = the perimeter, then the relationship between them is described by $p = 4n + 4$.

   a. Find the perimeter of the 18th design. 76

   b. Which design has perimeter 128? 31st

Name

5. Complete the chart at the right.

n = Design Number	s = Number of Squares
1	3
2	6
3	9
4	12
5	15

6. If one design has 45 squares, how many squares will the next design have? 48

7. Fill in the blanks to make a formula for this pattern. s = 0 + 3 n or $n + 2n$

8. How many squares will be in the 25th design? 75

9. Which design is made up of 66 squares? 22nd

In 10–12, use the chart at the right. It shows a price list for wallet-size pictures.

Number of Prints	Price
1 dozen	\$24
2 dozen	\$32
3 dozen	\$40
4 dozen	\$48
5 dozen	\$56

10. How much would 120 prints cost? \$96

11. Describe how the price changes as the number of prints increases.
The price increases \$8 for each additional dozen prints.

12. Write an equation for the cost c of p dozen prints. $c = 8p + 16$

13. The Central Valley Gas Company charges customers \$16.50 per month for up to 150 therms used and \$.06 for each therm after that.

   a. At the right make a table showing the cost of 100, 150, 200, 250, and 300 therms used during the month.

Therms	Cost
100	\$16.50
150	\$16.50
200	\$19.50
250	\$22.50
300	\$25.50

   b. Write a formula for the cost c in terms of the number t of therms used when $t \geq 150$.
   $c = 16.50 + .06(t - 150)$

   c. What is the cost of 680 therms used in a month?
   \$48.30

Name

LESSON MASTER 3-9 B Questions on SPUR Objectives

Skills Objective C: Add algebraic fractions.

In 1–14, find the sum.

1. $\frac{x}{z} + \frac{y}{z}$ $\frac{x + y}{z}$
2. $\frac{m}{5} + \frac{n}{5}$ $\frac{m + n}{5}$
3. $\frac{a}{9} + \frac{a}{9}$ $\frac{2a}{9}$
4. $\frac{1}{c} + \frac{2}{c} + \frac{3}{c}$ $\frac{6}{c}$
5. $\frac{3}{10} + \frac{9}{10}$ $\frac{6}{5}$, or $1\frac{1}{5}$
6. $-\frac{2}{5} + \frac{7}{5}$ $\frac{5}{5}$, or 1
7. $-\frac{4}{9} + -\frac{7}{9}$ $-\frac{11}{9}$, or $-1\frac{2}{9}$
8. $5\frac{7}{8} + \frac{5}{8}$ $6\frac{1}{2}$
9. $\frac{3}{r} + -\frac{12}{r}$ $-\frac{9}{r}$
10. $\frac{2m}{7} + \frac{6m}{7} + -\frac{m}{7}$ m
11. $-\frac{7}{8k} + \frac{15}{8k}$ $\frac{1}{k}$
12. $\frac{4}{3y} + -\frac{2}{3y} + \frac{10}{3y}$ $\frac{4}{y}$
13. $\frac{x + 7}{5u} + \frac{3x + 2}{5u}$ $\frac{4x + 9}{5u}$
14. $\frac{7p + -3}{2ab} + \frac{9p + 5}{2ab}$ $\frac{8p + 1}{ab}$

In 15 and 16, tell what common denominator you could use to add the fractions. Samples are given.

15. $\frac{x}{9}$ and $\frac{3x}{12}$ 36
16. $\frac{2v}{5}$ and $-\frac{7v}{6}$ 30

In 17-22, write as a single fraction.

17. $\frac{3x}{8} + \frac{5x}{4}$ $\frac{13x}{8}$
18. $-\frac{4a}{7} + \frac{12a}{3}$ $\frac{24a}{7}$
19. $-\frac{5m}{3} + -\frac{3m}{8}$ $-\frac{49m}{24}$
20. $h + \frac{h}{3}$ $\frac{4h}{3}$
21. $\frac{2y}{5} + \frac{3y}{2} + \frac{y}{15}$ $\frac{59y}{30}$
22. $9j + \frac{5j}{6}$ $\frac{59j}{6}$

In 23 and 24, simplify each expression.

23. $-\frac{4}{5}s + \frac{2}{3}s$ $-\frac{2}{15}s$
24. $\frac{2e + 7}{e} + \frac{-7}{e}$ 2

Name

25. On Monday, AFZ's stock dropped $2\frac{1}{4}$ points. On Tuesday it rose $\frac{7}{8}$ of a point. What was the net change? $-1\frac{3}{8}$ points

26. On Friday, the river rose $2\frac{1}{2}$ feet. On Saturday it rose another $2\frac{1}{4}$ feet. On Sunday it receded $1\frac{3}{4}$ feet. What was the net change in the level of the river? 3-ft rise

Properties Objective E: Identify and apply the Distributive Property.

In 27–30, tell if the equation involves the Distributive Property.

27. $\frac{5}{9} + \frac{1}{2} = \frac{10}{18} + \frac{9}{18}$ no
28. $a\left(\frac{1}{9}\right) + b\left(\frac{1}{9}\right) = (a + b)\frac{1}{9}$ yes
29. $\frac{e}{k} + \frac{2}{k} = \frac{e + 2}{k}$ yes
30. $\frac{9m}{m} = 9$ no

Review Objective C, Lesson 2-8

In 31–36, solve and check the inequality. Sample checks are given.

31. $9n > 36$
$n > 4$
$9 \cdot 4 = 36$
$9 \cdot 5 > 36?$
$45 > 36$

32. $84 \leq 12c$
$c \geq 7$
$84 = 12 \cdot 7$
$84 < 12 \cdot 8?$
$84 < 96$

33. $-5p < 5$
$p > -1$
$-5 \cdot -1 = 5$
$-5 \cdot 0 < 5?$
$0 < 5$

34. $58 \geq -2v$
$v \geq -29$
$58 = -2 \cdot -29$
$58 > -2 \cdot -20?$
$58 > 40$

35. $-\frac{3}{4}j < 27$
$j > -36$
$-\frac{3}{4} \cdot -36 = 27$
$-\frac{3}{4} \cdot -20 < 27?$
$15 < 27$

36. $-0.8u \leq -0.64$
$u \geq 0.8$
$-0.8 \cdot 0.8 = -0.64$
$-0.8 \cdot 1 < -0.64?$
$-0.8 < -0.64$

Name

LESSON MASTER 3-10 B **Questions on SPUR Objectives**

Skills Objective D: Solve and check inequalities of the form $ax + b < c$.

1. Scott solved $-4x + 3 > 43$ and got a solution of $x > -10$. He thought it was right because he checked it like this:

Does $-4(-10) + 3 = 43$?

Yes; $-4(-10) + 3 = 40 + 3 = 43$.

Scott's solution is incorrect. Explain why his check did not point this out.

Sample: Scott failed to do the second part of the check; if $x = 0$, then $-4 \cdot 0 + 3 \not> 43$.

Sample checks are given.

In 2–7, solve and check the inequality.

2. $4k + 8 > 52$

$k > 11$
$4 \cdot 11 + 8 = 52$
$4 \cdot 12 + 8 > 52$?
$56 > 52$

3. $-1 \geq 5e + 9$

$e \leq -2$
$-1 = 5 \cdot -2 + 9$
$-1 > 5 \cdot -3 + 9$?
$-1 > -6$

4. $-5p + 16 < 11$

$p > 1$
$-5 \cdot 1 + 16 = 11$
$-5 \cdot 2 + 16 < 11$?
$6 < 11$

5. $-6 \leq -m + 4$

$m \leq 10$
$-6 = -10 + 4$
$-6 < -9 + 4$?
$-6 < -5$

6. $18 + \frac{k}{8} < 21$

$k < 24$
$18 + \frac{24}{8} = 21$
$18 + \frac{16}{8} < 21$?
$20 < 21$

7. $3(4.1s + 10) \geq -43.8$

$s \geq -6$
$3(4.1 \cdot -6 + 10) = -43.8$?
$3(-14.6) = -43.8$
$3(4.1 \cdot 0 + 10) > -43.8$?
$30 > -43.8$

Name

Uses Objective G: Apply models for addition to write and solve inequalities of the form $ax + b < c$.

In 8 and 9, write an inequality to describe the situation and solve the inequality to answer the question.

8. During an eight-hour day, Ms. Swenson earns $95 plus 12% of the cost of the clothing she sells. What is the cost of the clothing she must sell if she wants to earn at least $150?

$95 + .12c \geq 150$ (inequality) — at least $458.34 (answer)

9. Student Council has $55 budgeted for service awards. They plan to buy a plaque for $19 and spend the rest on service pins. How many service pins can they purchase if each one costs 75¢?

$19 + .75s \leq 55$ (inequality) — no more than 48 pins (answer)

Representations Objective K: Use balance scales to represent sentences.

10. a. Write an inequality to describe the diagram at the right.

$5w + 1 < 16$

b. Solve the inequality from Part **a**.

$w < 3$

Representations Objective L: Graph solutions to inequalities of the form $ax + b < c$ on a number line.

11. *Multiple choice.* Which of the graphs below shows the solutions of $-4d + 7 \geq -5$? b

(a) 3 *d* (b) 3 *d*

(c) -3 *d* (d) -3 *d*

In 12–15, graph the solution to the inequality you solved in

12. Question 2. 9 10 11 12 13 14 *k*

13. Question 3. -5 -4 -3 -2 -1 0 *e*

14. Question 6. 21 22 23 24 25 26 *k*

15. Question 7. -8 -7 -6 -5 -4 -3 *s*

Name

LESSON MASTER 4-1 B **Questions on SPUR Objectives**

Skills Objective A: Simplify expressions involving subtraction.

In 1–13, simplify the expression.

1. $4 - 13$ -9

2. $-6 - 19$ -25

3. $20 - -10$ 30

4. $-7 - -15$ 8

5. $-17 - -17$ 0

6. $\frac{5}{6} - \frac{11}{12}$ $-\frac{1}{12}$

7. $-8.3 - -9.44$ 1.14

8. $10m - 4m + 3m$ $9m$

9. $13u - u$ $12u$

10. $p + 5 - 4p$ $-3p + 5$

11. $-4d - 8e + -4 + 6d - -9e - 11$ $2d + e - 15$

12. $-\frac{9}{10}a - \frac{3}{5}a - \frac{1}{2}a$ $-2a$

13. $\frac{4r}{s} - \frac{7r}{s}$ $\frac{-3r}{s}$

14. Evaluate $h^2 - h$, when $h = -3$. 12

15. Evaluate $18 - g^2$, when $g = 5$. -7

16. Evaluate $-a - -b$, when $a = -10$ and $b = 6$. 16

17. Evaluate $100 - 200 + 300 - 400 + \ldots + 900 - 1{,}000$. -500

Name

18. Let E = the height of the Wicked Witch of the East and let W = the height of the Wicked Witch of the West. If $E - W < 0$, which Witch is taller? Explain how you know.

Wicked Witch of the West; sample: when a larger number is subtracted from a smaller number, the difference is negative.

Properties Objective E: Apply the Algebraic Definition of Subtraction.

In 19–22, use the table below. It shows how a financial adviser records the weekly closing prices for shares of KDmetro stock. The numbers in the Change row show how the price compares to the price the previous week. Complete the table.

WEEK	1	2	3	4	5	6
CLOSING PRICE	144.25	142.50	145.375	145.875	143.00	144.375
CHANGE		-1.75	2.875	**19.** ?	**20.** ?	**21.** ?

19. 0.5 **20.** -2.875 **21.** 1.375

22. How could you find the change in price for Week 2

a. using subtraction? 142.50 − 144.25

b. using addition? 142.50 + -144.25

23. Write a calculator key sequence to find $44 - -19$

a. by subtracting. 44 ⊖ 19 [+/-] ⊜

b. by adding. 44 ⊕ 19 ⊜

In 24–29 rewrite each subtraction as an addition. Do not simplify.

24. $-8 + u - 14$ $-8 + u + -14$

25. $12 - 9y - 4y$ $12 + -9y + -4y$

26. $32 - -41$ $32 + 41$

27. $5e - -e$ $5e + e$

28. $1 - 100$ $1 + -100$

29. $-r - 7r + 2r - -4r^2$ $-r + -7r + 2r + 4r^2$

Name

LESSON MASTER 4-2 B Questions on SPUR Objectives

Uses Objective H: Use the Take-Away and Comparison Models for Subtraction to write expressions and equations involving subtraction.

In 1–6, use the table below. Remember that a negative profit is a loss.

PROFITS FOR SMITH ENTERPRISES (IN MILLIONS OF DOLLARS)			
CLOTHING		OTHER VENTURES	
Women's Apparel	4.6	Sunglasses	-0.6
Men's Apparel	3.1	Toiletries	1.9
Children's Apparel	-1.5	Watches	-0.2
Shoes	0.8		

1. Which enterprise was the most profitable? **Women's Apparel**
2. Which enterprise was the least profitable? **Children's Apparel**
3. How much more did the most profitable enterprise earn than the least profitable did? **$6.1 million**
4. What was the range of earnings for the clothing enterprises? **$6.1 million**
5. What was the range of earnings for the other ventures? **$2.5 million**
6. What was the range of earnings for all seven enterprises? **$6.1 million**
7. Let C = the weight of Gloria's cat and D = the weight of Gloria's dog. The dog weighs more than the cat. Which difference is positive, $C - D$, or $D - C$? **$D - C$**
8. Let K = Kyoto's age now. Write an expression for Kyoto's age
   a. 9 years ago. **$K - 9$** b. 5 years from now. **$K + 5$**

In 9 and 10, write a subtraction expression for the length of the segment marked with a question mark (?).

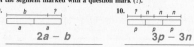

9. 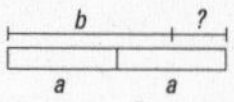

$2a - b$

10. 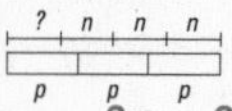

$3p - 3n$

Name

► **LESSON MASTER 4-2 B** *page 2*

11. At the right are the attendance figures for Crestville's Pioneer Festival.

1991	3,043
1992	2,945
1993	2,760
1994	3,178

   a. What was the change from 1992 to 1993? **-185; decrease of 185 people**
   b. What was the change from 1993 to 1994? **418; increase of 418 people**

12. Each spring, Lurvelle's discounts all winter merchandise 40%.
   a. If a winter coat was originally priced at $256, what is the amount of discount? **$102.40**
   b. What is the sale price of the coat in Part **a**? **$153.60**
   c. If a winter jacket was originally priced at J dollars, what is the sale price of the jacket? **$J - .4J$, or $.6J$**

13. Let M = Meg's age. Sam's age is $M - 8$, and Lill's age is $M + 2$.
   a. Arrange the three ages in order from least to greatest. **$M - 8$, M, $M + 2$; Sam, Meg, Lill**
   b. How much older is the oldest person than the youngest person? Explain how you determined the answer. **10 years; subtracted; $(M + 2) - (M - 8) = 10$**

14. Point M is x units to the right of -16. N is 8 units to the left of 10.

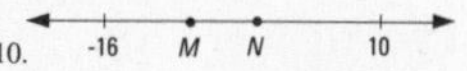

   a. Write an expression for the coordinate of M. **$-16 + x$**
   b. Find the coordinate of N. **$10 - 8 = 2$**

15. At the right are the weights of four of Dr. Norton's weight-loss patients.
   a. Complete the table.
   b. Which patient lost the most weight? **Morgan, S.**

Patient	Jan.	Oct.	Change
Morgan, S.	192	166	-26
Rojas, F.	214	195	**-19**
Ozu, D.	166	**155**	-11
Lake, M.	**183**	189	6

Name

LESSON MASTER 4-3 B Questions on SPUR Objectives

Skills Objective B: Solve and check linear equations involving subtraction.

In 1–9, solve and check each equation.

1. $5m - 12 = 38$
   $m = 10$
   $5 \cdot 10 - 12 = 38?$
   $38 = 38$

2. $-8g - 13 = 43$
   $g = -7$
   $-8 \cdot -7 - 13 = 43?$
   $43 = 43$

3. $-50 = 6e - 44$
   $e = -1$
   $-50 = 6 \cdot -1 - 44?$
   $-50 = -50$

4. $84 - x = 27$
   $x = 57$
   $84 - 57 = 27?$
   $27 = 27$

5. $-18.4 = -0.3y - -3.4$
   $y = 50$
   $-18.4 = -0.3 \cdot 50 - 3.4?$
   $-3.4 = -3.4$

6. $\frac{5}{6}u - -17 = 102$
   $u = 102$
   $\frac{5}{6} \cdot 102 - -17 = 102?$
   $102 = 102$

7. $7(19h - 3) = 112$
   $h = 1$
   $7(19 \cdot 1 - 3) = 112?$
   $112 = 112$

8. $-3(a + 20) - 2a = 25$
   $a = -17$
   $-3(-17 + 20) - 2(-17) = 25?$
   $25 = 25$

9. $102 - 7d = 11$
   $d = 13$
   $102 - 7 \cdot 13 = 11?$
   $11 = 11$

Skills Objective C: Solve and check linear inequalities involving subtraction.

10. *Skill sequence.* Solve.
   a. $8x - 40 = 360$ **$x = 50$** b. $8x - 40 < 360$ **$x < 50$**
   c. $8 - 40x = 360$ **$x = -8.8$** d. $8 - 40x < 360$ **$x > -8.8$**

Name

► **LESSON MASTER 4-3 B** *page 2*

In 11–13, a. solve and b. graph each inequality.

11. $-5t - 37 > -77$ a. **$t < 8$** b. 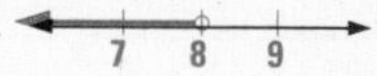

12. $23 - p \leq -47$ a. **$p \geq 70$** b. 

13. $-67 < 7g - 18$ a. **$g > -7$** b. 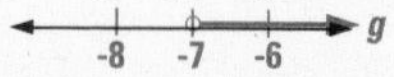

Uses Objective H: Use models for subtraction to write sentences involving subtraction.
Objective I: Solve problems using linear sentences involving subtraction.

In 14–18, write a subtraction sentence to describe the situation. Then solve the sentence to answer the question.

14. Mrs. Franco's initial investment of $3620 lost $12 per week. After x weeks, its value was $3464. How many weeks had elapsed?
   $3620 - 12x = 3464$ (equation) **13 weeks** (answer)

15. When a certain number is multiplied by 15 and the product is subtracted from 18, the answer is -87. What is the number?
   $18 - 15n = -87$ (equation) **7** (answer)

16. In the morning, there were 284 bottles of suntan lotion at Sunny's Beach Shop. By the end of the day, fewer than 3 dozen remained. How many bottles were sold?
   $284 - b < 3 \cdot 12$ (equation) **more than 248 bottles** (answer)

17. Farmer's State Bank provides free travelers' checks to customers having at least $1000 in a savings account. Susan Chin wants to withdraw $1750 from her savings account for a trip. How much must be in her account in order for her to get free travelers' checks?
   $S - 1750 \geq 1000$ (equation) **at least $2750** (answer)

18. The SFM Corporation bought a 12,000-ft² piece of property for a new office building. The building is to occupy 4,800 ft². How much of the area will be landscaped if the area left for the parking lot is 3,500 ft²?
   $12{,}000 - 4{,}800 - L = 3{,}500$ (equation) **3,700 ft²** (answer)

Name

LESSON MASTER 4-4 B

Questions on SPUR Objectives

Representations Objective K: Use a spreadsheet to show patterns and make tables from formulas.

In 1–4, use the spreadsheet below, which shows the enrollment figures at Eaglecrest High School.

	A	B	C
1	Class	Girls	Boys
2	Freshmen	112	105
3	Sophomores	133	136
4	Juniors	120	124
5	Seniors	118	110
6			
7			

1. What is in cell B4? **120**

2. Which cell contains the number 136? **C3**

3. Suppose the formula =B2+B3+B4+B5 is entered in cell B6.
   a. What value will appear in cell B6? **483**
   b. What quantity does this value represent? **the total number of girls in the school**

4. What formula should be entered in cell C7 to find the average number of boys per class? **=(C2+C3+C4+C5)/4**

In 5–8, the Broadstreet Theater sells first-floor tickets for $35.00 each and balcony seats for $22.00. The spreadsheet below shows the ticket sales for last month's concerts.

	A	B	C	D
1	Concert	First-floor	Balcony	Ticket sales
2	Horton Quintet	418	277	20724.00
3	Red Magnets	533	245	24045.00
4	LaGrange Choir	404	183	18166.00
5	Dora Chalmers	351	216	17037.00
6	Sioux Dancers	430	238	
7	TOTAL	2136	1159	

5. What is the formula used in cell C7 to calculate the total number of tickets sold for balcony seats? **=C2+C3+C4+C5+C6**

Name

► LESSON MASTER 4-4 B *page 2*

6. a. What formula could be entered in cell D6 to find the total ticket sales for the Sioux Dancers' concert? **=35*B6+22*C6**
   b. What number will appear in cell D6? **20,286.00**

7. Give two different formulas that could be entered in cell D7 to give the total ticket sales for all five concerts.
   =D2+D3+D4+D5+D6 **=35*B7+22*C7**

8. Suppose 200 balcony seats had been sold for the LaGrange Choir concert. Besides cell C4 changing to show 200, what other cells would show a different amount? **D4, C7, D7**

In 9 and 10, use the spreadsheet below. Chad, who is treasurer of the Student Council uses the spreadsheet to keep track of the dance committee's funds. He has columns for how much they take in each month through ticket sales, donations, and bake sales, and also for what they spend during the month financing the dances.

	A	B	C	D	E	F	G
1	MONTH	START	TICKETS	DONATIONS	BAKE SALES	EXPENSES	BALANCE
2	J	110.38	214.00	25.00	40.75	181.66	208.47
3	F	208.47	190.00	40.00	22.11	208.16	252.42
4	M	252.47	154.00	0.00	15.16	244.05	177.58

9. What formula could Chad be using in cell G2 for the committee's balance at the end of the month. **=B2+C2+D2+E2−F2**

10. Chad decides to add a column to show how the end-of-the-month funds change from month to month.
   a. If cell H3 has the formula =G3−G2, what number will appear? **43.95**
   b. If cell H4 has the formula =G4−G3, what number will appear? **-74.84**
   c. Why do the answers to Parts **a** and **b** have different signs? **Sample: There was an increase in the balance from January to February but a decrease from February to March.**

11. In a spreadsheet, suppose cell A6 contains the number 18 and cell C6 contains the number 25. If cell F6 contains the formula = (2*C6−A6)^2, what number will appear in cell F6? **1024**

Name

LESSON MASTER 4-5 B

Questions on SPUR Objectives

Skills Objective D: Use the Opposite of a Sum or Difference Property to simplify expressions and solve equations.

1. *Multiple choice.* Which expression is *not* equal to $-(12x - 4)$? **b**
   (a) $-4(3x - 1)$ (b) $-12x - 4$
   (c) $-12x + 4$ (d) $-12x - -4$

2. Teresa simplified $-3(9y - 5)$ and got $-27y - 15$.
   a. Substitute 10 for y to show that Teresa did the problem incorrectly.
   $-3(9 \cdot 10 - 5) = -3(85) = -255; -27(10) - 15 = -270 - 15 = -285$
   b. How do you think Teresa got the wrong answer?
   Sample: She multiplied -3 by 5 rather than by -5.

In 3–16, simplify the expression.

3. $-(m + n)$ **$-m - n$**
4. $-(m - n)$ **$-m + n$**
5. $-(4e - 13)$ **$-4e + 13$**
6. $-(-4e + 13)$ **$4e - 13$**
7. $-6(-3a + 15)$ **$18a - 90$**
8. $-5(x - y + 7)$ **$-5x + 5y - 35$**
9. $13v - (3v + 10)$ **$10v - 10$**
10. $(6s + 4) - (7s + 3)$ **$-s + 1$**
11. $24 - (6r - 12)$ **$-6r + 36$**
12. $-(5.3x + 3) - (2y - 8.7)$ **$-5.3x - 2y + 5.7$**
13. $5b - (7b + 2) + (3b + 2)$ **b**
14. $\frac{2x}{3} - \frac{7x + 1}{3}$ **$\frac{-5x - 1}{3}$**
15. $\frac{3m}{4} - \frac{3m - 3}{8}$ **$\frac{3m + 3}{8}$**
16. $\frac{2u + 4}{5} - \frac{u - 9}{4} - \frac{1 - 5u}{2}$ **$\frac{53u + 51}{20}$**

Name

► LESSON MASTER 4-5 B *page 2*

In 17–22, solve the equation.

17. $-(j + 9) = 15$ **$j = -24$**
18. $8 - (6x - 4) = -48$ **$x = 10$**
19. $7h - (6 + 9h) = 8$ **$h = -7$**
20. $-56 = -2(5w + 8) - (3w - 12)$ **$w = 4$**
21. $9x - 6(-2x + 1) = -6$ **$x = 0$**
22. $-3(y - 6) - (2y + 8) = 20$ **$y = -2$**

Review Objective I, Lesson 3-3

23. The table below compares the first 10 days the municipal pool was open, showing the temperature at noon and the number of swimmers.

Day	Noon Temperature	Number of Swimmers
June 11	73	221
June 12	71	163
June 13	74	180
June 14	84	209
June 15	93	311
June 16	90	266
June 17	90	206
June 18	92	271
June 19	85	240
June 20	81	188

Number of Swimmers: 100, 200, 300
Noon Temperature: 70° 80° 90°

   a. Graph the data on the grid, showing noon temperature on the horizontal axis and number of swimmers on the vertical axis.
   b. Describe any trends you see. Are there any days that do not follow this trend? What factors might explain this?
   Sample: The warmer the temperature, the more swimmers there are; June 11 is an exception; perhaps June 11 was opening day.

Name

LESSON MASTER 4-6 B

Questions on SPUR Objectives

Representations Objective L: Graph equations of the forms $x + y = k$ and $x - y = k$.

1. *Multiple choice.* Choose the equation that describes all four of the points in the graph at the right.
(a) $x + y = -1$
(b) $x + y = 1$
(c) $x - y = -1$
(d) $x - y = 1$

b

2. There are 3 more people in the Artrip family than in the Barrios family. Let a be the number of people in the Artrip family and let b be the number of people in the Barrios family.

a. Which equation describes this, $b = a + 3$ or $b = a - 3$? $b = a - 3$

b. Complete the table below with some possible numbers for sizes of the two families.

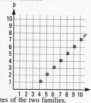

Size of Artrip family, *a*	Size of Barrios family, *b*	Ordered pair (*a*, *b*)
7	4	(7, 4)
8	5	(8, 5)
9	6	(9, 6)
10	7	(10, 7)

c. Graph the possible numbers for the sizes of the two families.

d. If together the two families have 13 members, how many people are in each family? 8 and 5

e. Does the ordered pair (2, -1) satisfy the equation you chose in Part **a**? Can this ordered pair be used in the situation about the two families? Tell why or why not.

Yes; no; sample: a family cannot have a negative number of people.

Name

3. There are 12 magazines on a table. Ron owns r of them and Sam owns the rest of them s.

a. Write an equation to describe this situation. $r + s = 12$

b. Complete the table below to show some of the possible numbers of magazines belonging to the two boys.

r	*s*	(*r*, *s*)
1	11	(1, 11)
2	10	(2, 10)
3	9	(3, 9)
4	8	(4, 8)
5	7	(5, 7)

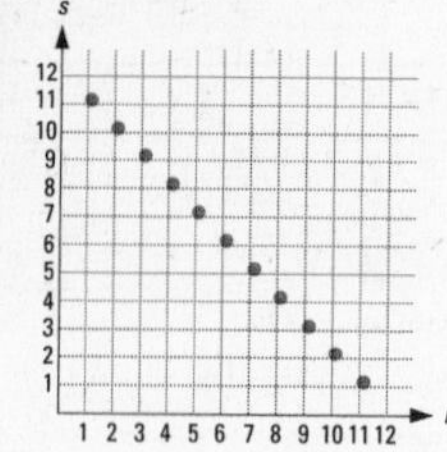

c. Graph *all* the possible numbers of magazines belonging to each boy.

d. If Sam has 3 times as many magazines as Ron does, how many magazines does each boy have? Sam, 9; Ron, 3

4. Consider the equation $x + y = 6$. Sample points are given.

a. Pick four x-coordinates to use in the table below.

b. For each x-coordinate find the y-coordinate that satisfies $x + y = 6$.

x	*y*	(*x*, *y*)
1	5	(1, 5)
-1	7	(-1, 7)
0	6	(0, 6)
3	3	(3, 3)

c. Graph *all* ordered pairs that satisfy the equation.

Name

LESSON MASTER 4-7 B

Questions on SPUR Objectives

Vocabulary

1. Define *supplementary angles.*
Supplementary angles are two angles whose measures add to 180°.

2. Define *complementary angles.*
Complementary angles are two angles whose measures add to 90°.

Properties Objective F: Use the definitions of supplements and complements and the Triangle Sum Theorem.

3. Use a protractor.

a. Find the measure of the angle at the right. 56°

b. Draw a complement of this angle. c. Draw a supplement of this angle.

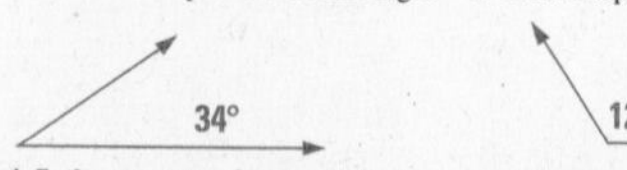

In 4–7, the measure of an angle is given. Find the measure of **a.** a complement **b.** a supplement.

4. 24° a. 66° b. 156°
5. 45° a. 45° b. 135°
6. 126° a. none b. 54°
7. $b°$ a. $(90-b)°$ b. $(180-b)°$

8. a. Write an equation relating the measures of the angles shown at the right. $(3x+2)+(6x-2)=180$

b. Find the value of x. $x = 20$

c. Find the measure of the smaller angle. 62°

9. $\angle A$ and $\angle B$ are supplements. The measure of $\angle A$ is 10 more than 4 times the measure of $\angle B$. Write and solve an equation to find the measure of each angle.
$b+(4b+10)=180$ (equation) $m\angle A =$ 146° $m\angle B =$ 34°

Name

10. Write an expression to represent the measure of $\angle SUN$ in terms of p and q. $180 - (p + q)$

11. Use a protractor to draw a triangle with a 100° angle and a 35° angle. What is the measure of the third angle? 45°

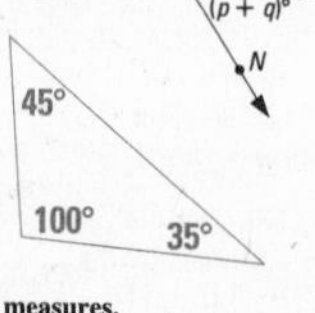

In 12–14, a. write an equation relating the angle measures. b. Find the value of the variable. c. Find the measures of any unknown angles.

12.

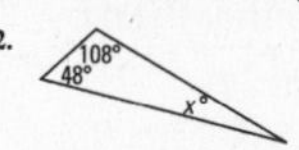

a. $x+48+108=180$
b. $x = 24$
c. 24°

13.

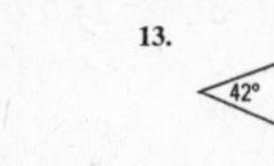

a. $2y + 42 = 180$
b. $y = 69$
c. 69°, 69°

14. a. $(3x + 8) + (5x - 2) + (7x - 6) = 180$
b. $x = 12$
c. 44°, 58°, 78°

In 15 and 16, find the angle measures.

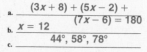

15. 16. *MNOP* is a square.

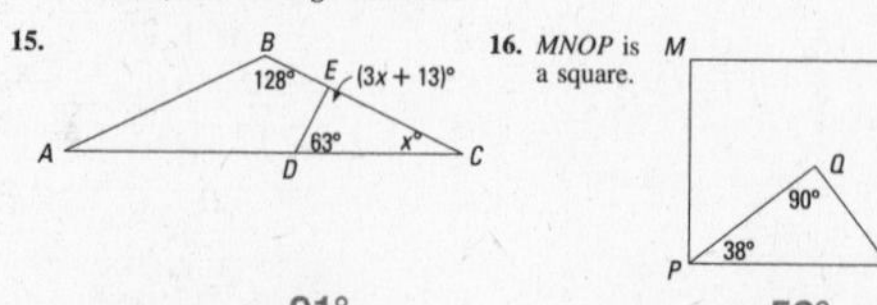

$m\angle CED =$ 91° $m\angle POQ =$ 52°
$m\angle BAC =$ 26° $m\angle QON =$ 38°

Name

LESSON MASTER 4-8 B **Questions on SPUR Objectives**

Properties Objective G: Use the Triangle Inequality to determine possible lengths of sides of triangles.

In 1–3, write an expression for the length of $\overline{YZ}$ in terms of a and b.

1. Z a X b Y — $a + b$

2. 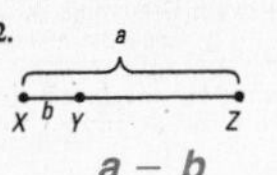 — $a - b$

3. 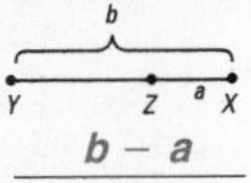 — $b - a$

4. Fill in the blanks.

a. $x <$ 53

b. $x >$ 9

c. 9 $< x <$ 53

In 5–10, tell whether the three numbers can be the lengths of sides in a triangle.

5. 3, 7, 9 yes

6. 4, 6, 4 yes

7. 2, 10, 14 no

8. 7, 17, 7 no

9. 12, 1, 13 no

10. 15, 3, 16 yes

11. In ΔBIG, $BG = 13.7$ and $IG = 30.4$. The length of BI must be between what two numbers? 16.7 and 44.1

12. Fill in the blanks with simplified expressions.

$2m + 9 < JK < 8m + 5$

Uses Objective J: Apply the Triangle Inequality in real situations.

13. Southcrest is 25 miles from Franklin and 48 miles from Granville. Is it possible that Franklin is 76 miles from Granville? Explain why or why not.

No; sample: by the Triangle Inequality, Franklin cannot be more than 73 miles from Granville.

Name

▸ LESSON MASTER 4-8 B *page 2*

In 14 and 15, assume there are direct paths between the buildings involved.

14. It takes Kirk 10 minutes to bike to Ramon's house and 22 minutes to bike to Matt's house. Assuming Matt bikes at the same speed, how long would it take for him to bike to Ramon's house?

between 12 and 32 min

15. Every morning Kate leaves her dormitory and walks to the library, then to Cragin Hall, and then back to the dormitory. The dormitory is 5 blocks from the library and 4 blocks from Cragin Hall. Make a sketch showing the locations of Kate's dormitory, the library, and Cragin Hall for each of the following scenarios. Samples are given.

a. Best-case scenario: Kate's trip is as short as possible. $CL = 1$

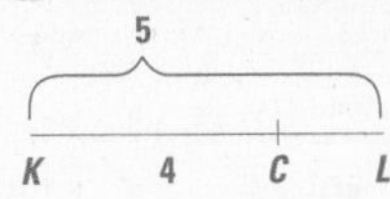

b. Worst-case scenario: Kate's trip is as long as possible. $CL = 9$

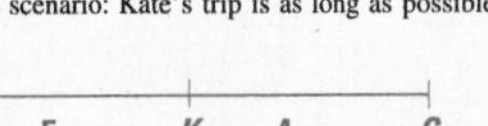

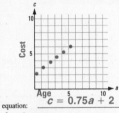

c. Kate's trip is somewhere between the best and worst cases.

$1 < CL < 9$

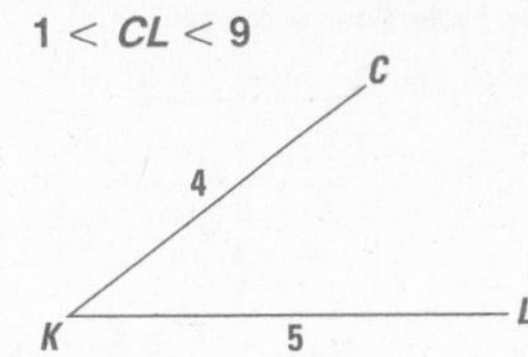

Name

LESSON MASTER 4-9 B **Questions on SPUR Objectives**

Representations Objective L: Graph equations of the forms $y = ax + b$ and $y = ax - b$ by making a table of values.

In 1–3, use the following information: At an all-you-can-eat buffet, the Pasta Emporium charges children under twelve \$2 plus \$0.50 for each year of age.

1. a. Complete the table showing the age of the child a and the cost of the child's meal c.

Age a	Cost c	(a, c)
0	2	(0, 2)
1	2.5	(1, 2.5)
2	3	(2, 3)
3	3.5	(3, 3.5)
4	4	(4, 4)
5	4.5	(5, 4.5)

b. Graph the ordered pairs (a, c).

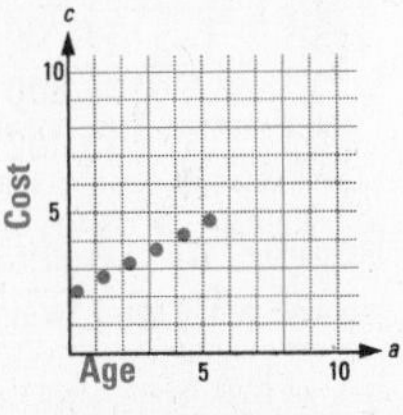

c. Write an equation that represents c in terms of a. $c = 0.5a + 2$

d. What would be a suitable domain for this graph? whole numbers < 12

In 2 and 3, use this information: Pasta Emporium decides to charge more for children. For each plan given below, complete the table, make a graph, and write an equation. Then describe how the graph is different from the first graph.

2. Plan A: Raise the basic charge to \$3, but continue to charge \$0.50 per year.

Age a	Cost c	(a, c)
0	3	(0, 3)
1	3.5	(1, 3.5)
2	4	(2, 4)
3	4.5	(3, 4.5)
4	5	(4, 5)
5	5.5	(5, 5.5)

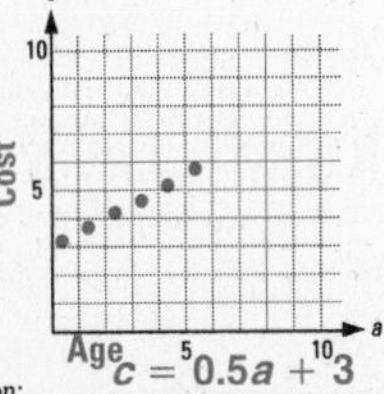

equation: $c = 0.5a + 3$

Sample: This graph is 1 unit "higher."

Name

▸ LESSON MASTER 4-9 B *page 2*

3. Plan B: Keep the basic charge at \$2, but charge \$0.75 per year.

Age a	Cost c	(a, c)
0	2	(0, 2)
1	2.75	(1, 2.75)
2	3.5	(2, 3.5)
3	4.25	(3, 4.25)
4	5	(4, 5)
5	5.75	(5, 5.75)

equation: $c = 0.75a + 2$

Sample: This graph is steeper.

4. The temperature was 5° and was dropping 2° each hour.

a. Complete the table.

Hours h	Temperature c
0	5
1	3
2	1
3	-1

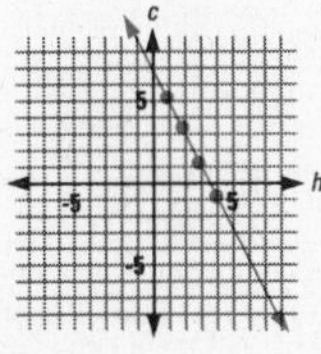

b. Draw the graph.

c. Write an equation to describe the temperature in terms of hours that have passed. $c = -2h + 5$

5. Consider the equation $y = -3x + 4$.

a. Make a table of values.

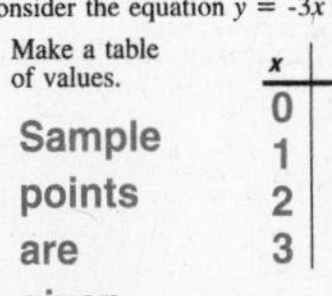

Sample points are given.

x	y
0	4
1	1
2	-2
3	-5

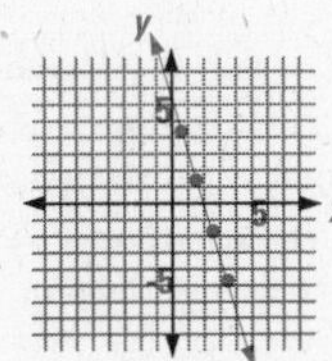

b. Draw the graph.

Name

LESSON MASTER 5-1 B **Questions on SPUR Objectives**

Representations Objective H: Graph horizontal and vertical lines.

In 1–3, an equation is given. a. Give the coordinates of three points that satisfy the equation. b. Graph the equation. Sample points are given.

1. $x = -2$	2. $y = 1$	3. $y = -3.5$
(-2, 3)	(0, 1)	(1, -3.5)
(-2, 0)	(-3, 1)	(-2, -3.5)
(-2, -1)	(3, 1)	(3, -3.5)

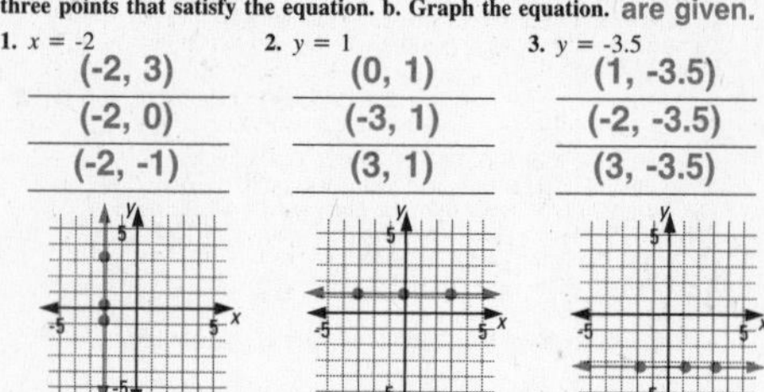

In 4–6, graph the given line and the point (-1, 4). Tell where (-1, 4) lies in relation to the line: *on, above, below, to the left,* or *to the right.*

4. $y = 4$ on
5. $y = 0$ above
6. $x = 4$ to left

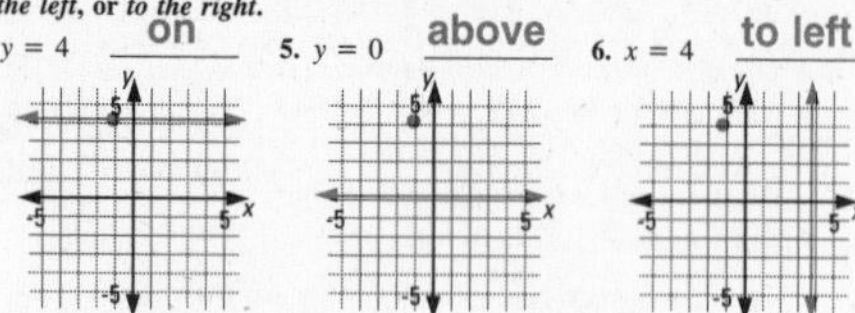

In 7–11, give an equation for the line shown or described.

7.
8.

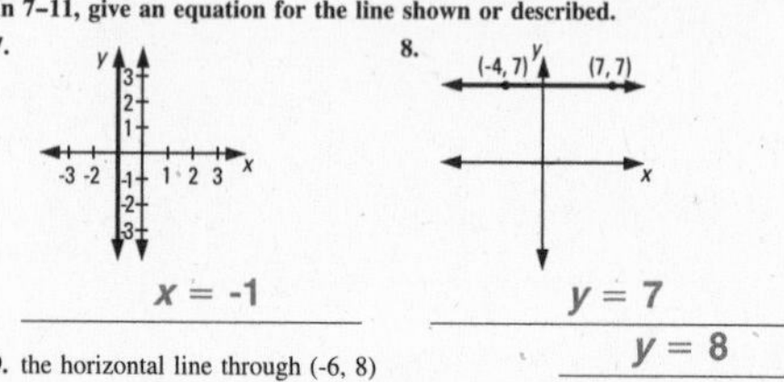

7. $x = -1$
8. $y = 7$

9. the horizontal line through (-6, 8) $y = 8$

Name

▶ **LESSON MASTER 5-1 B** *page 2*

10. the vertical line through (0, 4) $x = 0$

11. the line through (3, 3), (3, -4.1) and (3, 0) $x = 3$

Representations Objective I: Use graphs to solve problems involving linear equations.

12. Tommy owes his parents \$140. He gave them \$36 and promised to pay back another \$8 each week.

a. On a coordinate grid, graph $y = 140$ to represent the total amount Tommy owes his parents.

b. Write an equation to describe the amount y he has paid back after x weeks. $y = 8x + 36$

c. Graph your equation from Part **b** on the same coordinate grid as Part **a**.

d. Use the graph to estimate when Tommy's debt will be paid. in 13 weeks

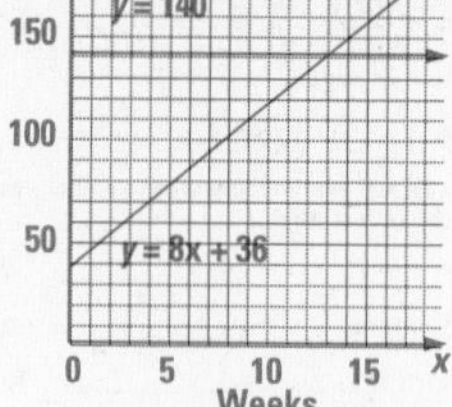

e. Check your answer to Part **d** by solving an equation. $x = 13$

13. Tonya purchased a sofa priced at \$600 and made a deposit of \$300. She agreed to pay off the balance with monthly payments of \$50.

a. On a coordinate grid, graph $y = 600$ to represent the total cost of the sofa.

b. Write an equation to describe the amount y she has paid after x months. $y = 300 + 50x$

c. Graph your equation from Part **b** on the same grid as Part **a**.

d. Use the graph to tell when Tonya will have completed her payments. in 6 months

e. Check your answer to Part **d** by solving an equation. $x = 6$

Name

LESSON MASTER 5-2 B **Questions on SPUR Objectives**

Representations Objective G: Use tables or spreadsheets to solve real-world problems involving linear situations.

1. At the Children's Museum, children can watch chicks and ducks hatch. Today there are 40 baby chicks and 25 ducks. Each day, 4 chicks and 7 ducks are expected to hatch.

a. Complete the table below.

DAY	CHICKS	DUCKS
0	40	25
1	44	32
2	48	39
3	52	46
4	56	53
5	60	60
6	64	67

b. At the end of 6 days, will there be more chicks or ducks? ducks

c. Write an equation for the number of chicks C in terms of the day d. $C = 40 + 4d$

d. Write an equation for the number of ducks D in terms of the day d. $D = 25 + 7d$

e. What equation could be used to find when there will be an equal number of chicks and ducks? $40 + 4d = 25 + 7d$

2. Marta uses a spreadsheet (shown on the next page) to compare the salaries between two companies that have offered her a job. The O'Connell Company offers \$29,000 the first year with annual raises of \$900. Tri-Tech, Inc. pays \$27,800 the first year and gives annual raises of \$1,200. The cells of the spreadsheet contain yearly salaries.

a. What formula could be used in cell B3? =B2+900

b. What formula could be used in cell C3? =C2+1200

c. Complete the spreadsheet.

Name

▶ **LESSON MASTER 5-2 B** *page 2*

	A	B	C
1	YEAR	O'CONNELL	TRI-TECH
2	1	29,000	27,800
3	2	29,900	29,000
4	3	30,800	30,200
5	4	31,700	31,400
6	5	32,600	32,600
7	6	33,500	33,800

d. Describe how the two jobs compare over a six-year period.
Sample: By the 6th year, Tri-Tech is paying more; total pay is more for O'Connell.

3. Over the years, the O'Connell Company has been switching from typewriters to computers. At one time the company had 815 typewriters which were wearing out at a rate of about 60 per year. At the same time, they had 500 computers and were adding 75 per year. Assume that the company continues buying computers and eliminating typewriters at the same rate.

a. Write an expression for the number of typewriters after y years. $815 - 60y$

b. Write an expression for the number of computers after y years. $500 + 75y$

c. Make a table and use it to find the number of years it takes for O'Connell to have an equal number of typewriters and computers.

d. Write an inequality of the form $y < k$ or $y > k$ to describe when there are more computers than typewriters. $y > 2$

Yr	Type.	Comp.
0	815	500
1	755	575
2	695	650
3	635	725
4	575	800
5	515	875
6	455	950
7	395	1025
8	335	1100

Name

LESSON MASTER 5-3 B Questions on SPUR Objectives

Skills Objective A: Solve linear equations of the form $ax + b = cx + d$.

1. a. Write the equation that is represented by this drawing.
$3w + 5 = 9w + 3$

b. Solve the equation to find the weight w of one box.
$\frac{1}{3}$ oz

In 2–7, solve the equation and check the result.

2. $m + 12 = 2m + 77$
$m = -65$
$-65 + 12 = 2(-65) + 77?$
$-53 = -53$

3. $7w = 2w + 45$
$w = 9$
$7 \cdot 9 = 2 \cdot 9 + 45?$
$63 = 63$

4. $5g + .6 = -3g - 4.4$
$g = -.625$
$5(-.625) + .6 = -3(-.625) - 4.4?$
$-2.525 = -2.525$

5. $\frac{1}{6}m + 33 = 5 - m$
$m = -24$
$\frac{1}{6}(-24) + 33 = 5 - (-24)?$
$29 = 29$

6. $7(8h - 3) + 2h = 72 - 4h$
$h = 1.5$
$7(8 \cdot 1.5 - 3) + 2(1.5) = 72 - 4(1.5)?$
$66 = 66$

7. $-3(a + 14) = 6(2a + 3)$
$a = -4$
$-3(-4 + 14) = 6(2 \cdot -4 + 3)?$
$-30 = -30$

Name

Properties Objective E: Apply and recognize properties associated with linear equations.

In 8 and 9, tell what should be done to both sides of the equation first in order to solve.

8. $10u + 16 = 5 - 5u$
Add $5u$ or $-10u$.

9. $7x + 18 = 20x$
Add $-7x$.

10. Fill in each blank with a number or operation to explain the steps in the solution shown below. Then complete the solution and check your result.

$1.6n + 4.2 = 0.7n + 6.9$ Add $-0.7n$ to each side.
$0.9n + 4.2 = 6.9$ Add -4.2 to each side.
$0.9n = 2.7$ Multiply each side by $\frac{1}{0.9}$.

Uses Objective F: Use linear equations of the form $ax + b = cx + d$ to solve real-world problems.

11. A mountain climber is injured. His partner radios for help, then the two begin to descend from the 12,500-foot mountain at a speed of about 200 feet per hour. The rescue team starts at an altitude of 6,500 feet and climbs 1,000 feet per hour.

a. Write an equation to show that the rescuers meet the climbers after h hours. (In other words, their altitudes are the same.)
$1{,}000h + 6{,}500 = -200h + 12{,}500$

b. How long does it take the rescuers to reach the climbers?
5 hours

c. At what height will they meet?
11,500 feet

12. Raul and Tom both wish to wrestle at the same weight. Raul, who weighs 148 pounds, plans to gain a pound a week. Tom who weighs 166 pounds, plans to lose two pounds a week.

a. Write an equation to tell when the boys will have reached the same weight.
$148 + w = 166 - 2w$

b. How long will it take the boys to reach the same weight?
6 weeks

c. At what common weight will the boys wrestle?
154 pounds

Name

LESSON MASTER 5-4 B Questions on SPUR Objectives

Uses Objective F: Use linear equations of the form $ax + b = cx + d$ to solve real-world problems.

Representations Objective I: Use graphs to solve problems involving linear expressions.

1. The graph below shows the price of buying a vase of roses at two florists. Each shop charges a certain amount for a vase and then adds an additional charge per rose.

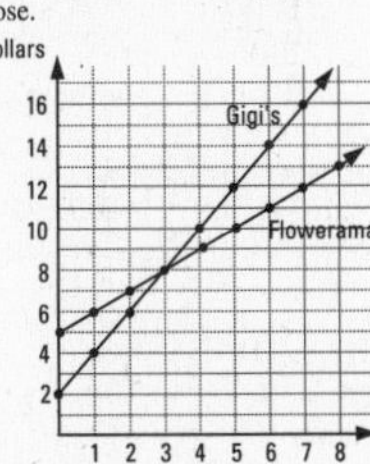

a. How much does an empty vase cost at Gigi's Flowers?
$2

b. Brad wants to send his fiancée a half-dozen roses. Which shop would have a lower price? How much lower?
Flowerama; $3

c. For how many roses do the two shops charge the same amount?
3 roses

d. For how many roses is Flowerama more expensive?
0, 1, and 2 roses

2. The graph below shows the estimated enrollment of two universities t years from now.

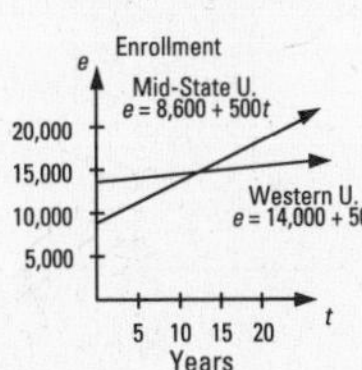

a. Use an equation to find in how many years the estimated enrollments will be equal. Use the graph to check your answer.
$8{,}600 + 500t = 14{,}000 + 50t$; 12 yr

b. When is Mid-State's estimated enrollment less than Western's?
up to 12 years from now

c. When is Mid-State's estimated enrollment greater than Western's?
more than 12 years from now

Name

3. Downtown Deli normally charges 55¢ for an onion roll. But they also offer the rolls at 15¢ each with the purchase of a pound of salami at $4.80.

Let r = the number of rolls purchased and c = cost.

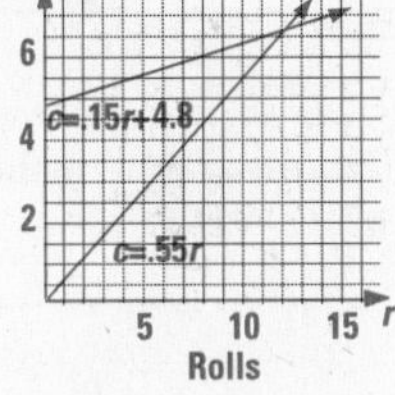

a. Write an equation describing the cost of r rolls at the regular price.
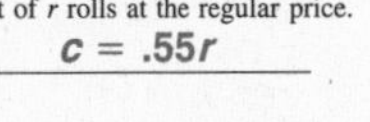
$c = .55r$

b. Write an equation describing the cost of r rolls with the purchase of a pound of salami.
$c = .15r + 4.8$

c. Graph the two equations from Parts **a** and **b** on the same grid.

d. Use your graph to tell when the cost of the rolls is the same with or without the salami.
for 12 rolls

e. What equation could be used to answer the question in Part **d**?
$.55r = .15r + 4.8$

f. Lucas needs 15 rolls. Is it cheaper to get the salami also?
yes

4. In Truetown, Bad Bart jumped aboard a freight train traveling at 25 mph. When the train was 50 miles from Truetown, Good Gus left Truetown, and followed the train doing 35 mph in his Stutz Wildcat.

Let r = the speed in mph and t = the time in hours.

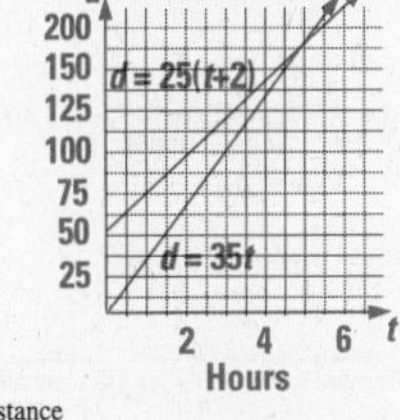

a. Write an equation describing Good Gus's distance from Truetown t hours after starting out.
$d = 35t$

b. Write an equation describing the distance of the train from Truetown t hours after Good Gus started out.
$d = 25(t + 2)$

c. Graph the two equations from Parts **a** and **b** on the same grid.

d. Use your graph to tell when Good Gus will catch up to the train. Then write and solve an equation to verify your answer.

after 5 hr	$35t = 25(t + 2)$	$t = 5$
answer in graph	equation	solution

Name

LESSON MASTER 5-5 B

Questions on SPUR Objectives

Representations Objective L: Given an equation, be able to use an automatic grapher to draw and interpret a graph.

In 1–3, use the window at the right.

1. Write two inequalities to describe this window.
$-6 \le x \le 6, -2 \le y \le 5$

2. As you move from $x = -5$ to $x = 1$ on the graph, what happens to the height of the graph?
It decreases.

3. What are the coordinates of the point where the graph crosses the y-axis? (0, 1)

4. What are the coordinates of the lowest point on the graph? (3, -1)

5. Describe a window that would show the lowest point in the center of the graph.
Sample: $-3 \le x \le 9, -5 \le y \le 3$

In 6–7, graph $y = x^2 - 4x - 12$ on an automatic grapher, using the given window. Sketch the graph, being sure to show the limits of the window and the axes, if they appear.

6. window: $-5 \le x \le 5$, $-5 \le y \le 5$

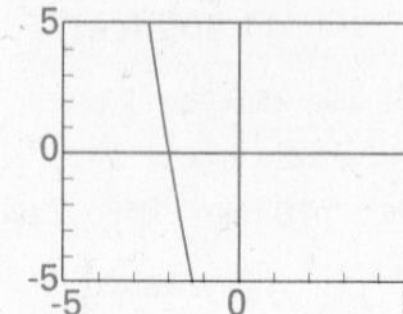

7. window: $-10 \le x \le 10$, $-20 \le y \le 40$

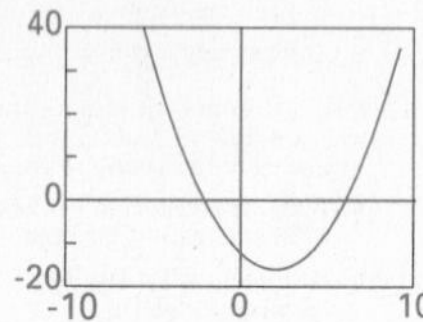

ALGEBRA © Scott, Foresman and Company

85 ▶

Name

▶ LESSON MASTER 5-5 B *page 2*

8. a. Use the window $-10 \le x \le 10$, $-10 \le y \le 10$, and graph the two equations $y = 2x$ and $y = x^2$. Sketch the graph.

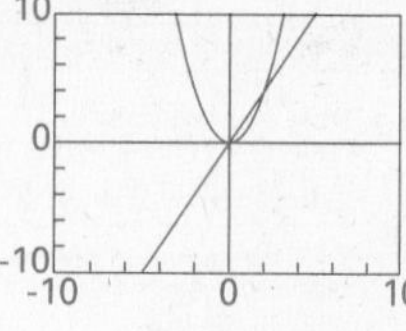

b. Use the graph to find a value of x for which $2x \ne x^2$.
Sample: $x = -3$

c. Use the graph to find a value of x for which $2x = x^2$
Sample: $x = 2$

9. a. Use the window $-15 \le x \le 15$, $-10 \le y \le 10$, and graph the two equations $y = 5 - x$ and $y = x - 5$. Sketch the graphs.

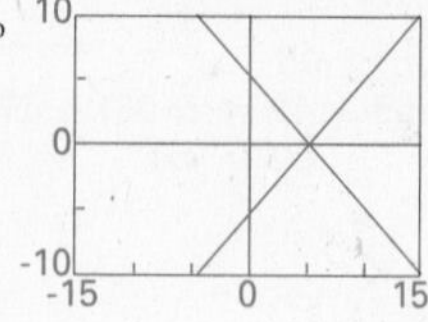

b. Use the graph to find a value of x for which $x - 5 \ne 5 - x$.
Sample: $x = 0$

c. Use the graph to find a value of x for which $x - 5 = 5 - x$.
$x = 5$

10. Use an automatic grapher to graph the two equations $y = -6x + 31$ and $y = .3x - 80$ on the same window of $-100 \le x \le 100$, $-100 \le y \le 100$.

a. Use the trace and zoom features to estimate the value of x for which $-6x + 31 = .3x - 80$. $x \approx 17.6$

b. For what values of x is $-6x + 31 < .3x - 80$? $x > 17.6$

ALGEBRA © Scott, Foresman and Company

86

Name

LESSON MASTER 5-6 B

Questions on SPUR Objectives

Skills Objective B: Solve linear inequalities of the form $ax + b < cx + d$.

1. Write an inequality to find the values of x that make $12x + 14$ less than $20x - 8$. $12x + 14 < 20x - 8$

In 2–5, solve and check. Sample checks are given.

2. $5a + 7 < 2a + 13$

$a < 2$
$5(2) + 7 = 2(2) + 13$
$5(0) + 7 < 2(0) + 13?$
$7 < 13$

3. $6x > 11x + 35$

$x < -7$
$6(-7) = 11(-7) + 35$
$6(-8) > 11(-8) + 35?$
$-48 > -53$

4. $6m + 8 + 2m \ge 4(3m + 2)$

$m \le 0$
$6(0) + 8 + 2(0) = 4(3 \cdot 0 + 2)$
$6(-1) + 8 + 2(-1) > 4(3 \cdot -1 + 2)?$
$0 > -4$

5. $-1.6e - 8 < 2.2e + 30$

$e > -10$
$-1.6(-10) - 8 = 2.2(-10) + 30$
$-1.6(0) - 8 < 2.2(0) + 30?$
$-8 < 30$

In 6 and 7, solve the inequality and graph all solutions on a number line.

6. $u + 19 \le 3u - 1$

7. $45 - 7b < 30 - 10b$

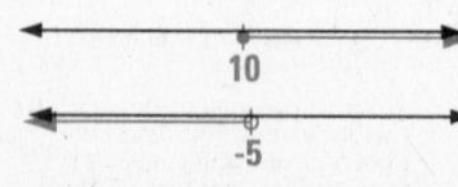

Properties Objective E: Apply and recognize properties associated with linear inequalities.

8. Solve for $6x - 10 > 18 - 2x$ as directed. Show your work. Student work is not shown.

a. Add $-6x$ to both sides. $-x > 3.5$

b. Add $2x$ to both sides. $x > 3.5$

9. Which solution method above do you prefer, and why?
Sample: Part b, because the sense of the inequality does not need to be reversed.

ALGEBRA © Scott, Foresman and Company

87 ▶

Name

▶ LESSON MASTER 5-6 B *page 2*

Uses Objective F: Use linear inequalities of the form $ax + b < cx + d$ to solve real-world problems.

10. To ship an order weighing 10 pounds or less, McGann's charges \$4 plus 90¢ per pound of merchandise. Northern Traders charges \$6 plus 50¢ per pound.

a. For what size order will the two shipping charges be the same?
5 pounds

b. Sketch a graph showing the two shipping charges over the interval $0 \le x \le 10$ pounds.

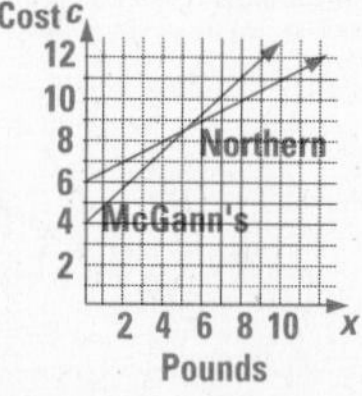

c. For what weight of merchandise does McGann's charge less?
less than 5 pounds

11. For a long-distance call, Dash charges 20¢ for the first minute plus 15¢ for each additional minute. AB&C charges 26¢ for the first minute plus 13¢ for each additional minute.

a. For what length of time will the two companies charge the same amount for a long-distance call?
3 minutes

b. Sketch a graph showing the two long-distance charges.

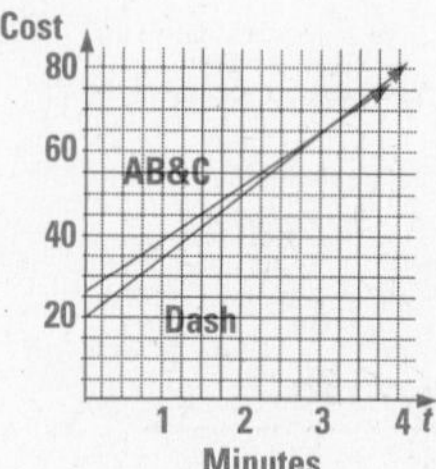

c. For what lengths of time does AB&C charge less?
more than 3 min

ALGEBRA © Scott, Foresman and Company

88

Name

LESSON MASTER 5-7 B

Questions on SPUR Objectives

Skills Objective D: Find equivalent forms of formulas and equations.

In 1–10, solve the formula for the given variable.

1. $C = K - 273$ for K
   $K = C + 273$

2. $d = 7w$ for w
   $w = \frac{d}{7}$

3. $p = 2a + b + c$ for a
   $a = \frac{p - b - c}{2}$

4. $C = \pi d$ for d
   $d = \frac{C}{\pi}$

5. $p = 2(\ell + w)$ for w
   $w = \frac{p}{2} - \ell$

6. $V = \frac{1}{3}Bh$ for B
   $B = \frac{3V}{h}$

7. $F + V = E + 2$ for E
   $E = F + V - 2$

8. $I = prt$ for p
   $p = \frac{I}{rt}$

9. $s = \frac{n}{2}(f + \ell)$ for f
   $f = \frac{2s - \ell n}{n}$

10. $S = (n - 2)180$ for n
    $n = \frac{S}{180} + 2$

11. The formula $C = p\left(\frac{\ell w}{5000}\right)$ gives the cost C of fertilizing a lawn with length ℓ ft and width w ft, where p = price per bag of fertilizer. Solve $C = p\left(\frac{\ell w}{5000}\right)$ for w.
    $w = \frac{5000C}{p\ell}$

In 12–17, solve the equation for y.

12. $9x + y = 15$
    $y = -9x + 15$

13. $8 = x - y$
    $y = x - 8$

14. $12 = 6x - 3y$
    $y = 2x - 4$

15. $-5x + 2y = 7$
    $y = \frac{5}{2}x + \frac{7}{2}$

Name

Properties Objective E: Apply and recognize properties associated with linear sentences.

16. Tech Tasks puts a customer's snapshot prints onto CDs for use with CD-Rom. The formula $C = 2.5p + 14$ relates the cost in dollars C to the number of prints p.
    a. Find the cost for 29 prints. **\$86.50**
    b. Solve $C = 2.5p + 14$ for p. $p = \frac{C - 14}{2.5}$
    c. Use your answer to find the number of prints in an order that cost \$59. **18 prints**

17. Fill in the blanks to explain the steps taken to solve $T = .15(C - S)$ for C.

    $T = .15(C - S)$
    $T = .15C - .15S$ — **Distributive** Property
    $T + .15S = .15C$ — **Add .15S** to each side.
    $\frac{T}{.15} + S = C$ — **Multiply** each side by $\frac{1}{.15}$.

Review Objective A, Lesson 3-7

In 18–23, write the expression without parentheses.

18. $12\left(\frac{7x}{12} + \frac{9x}{4}\right)$ — $12 \cdot \frac{7x}{12} + 12 \cdot \frac{9x}{4}$

19. $-18\left(\frac{4u}{9} + \frac{11u}{6}\right)$ — $-18 \cdot \frac{4u}{9} + -18 \cdot \frac{11u}{6}$

20. $-8\left(\frac{5e}{3} + \frac{.3e}{8}\right)$ — $-8 \cdot \frac{5e}{3} + -8 \cdot \frac{.3e}{8}$

21. $5\left(v + \frac{v}{5}\right)$ — $5 \cdot v + 5 \cdot \frac{v}{5}$

22. $100(.3c + .15c + .05c)$ — $100 \cdot .3c + 100 \cdot .15c + 100 \cdot .05c$

23. $.5(8m + 12m + 10m)$ — $.5 \cdot 8m + .5 \cdot 12m + .5 \cdot 10m$

Name

LESSON MASTER 5-8 B

Questions on SPUR Objectives

Skills Objective A: Clear fractions or multiply through by a fraction to solve linear equations of the form $ax + b = cx + d$.

In 1–6, solve the equation.

1. $\frac{3a}{4} + 4 = 13$
   $a = 12$

2. $\frac{4}{5}h + \frac{1}{6} = \frac{11}{30}$
   $h = \frac{1}{4}$

3. $\frac{5x}{4} - 8 = 3 + \frac{3x}{4}$
   $x = 22$

4. $\frac{1}{9}x + \frac{5}{6} = \frac{1}{2}x - \frac{1}{3}$
   $x = 3$

5. $6m - .3 = 2.8m + 2.9$
   $m = 1$

6. $.5(2x + 7) = .2x - 2.1$
   $x = -7$

Skills Objective A: Clear fractions or multiply through by a fraction to solve linear inequalities of the form $ax + b < cx + d$.

In 7–12, solve the inequality.

7. $\frac{7b}{8} + 4 \leq 3b - \frac{1}{4}$
   $b \geq 2$

8. $4 - \frac{w}{3} < w$
   $w > 3$

9. $\frac{a}{2} + \frac{a}{5} - \frac{3}{10} > \frac{4a}{5} + \frac{1}{4}$
   $a < -\frac{11}{2}$

10. $400n + 600 \geq 1500 - 200n$
    $n \geq \frac{3}{2}$

11. $1.3a + 1 < 2 - .7a$
    $a < .5$

12. $55y + 44 > 22y + 66$
    $y > \frac{2}{3}$

Properties Objective E: Apply and recognize properties associated with linear sentences.

In 13 and 14, write the equation or inequality that results from multiplying through by the given number.

13. $\frac{11}{12}u + \frac{1}{4} = 8$ Multiply both sides by 12. — $11u + 3 = 96$

14. $1.66 - 3.8r > .92 + .95r$ Multiply both sides by 100. — $166 - 380r > 92 + 95r$

Name

15. Consider the equation $\frac{x}{3} + \frac{5}{6} = \frac{5}{2}$.
    a. Multiplying through by 6 is an application of which property? **Multiplication Property of Equality**
    b. Give two other numbers by which you could multiply through. **Sample: 12** **Sample: 18**

16. Tell what to multiply each side by to solve more easily. **Samples are given.**
    a. $12{,}000e + 16{,}000 = 19{,}000e - 3{,}000$ — $\frac{1}{1{,}000}$
    b. $1.6 - .5u \leq 2.2$ — **10**
    c. $\frac{1}{5}(12y + 7) > \frac{3y}{4}$ — **20**

Uses Objective F: Use linear equations of the form $ax + b = cx + d$ and linear inequalities of the form $ax + b < cx + d$ to solve real-world problems.

17. For an upcoming election, $\frac{1}{4}$ of the registered voters support Candidate A, $\frac{2}{5}$ support Candidate B, and the rest, 7,700, are undecided.
    a. Write an equation to find the number of registered voters. $\frac{1}{4}v + \frac{2}{5}v + 7{,}700 = v$
    b. How many registered voters are there? **22,000 reg. vot.**
    c. Check your answer to Part **b** by finding the number of registered voters who support each candidate. **5,500 for A; 8,800 for B**

18. In Adeline County, 22% of the elementary-school children attend Jackson School, 18% attend Traynor School, and 240 students attend Claridge School. The students at these three schools make up more than 50% of the county's elementary-school children.
    a. Write an inequality to describe this situation. $.22c + .18c + 240 > .5c$
    b. How many elementary-school children live in Adeline County? **fewer than 2400**
    c. How many children attend the other schools in Adeline County? **fewer than 1200**

Name

LESSON MASTER 5-9 B

Questions on SPUR Objectives

Skills Objective C: Use chunking to simplify or evaluate expressions and to solve equations.

1. If $6x = 5$, find the value of
   a. $12x$. **10** b. $60x$. **50** c. $3x$. **2.5**
2. If $2c = 3.3$, find the value of $10c + 2$. **18.5**
3. If $25y + 4 = 817$, find the value of $25y + 5$. **818**
4. If $.77p - .3 = 21.9$, find the value of $10(.77p - .3)$. **219**
5. If $3n = 8$, find the value of $(3n)^2$. **64**
6. If $5c + 4 = 19$, find the value of $25c + 20$. **95**
7. If $12t - 4a = 16$, find the value of $3t - a$. **4**
8. If $2s = 3$, find the value of $(2s)^3 + 8$. **35**

In 9–20, use chunking to simplify.

9. $3(2a + 7) + 6(2a + 7)$ — $18a + 63$
10. $7(r + 6) - 10(r + 6)$ — $-3r - 18$
11. $-2(x^2 + 1) + 4(x^2 + 1) - 8(x^2 + 1)$ — $-6x^2 - 6$
12. $9\sqrt{6} + 3\sqrt{6} - \sqrt{6} - 4\sqrt{6}$ — $7\sqrt{6}$
13. $\frac{2}{7m - 4} + \frac{5}{7m - 4}$ — $\frac{7}{7m - 4}$
14. $\frac{-8}{5abc} + \frac{4}{5abc}$ — $\frac{-4}{5abc}$
15. $\frac{8}{12d - 1} - \frac{11}{12d - 1} + \frac{5}{12d - 1}$ — $\frac{2}{12d - 1}$
16. $\frac{6u + 1}{d - 2} + \frac{2u}{d - 2} - \frac{5u + 3}{d - 2}$ — $\frac{3u - 2}{d - 2}$
17. $\frac{e + 9}{8} \cdot \frac{5}{e + 9}$ — $\frac{5}{8}$
18. $\frac{x^2 + 7}{3} \cdot \frac{9}{x^2 + 7}$ — 3
19. $\frac{4}{3(b - 5)} \cdot \frac{5(b - 5)}{9}$ — $\frac{20}{27}$
20. $\frac{2}{\sqrt{7} + 2} \cdot \frac{3(\sqrt{7} + 2)}{10}$ — $\frac{3}{5}$

Name

► LESSON MASTER 5-9 B *page 2*

In 21–28, solve the equation.

21. $2(4a + 6) + 6(4a + 6) = 80$ — $a = 1$
22. $(2a + 3)^2 = 49$ — $a = 2$ or $a = -5$
23. $(x + 3)^2 = 36$ — $x = 3$ or $x = -9$
24. $(m - 8)^2 = 121$ — $m = 19$ or $m = -3$
25. $(u^2)^2 = 625$ — $u = 5$ or $u = -5$
26. $3(x^2 + 1) - 4(x^2 + 1) = -26$ — $x = 5$ or $x = -5$
27. $10(w + 1) - 5(w + 1) + (w + 1) = -42$ — $w = -8$
28. $12(2w^2 + 4) - 5(2w^2 + 4) - (2w^2 + 4) = 24$ — $w = 0$
29. If $\sqrt{x + 3} = 81$, what is the value of $x + 3$? **6,561**
30. If $\sqrt{x + 3} = 81$, what is the value of x? **6,558**
31. If $\sqrt{x + 3} = 81$, what is the value of $3\sqrt{x + 3}$? **243**
32. If $14y + 21 = 17$, what is the value of $2y + 3$? $\frac{17}{7}$

Name

LESSON MASTER 6-1 B

Questions on SPUR Objectives

Skills Objective A: Divide real numbers and algebraic fractions.

In 1–15, fill in the blanks or boxes.

1. $\frac{7}{a} =$ **7** $\div$ **a**
2. $-5 \div 8 =$ **-5** $\cdot$ $\frac{1}{8}$
3. $\frac{5}{12} =$ **5** $\cdot$ $\frac{1}{12}$
4. $\frac{x}{y} =$ **x** $\cdot$ $\frac{1}{y}$
5. $b \cdot \frac{1}{3} = \frac{\boxed{b}}{\boxed{3}}$
6. $c \cdot \frac{1}{e} = \frac{\boxed{c}}{\boxed{e}}$
7. $10 \cdot \frac{1}{7} = \frac{\boxed{10}}{\boxed{7}}$
8. $\frac{\frac{5}{6}}{\frac{2}{3}} =$ $\frac{5}{6}$ $\div$ $\frac{2}{3}$
9. $\frac{\frac{e}{2r}}{\frac{w}{x}} =$ $\frac{e}{2r}$ $\cdot$ $\frac{x}{w}$
10. $\frac{1}{2} \div \frac{7}{8} =$ $\frac{1}{2}$ $\cdot$ $\frac{8}{7}$
11. $\frac{a}{b} \div \frac{2}{7c} =$ $\frac{a}{b}$ $\cdot$ $\frac{7c}{2}$
12. $\frac{1}{m} \div -27 = \frac{1}{m} \cdot$ $-\frac{1}{27}$
13. $\frac{s}{\frac{x}{y}} =$ **s** $\cdot$ $\frac{y}{x}$
14. $3d \div \frac{4}{7 + u} = \frac{3d}{\boxed{\frac{4}{7 + u}}}$
15. $21 \cdot \frac{3y}{8} = \frac{\boxed{21}}{\boxed{\frac{8}{3y}}}$

Multiple choice. **Tell which expression is *not* equivalent to the others.**

16. (a) $\frac{-6}{-5}$ (b) $-\frac{6}{5}$ (c) $\frac{-6}{5}$ (d) $\frac{6}{-5}$ — **a**
17. (a) $\frac{x}{a + b}$ (b) $x\left(\frac{1}{a + b}\right)$ (c) $\frac{1}{x}(a + b)$ (d) $x \div (a + b)$ — **c**

Name

► LESSON MASTER 6-1 B *page 2*

In 18–29 simplify.

18. $\frac{1}{6} \div \frac{4}{9}$ — $\frac{3}{8}$
19. $\frac{7}{8} \div 10$ — $\frac{7}{80}$
20. $\frac{a}{b} \div \frac{2a}{b}$ — $\frac{1}{2}$
21. $-y \div \frac{3}{m}$ — $-\frac{my}{3}$
22. $\frac{3 + n}{8} \div \frac{3 + n}{10}$ — $\frac{5}{4}$
23. $\frac{7}{3bc} \div \frac{2b}{5c}$ — $\frac{35}{6b^2}$
24. $\frac{\frac{3}{4}}{\frac{1}{12}}$ — 9
25. $\frac{\frac{y}{6}}{\frac{y}{12}}$ — 2
26. $\frac{m}{\frac{2}{m}}$ — $\frac{m^2}{2}$
27. $\frac{\frac{7}{b}}{ac}$ — $\frac{7}{abc}$
28. $\frac{-4\frac{1}{3}}{\frac{5}{6}}$ — $-\frac{26}{5}$
29. $\frac{\frac{\pi}{6}}{\frac{2\pi}{3}}$ — $\frac{1}{4}$

Review Objective J, Lesson 3-4

For 30–33, use the grid at the right.

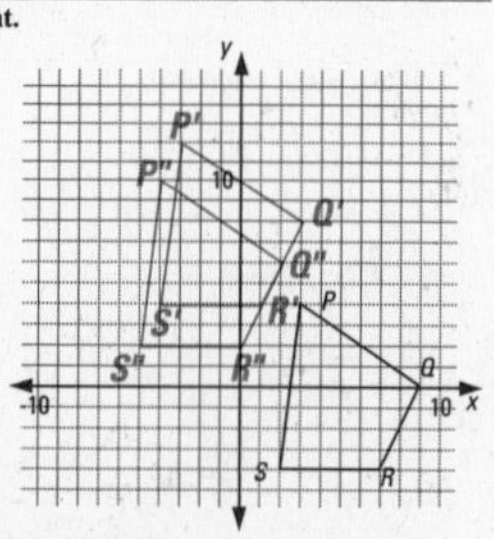

30. Graph $P'Q'R'S'$, the image of sliding quadrilateral $PQRS$ 6 units left and 8 units up.
31. Slide $P'Q'R'S'$ 1 unit left and 2 units down. Label the image $P''Q''R''S''$.
32. Give the coordinates of Q''. **(2, 6)**
33. The coordinates of P and R are (3, 4) and (7, -4), respectively. Explain how to find the coordinates of each point without using a graph.
    a. point P' Add -6 to x-coordinate and 8 to y-coordinate and get (-3, 12).
    b. point R'' Add -7 to x-coordinate and 6 to y-coordinate and get (0, 2).

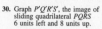

Name

LESSON MASTER 6-2 B Questions on SPUR Objectives

Uses Objective E: Use the rate model for division.

1. Automobile racing first appeared as a sport in 1894. Only 15 of the 21 starting vehicles completed the race. It took the winner about 5.2 hours to complete the 125-km run between Paris and Rouen, France.
   a. What was the winner's average speed in kilometers per hour? $\approx$ 24 km/h
   b. How long did it take the winning car to travel 1 kilometer? $\approx$ 2.5 min

2. During a meteor shower, some meteors approach the earth's atmosphere at speeds of 95 kilometers per second. Give the reciprocal rate and explain its meaning.
   $\frac{1}{95}$ second/km; it takes $\frac{1}{95}$ second for the meteor to travel 1 km.

3. Explain how considering a rate of $\frac{12 \text{ miles}}{0 \text{ seconds}}$ illustrates that dividing by zero is impossible.
   Sample: To travel 12 mi in 0 sec means you are in two places at one time.

In 4–13, calculate a rate for the situation described.

4. Clarissa drove 135 miles in 3 hours. 45 mph
5. The car traveled 315 miles on 15 gallons of gasoline. 21 mi/gal
6. In 15 almonds there are about 90 calories. 6 cal/alm.
7. The roast weighed 5.6 pounds and cost $21.22. $3.79/lb
8. Craig answered 186 questions in 12 minutes. 15.5 ques./min
9. There were 19,500 bushels of corn grown on 300 acres of farmland. 65 bu/acre
10. The tree grew 18 feet in 5 years. 3.6 ft/yr
11. On January 8, 26 inches of snow fell in 6 hours. $4\frac{1}{3}$ in./hr

Name

12. In 1990, the population of Alaska was 550,403 and its area was 656,424 square miles. Give two rates suggested by this information. .84 per./mi^2; 1.19 mi^2/per.
13. Mr. Santos stuffed 4200 envelopes in 3 hours. Give two rates, one using hours and one using minutes. 1400 env./hr; $23.\overline{3}$ env./min
14. For each situation, give a rate.
   a. The committee made 144 bean bags in 6 hours. 24 b.b./hr
   b. The committee made 200 bean bags in h hours. $\frac{200}{h}$ b.b./hr
   c. The committee made b bean bags in $\frac{1}{2}$ hour. $2b$ bb./hr
15. A 20-oz jar of lotion costs $4.09 and a 12-oz jar costs $2.49.
   a. Find the unit cost (cost per ounce) for 20 ounces. $.2045/oz
   b. Find the unit cost of the smaller bottle. $.2075/oz
   c. Which is the better buy? 20-oz jar
16. If it takes 7 minutes to call the names of 100 graduates, how long will it take to call the names of 448 graduates? $\approx$31 min

In 17–19, give the density (weight per volume) of each item.

		WEIGHT	VOLUME	DENSITY
17.	aluminum	8,097 grams	3,000 cubic centimeters	2.699 g/cm^3
18.	copper	4,928 grams	550 cubic centimeters	8.96 g/cm^3
19.	gold	4,338 grams	225 cubic centimeters	19.28 g/cm^3

20. Which is faster, typing $5p$ pages in $4h$ hours or $4p$ pages in $3h$ hours? Explain your answer.
   $4p$ pages in $3h$ hr; $\frac{5p}{4h} = 1.25\frac{p}{h}$ and $\frac{4p}{3h} = 1.33\frac{p}{h}$; $1.33 > 1.25$; so $4p$ pages in $3h$ hr is faster.
21. Which is less expensive, $6c$ cases of juice for $10 or $4c$ cases of juice for $6? Explain your answer.
   $4c$ cases for \$6; $\frac{\$10}{6c} = 1.6\overline{6}\frac{\$}{c}$ and $\frac{\$6}{4c} = 1.50\frac{\$}{c}$; $1.5 < 1.\overline{66}$; so $4c$ cases for \$6 is less expensive.

Name

LESSON MASTER 6-3 B Questions on SPUR Objectives

Vocabulary

1. There are 14 teachers for 280 students. What is the ratio of teachers to students? $\frac{1}{20}$
2. Out of 26 kindergartners, 15 are girls. What is the ratio of girls to boys? $\frac{15}{11}$
3. A farm has 800 acres of corn and 2,000 acres of wheat. What is the ratio of corn to wheat? $\frac{2}{5}$
4. In a survey, 125 people out of 300 said they like spring best. What ratio is this? $\frac{5}{12}$

Uses Objective F: Use ratios to compare two quantities.

5. *Multiple choice.* Which of the following is (are) *not* equal to the ratio of 5 to 4? c, d, e
   (a) $\frac{20}{16}$ (b) $\frac{5x}{4x}$ (c) $\frac{4}{5}$
   (d) 80% (e) 400 to 500 (f) 30 ft to 24 ft
6. *Multiple choice.* Which of the following is (are) *not* equal to the ratio of a to b? c
   (a) $\frac{a}{b}$ (b) $\frac{ax}{bx}$ (c) $100b$ to $100a$ (d) a miles to b miles
7. At the pool, there were 118 swimmers in the morning, 420 in the afternoon, and 258 in the evening. What is the ratio of morning swimmers to all swimmers? $\frac{59}{398}$
8. At Central Electronics, the ratio of black-and-white TVs to all TVs is 1 to 24. What is the ratio of color TVs to all TVs? $\frac{23}{24}$
9. During his 17 years in the major leagues, Lou Gehrig was at bat 8,001 times and made 2,721 hits. Give his *batting average*, the ratio of hits to times at bat, as a decimal rounded to the nearest thousandth. 0.340
10. The children's section of a library has 8,410 books, of which 3,145 are fiction. The adult section has 98,875 books and 27,218 of them are fiction. Which section has more fiction books in relation to the total number of books in the section? children's

Name

11. A punch recipe calls for 3 parts juice, 2 parts soda, and 3 parts sherbet. How much of each ingredient is needed for 2 gallons of punch? (1 gallon = 16 cups)
   12c juice, 8c soda, 12c sherbet
12. In a "taste-test," 77 people out of 120 preferred smooth peanut butter to crunchy. Out of 4,000 jars of peanut butter purchased, how many were probably smooth? 2,567 jars

Uses Objective H: Solve percent problems in real situations.

In 13–18, give a ratio comparing the first quantity to the second. Then give the ratio as a percent.

13. 16 questions correct out of 20 $\frac{4}{5}$ 80%
14. 2,044 voters out of 6,820 for Candidate A $\frac{511}{1705}$ $\approx$30%
15. $56 discount on a coat regularly priced at $224 $\frac{1}{4}$ 25%
16. 2 hours for homework and 30 minutes for practicing $\frac{4}{1}$ 400%
17. 3 defective light bulbs out of 500 tested $\frac{3}{500}$ 0.6%
18. 64 germinated seeds out of 70 planted $\frac{32}{35}$ $\approx$91%
19. According to the 1900 census, the U.S. population was 76,212,168. Find the percent of the U.S. population that lived in each of these states.
   a. Iowa 2,231,853 $\approx$ 2.9%
   b. New York 7,268,894 $\approx$ 9.5%
   c. Louisiana 1,381,625 $\approx$ 1.8%
20. According to the 1990 census, the U.S. population was 248,709,873. Find the percent of the U.S. population that lived in each of these states.
   a. Iowa 2,776,755 $\approx$ 1.1%
   b. New York 17,990,455 $\approx$ 7.2%
   c. Louisiana 4,219,973 $\approx$ 1.7%
21. An electronic note pad originally costing $259 is on sale for $207.20. After tax is added, the price is $223.78.
   a. What is the percent of discount? 20%
   b. What is the percent of tax? 8%

Name

LESSON MASTER 6-4 B Questions on SPUR Objectives

Uses Objective G: Calculate relative frequencies or probabilities in situations with a finite number of equally likely outcomes.

1. A fair six-sided die was tossed 60 times. The number 5 came up 13 times.
   a. What was the relative frequency of tossing 5? $\frac{13}{60}$
   b. What is the probability of tossing 5? $\frac{1}{6}$
   c. Are your answers to Parts **a** and **b** the same? Explain why this is the case.
   No; sample: Relative frequency is found by experimentation; probability is deduced from assumptions.

2. In Franklin Heights, 1,300 of the 4,200 residents bought season passes to the swimming pool. Give the relative frequency of residents who bought passes
   a. as a fraction. $\frac{13}{42}$ b. as a percent. $\approx 31\%$

3. In 1993, it was estimated that out of 91,238,000 households in the United States that had television sets, 1,862,000 had only black-and-white television sets.
   a. What was the relative frequency, as a percent, of households with only black-and-white television sets? $\approx 2\%$
   b. How many households had color sets? 89,376,000 hh.
   c. What was the relative frequency, as a percent, of households with only color television sets? $\approx 98\%$

4. A survey asked students to name their favorite class. Give the relative frequency, as a fraction, of students who like art best if
   a. 68 students were polled and 59 did *not* pick art. $\frac{9}{68}$
   b. 187 students were polled and 161 did *not* pick art. $\frac{26}{187}$
   c. 275 students were polled and *x* did *not* pick art. $\frac{275 - x}{275}$
   d. *s* students were polled and *n* did *not* pick art. $\frac{s - n}{s}$

Name

5. A teacher filled a box with 700 yellow and 400 green centimeter cubes. A student randomly grabbed a handful of 22 cubes and found that 16 were yellow.
   a. Give the probability of randomly selecting a yellow cube. $\frac{7}{11}$
   b. Give the student's relative frequency of randomly selecting a yellow cube. $\frac{8}{11}$

6. Describe the complement of each event.
   a. Toss a number cube and get a number greater than 4.
   Toss a number cube and get a number less than or equal to 4.
   b. The lake is frozen.
   The lake is not frozen.
   c. The name of a state begins with a vowel.
   The name of a state begins with a consonant.

7. Music Boosters sold 814 raffle tickets. One ticket will be drawn at random, and the winner will receive tickets to a concert. Rose bought 12 tickets. Let the event E = Rose wins and S = set of outcomes. Find each of the following.
   a. $N(E)$ 12
   b. $N(S)$ 814
   c. $P(E)$ $\frac{6}{407}$
   d. P(Rose does not win.) $\frac{401}{407}$

8. A card is drawn at random from a regular deck. Find each of the following.
   a. P(four) $\frac{1}{13}$
   b. P(four of diamonds) $\frac{1}{52}$
   c. P(four, five, six, seven, or eight) $\frac{5}{13}$
   d. P(spade) $\frac{1}{4}$

9. Consider tossing a die. Give an example of an event
   a. with probability 0. Sample: tossing a 7
   b. with probability 1. Sample: tossing a number less than 7

Name

LESSON MASTER 6-5 B Questions on SPUR Objectives

Skills Objective B: Solve percent problems.

1. 24 out of 200 is what percent? 12%
2. What is 7% of 613? 42.91
3. 2.6 is what percent of 9.6? $\approx 27\%$
4. 19% of what number is 57? 300
5. What is 14.3% of 400? 57.2
6. 84 is what percent of 56? 150%
7. $2\frac{1}{2}\%$ of what number is 75? 3,000
8. What is 0.7% of $42,000? $294
9. 9 is what percent of 14,000? $\approx 0.06\%$
10. $3\frac{1}{3}\%$ of 600 is what number? 20
11. 7.44% of what number is 18.6? 250
12. What is 475% of 88? 418

Uses Objective H: Solve percent problems in real situations.

13. Last year 42% of the students at Roosevelt rode the bus. If there were 350 students, how many rode the bus? 147 students

14. Refer to the headline below.

CITY SCHOLARSHIPS AWARDED TO
12% OF SENIOR CLASS
36 Students Proudly Accept Grants

How many students are in the senior class? 300 students

15. About 2.2% of Tennessee's total area is water. The total area of Tennessee is 42,146 square miles.
   a. What is the water area in Tennessee? ≈ 927 mi²
   b. What is the land area in Tennessee? $\approx 41{,}219$ mi²

Name

16. Between 1980 and 1990 the population of Columbus grew 12%.
   a. *Fill in the blank.* If the 1980 population was P, then the 1990 population was $1.12P$
   b. The 1990 population of Columbus was 632,910. Write an equation and find the 1980 population.
   $1.12P = 632{,}910$ (equation) 565,098 (population)

17. Between 1980 and 1990 Baltimore's population dropped 6.4%.
   a. *Fill in the blank.* If the 1980 population was P, then the 1990 population was $0.936P$
   b. The 1990 population of Baltimore was 736,014. Write an equation and find the 1980 population.
   $0.936P = 736{,}014$ (equation) 786,340 (population)

18. The total cost of head phones, including 7% sales tax, was $35.15. What was the price of the head phones without tax? $32.85

19. A coat is on sale for 40% off. The sale price is $172.80. What is the regular price? $288

20. During the summer, the population of Golden Beach Shores increased 32% to 1,023. What was the population during the other seasons? 775

21. Mrs. Jin invested $4,500 in bonds. After 1 year, her investment was worth $5017.50. By what percent did her investment grow? 11.5%

22. In a 14-gram serving (1 tablespoon) of a certain brand of mayonnaise, there are 11 grams of fat. What percent of the mayonnaise is fat? $\approx 78.6\%$

23. In an 8th-grade class, 8 students have birthdays in fall, 6 in winter, 7 in spring, and 7 in summer. What percent of the students do not have summer birthdays? 75%

24. The figure at the right shows two rectangles. What percent of the larger rectangle is shaded? 16%

Name

LESSON MASTER 6-6 B **Questions on SPUR Objectives**

Representations Objective J: Find probabilities involving geometric regions.

In 1 and 2, give the probability that the spinner will land in region X.

1\.

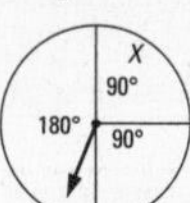

$\frac{1}{4}$, or 25%

2\.

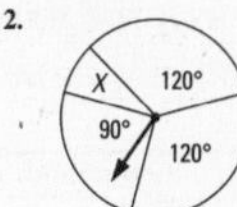

$\frac{1}{12}$, or $8\frac{1}{3}$%

In 3–5, the target at the right is made up of circles with radii of 10, 20, and 30 cm.

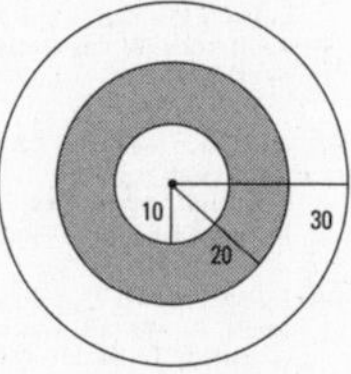

3\. Find the area of each circle.
100π, 400π, 900π in.^{2}

4\. Find the area of the shaded ring.
300π in.^{2}

5\. If a dart thrown at random hits the target, what is the probability that it will land in

a. the smallest circle? $\frac{1}{9}$, or ≈ 11%

b. the shaded ring? $\frac{1}{3}$, or ≈ 33%

c. the outermost ring? $\frac{5}{9}$, or ≈ 56%

6\. The land area of the United States is about 3,536,000 square miles and the water surface area is about 251,000 square miles. If a meteor hits the United States, what is the probability that it will

a. fall on land? $\frac{3,285}{3,536}$, or ≈ 93%

b. fall on water? $\frac{251}{3,536}$, or ≈ 7%

Name

7\. A park 200 ft by 300 ft contains a fountain 60 ft in diameter. Kelly, a sky diver, parachutes into the park. If Kelly lands at random, what is the probability she will land in the fountain?

$\frac{900\pi}{60,000}$, or ≈ 4.7%

8\. An electric clock with a second hand is stopped by a power failure. What is the probability that the second hand stopped between the following two numerals?

a. 5 and 6 $\frac{1}{12}$, or ≈ 8.3%

b. 3 and 6 $\frac{1}{4}$, or 25%

c. 7 and 12 $\frac{5}{12}$, or ≈ 41.7%

9\. The route from Mr. Santiago's office to his home is shown below. If his car runs out of gas at a random point on the path, what is the probability that it will be on the freeway?

OFFICE — 2 miles — 6 miles freeway — 2 miles — $2\frac{1}{2}$ miles — HOME

$\frac{12}{25}$, or 48%

10\. In baseball, the width of the strike zone is the 17-in. width of home plate. The height of the strike zone is the distance between the batter's chest and knees. The strike zones for two batters are shown as shaded areas in the diagrams below. Suppose a pitcher throws a ball within a square region 36 in. on a side which contains the strike zone. If the placement of the ball within this square is random, what is the probability that the ball will be in the strike zone of each batter?

a.

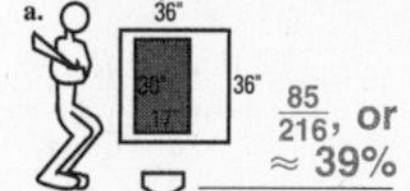

$\frac{85}{216}$, or ≈ 39%

b.

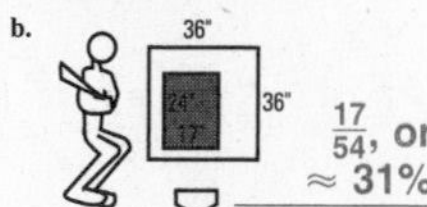

$\frac{17}{54}$, or ≈ 31%

Name

LESSON MASTER 6-7 B **Questions on SPUR Objectives**

Vocabulary

1\. If a size change is an *expansion*, what is true of the size-change factor?
It is greater than 1 or less than -1.

2\. If a size change is a *contraction*, what is true of the size-change factor?
It is between -1 and 1.

Uses Objective H: Solve percent problems from real situations.

3\. Gwen enlarged cartoon A on a photocopy machine by a factor of 150%. The result was cartoon B. Then she enlarged cartoon B by a factor of 125% to get cartoon C.

Find the widths of the other two cartoons if the width of

a. cartoon A is 12 cm.	b. cartoon B is 12 cm.	c. cartoon C is 27 cm.
B 18 cm	A 8 cm	A 14.4 cm
C 22.5 cm	C 15 cm	B 21.6 cm

4\. Jo's Catalog charges $3\frac{1}{2}$ times the normal cost to ship an order overnight. If it normally costs $4.50 to ship a jacket, what is the cost for overnight shipment? $15.75

Name

Representations Objective K: Apply the Size Change Model for Multiplication.

5\. a. Graph quadrilateral *ABCD* with $A = (6, -2)$, $B = (3, 3)$, $C = (0, 6)$, and $D = (0, 0)$.

b. Graph $A'B'C'D'$, the image of *ABCD* under a size change of magnitude $\frac{2}{3}$.

c. Graph $A''B''C''D''$, the image of *ABCD* under a size change of magnitude -2.

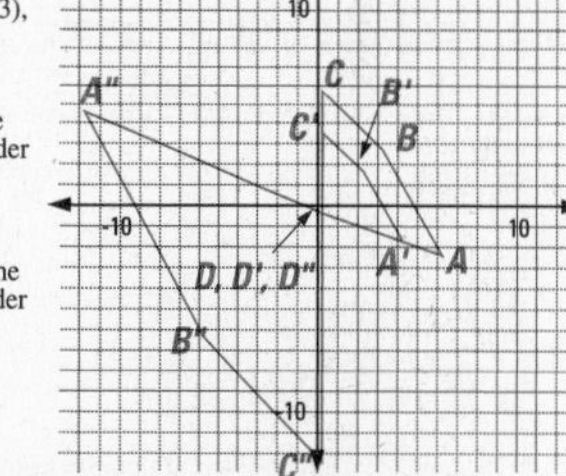

In 6–10, tell if the size change described is an *expansion*, a *contraction*, or *neither*. Then tell whether or not the original figure has been rotated 180°.

6\. $k = 8$ expansion no

7\. $k = -1$ neither yes

8\. $k = -.75$ contraction yes

9\. The image of (7, -2) is (3.5, -1). contraction no

10\. The image of (-4, 6) is (6, -9). expansion yes

In 11 and 12, consider two figures, Figure 1 and Figure 2. Figure 1 is the image of a triangle under a size change k_1. Figure 2 is the image of the same triangle under a size change k_2. Tell how the two images are <u>different</u> if

11\. $k_1 = 6$ and $k_2 = 2$.
Fig. 1 segments are 3 times as long as corresponding Fig. 2 segments.

12\. $k_1 = 3$ and $k_2 = -3$.
Fig. 2 is a 180° rotation image of Fig. 1.

Name

LESSON MASTER 6-8 B Questions on SPUR Objectives

Skills Objective C: Solve proportions.

In 1–10, use the Means-Extremes Property to solve.

1. $\frac{5}{12} = \frac{x}{30}$ $x = 12.5$

2. $\frac{-4}{5} = \frac{12}{a}$ $a = -15$

3. $\frac{5m}{14} = \frac{6}{21}$ $m = .8$

4. $\frac{1}{y+7} = \frac{8}{72}$ $y = 2$

5. $\frac{3}{x} = \frac{x}{12}$ $x = 6$ or $x = -6$

6. $\frac{b}{8} = \frac{18}{b}$ $b = 12$ or $b = -12$

7. $\frac{2e+9}{24} = \frac{e+1}{8}$ $e = 6$

8. $\frac{3(s+4)}{2} = \frac{14s}{4}$ $s = 3$

9. $\frac{4a-2}{3} = 2a$ $a = -1$

10. $\frac{c+12}{c+2} = 6$ $c = 0$

In 11 and 12, a proportion is given. a. Give the exact solution. b. Give the solution to the nearest hundredth.

11. $\frac{5}{x} = \frac{x}{2}$
 a. $x = \sqrt{10}$ or $x = -\sqrt{10}$
 b. $x = 3.16$ or $x = -3.16$

12. $\frac{k}{8} = \frac{3}{4k}$
 a. $k = \sqrt{6}$ or $k = -\sqrt{6}$
 b. $k = 2.45$ or $k = -2.45$

Properties Objective D: Use the language of proportions and the Means-Extremes Property.

In 13 and 14, identify the means and the extremes in each proportion.

13. $\frac{7}{8} = \frac{5}{40}$ means: 8, 5 extremes: 7, 40

14. $\frac{u+2}{10} = \frac{3u}{12}$ means: 10, $3u$ extremes: $u + 2$, 12

Name

15. Explain how you can use the Means-Extremes Property to determine if the fractions $\frac{4.5}{6}$ and $\frac{12}{16}$ are equal.
Sample: Find the product of the means (6 · 12) and the extremes (4.5 · 16). If the products are equal, the fractions are equal.

Uses Objective I: Solve problems involving proportions in real situations.

16. In three hours, 1,650 gallons were drained out of a swimming pool. At this rate, how many gallons will be drained out in 8 hours? 4,400 gal

17. One of the heaviest rainfalls ever recorded occurred in Holt, Missouri, when 12 inches of rain fell in 42 minutes. At this rate, how much rain would fall in an hour? ≈ 17.1 in.

18. A pollster found that 73 out of 120 people were in favor of an upcoming school referendum. If 4,500 people turn out to vote, how many can be expected to vote for the referendum? ≈ 2,738 people

19. Jimmy counted 23 raisins in 2 cups of his favorite cereal. At this rate, how many are in the entire box containing 11 cups of cereal? ≈ 127 raisins

20. As a library employee, Dawn found she was able to shelve 100 books in 3 hours. At this rate, how many books can she shelve in an 40-hour work week? ≈ 1,333 books

21. A ranger caught, tagged, and released 150 deer in a state park. Three months later, the ranger caught 80 deer. Of these, 6 had tags. Based on these findings, estimate the total number of deer in the park. 2,000 deer

22. If an animator needed to draw 3,600 frames for a $2\frac{1}{2}$-minute cartoon, how many frames would be needed for a 6-minute cartoon? 8,640 frames

Name

LESSON MASTER  Questions on SPUR Objectives

Vocabulary

1. *Similar* figures have the same shape.

Representations Objective L: Find lengths and ratios of similitude in similar figures.

In 2–4, ΔARM is similar to ΔLEG with corresponding sides parallel.

2. Which side in ΔARM corresponds to
 a. $\overline{LG}$? $\overline{AM}$
 b. $\overline{LE}$? $\overline{AR}$
 c. $\overline{GE}$? $\overline{MR}$

3. Write and solve a proportion to find the length of $\overline{AM}$.
 proportion: $\frac{AM}{12} = \frac{5}{8}$ solution: $AM = 7.5$

4. Give the two possible ratios of similitude. $\frac{5}{8}$ and $\frac{8}{5}$

5. Lilly made a 5-inch-by-7-inch enlargement of a $3\frac{1}{2}$-inch-by-5-inch snapshot. Are the two pictures similar? Why or why not?
No; sample: corresponding sides are not proportional; that is, $\frac{5}{3\frac{1}{2}} \neq \frac{7}{5}$.

In 6–8, the two quadrilaterals are similar. Find each length.

6. PQ ≈ 19.4

7. QR ≈ 11.1

8. RS ≈ 26.7

Name

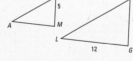

9. These two rectangles are similar. Find the dimensions of the smaller rectangle. 6 by 10

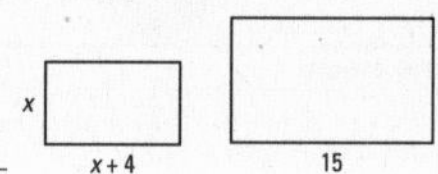

10. A smokestack casts a shadow that is 12 ft long. At the same time, a 6-foot man casts a $2\frac{1}{2}$-foot shadow. How tall is the smokestack? 28.8 feet

11. Quadrilaterals $BIRD$ and $LAMB$ are similar. $\overline{LA}$ is shown and corresponds to $\overline{BI}$. Complete a drawing of $LAMB$.

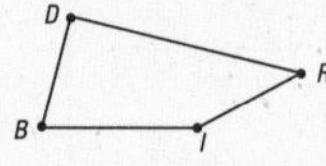

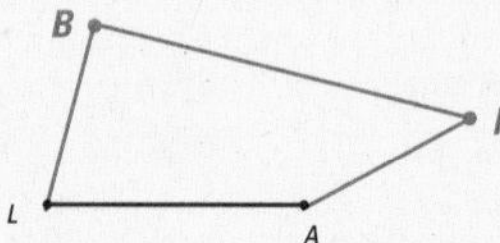

Name

LESSON MASTER 7-1 B Questions on SPUR Objectives

Uses Objective E: Calculate rates of change from real data.

In 1–3, fill in the blanks to give the rate of change for each situation.

1. A vine grew 30 inches in 10 weeks. 3 inches per week
2. Mr. Logan lost 15 pounds in 6 months. 2.5 pounds per month
3. Over a 3-year period, the company bought 7,500 new computers. 2,500 computers per year

In 4–7, use the chart below which shows the number of subscribers to the *Granville Gazette*.

Year	1970	1975	1980	1985	1990
Subscribers	866	948	1,007	1,219	1,485

Subscribers 1,500 1,000 500 '70 '80 '90 Year

4. Graph the information on the grid at the left. Connect the points.
5. a. Which segment is steeper, the one connecting (1975, 948) to (1980, 1,007), or the one connecting (1980, 1,007) to (1985, 1,219)? (1980, 1,007) to (1985, 1,219)

   b. Explain what this means. There was a greater rate of increase during those years than in earlier years.
6. What was the rate of change of the number of subscribers

   a. from 1970 to 1975? 16.4 subscribers/yr

   b. from 1985 to 1990? 53.2 subscribers/yr
7. For the years shown, was the rate of change ever negative? no

Name

In 8 and 9, use the table at the right. It shows some of the rental charges for a chain saw.

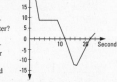

HOURS	COST
2	$20
3	$28
8	$45

8. a. What is the rate of change from a 2-hour rental to a 3-hour rental? $8/hr

   b. What is the unit of the rate of change? dollars/hr
9. Is the rate of change from 2 hours to 3 hours the same as the rate of change from 3 hours to 8 hours? no

In 10–12, use the graph at the right. It shows the altitude of an otter on rocks and in the water.

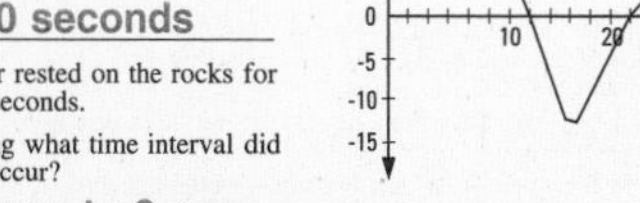

10. How many seconds pass before the otter enters the water? 12 seconds
11. How long is the otter in the water? 10 seconds
12. The otter rested on the rocks for several seconds.

    a. During what time interval did this occur? 4 sec to 9 sec

    b. Give the rate of change during this time interval. 0 ft/sec
13. Use the spreadsheet below, which shows the average number of cars produced each month in Mexico.

	A	B	C
1	YEAR	CARS PER MONTH (in thousands)	RATE OF CHANGE PER YEAR (in thousands)
2	1987	19.0	
3	1988	29.0	120.0
4	1989	37.9	106.8
5	1990	51.2	159.6
6	1991	61.1	118.8

   a. What formula could be in cell C5? =(B5−B4)*12

   b. Complete the spreadsheet.

Name

LESSON MASTER 7-2 B Questions on SPUR Objectives

Skills Objective A: Find the slope of the line through two given points.

In 1–6, calculate the slope of a line through the two points.

1. (4, 8) and (6, 12) 2
2. (-3, 2) and (5, -1) $-\frac{3}{8}$
3. (0, 11) and (6, 14) $\frac{1}{2}$
4. (-8, -1) and (-6, -4) $-\frac{3}{2}$
5. (4, 9) and (7, 9) 0
6. (3, 4) and (4, -18) -22

In 7–10, find the slope of the line.

7. 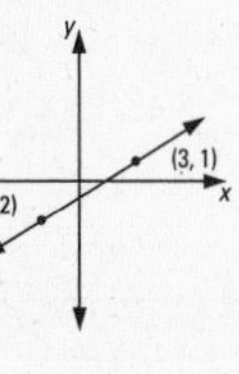

$\frac{3}{5}$

8. 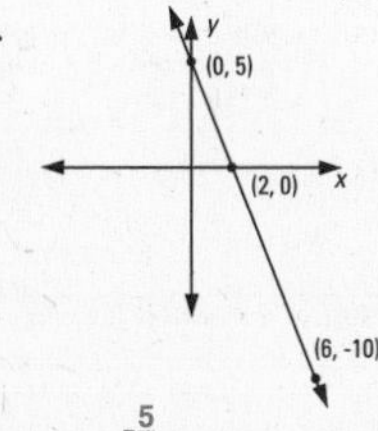

$-\frac{5}{2}$

9. 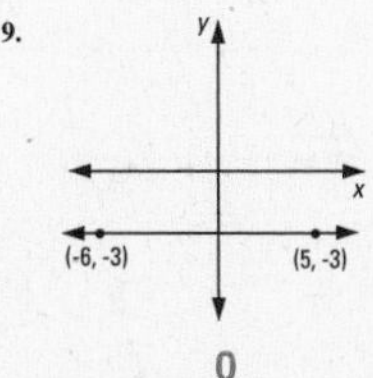

0

10. 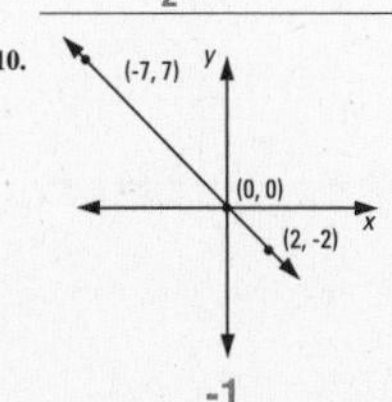

-1

Name

11. The points (2, -3) and (n, 6) are on a line with slope -3. Find the value of n. $n = -1$
12. The points (0, c) and (-4, -4) are on a line with slope $\frac{1}{2}$. Find the value of c. $c = -2$

In 13 and 14, an equation is given. a. Find two points on the line. b. Find the slope of the line. Sample points are given.

13. $x - y = 11$

    a. (12, 1), (15, 4)

    b. 1
14. $4x + 3y = 2$

    a. ($\frac{1}{2}$, 0), (2, -2)

    b. $-\frac{4}{3}$

Properties Objective D: Use the definition of slope.

15. Give the slope of the line passing through the points (p, q) and (r, s). $\frac{q-s}{p-r}$ or $\frac{s-q}{r-p}$
16. **On the grid at the right, draw and label**

    a. a line a with slope -4.

    b. a line b with slope $\frac{3}{2}$.

    Samples are given.

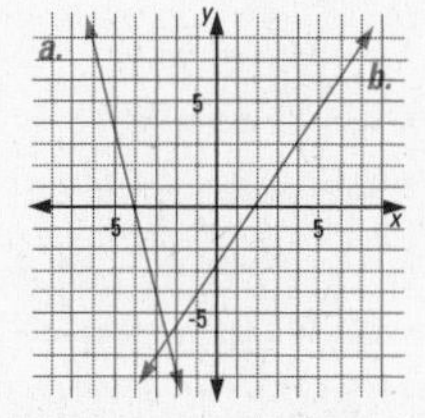

17. Tell if the slope of each line is *positive*, *negative*, or *zero*.

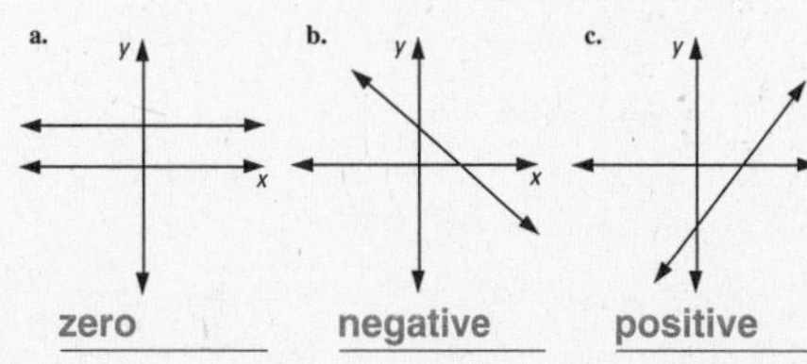

a. zero b. negative c. positive

Name

LESSON MASTER 7-3 B Questions on SPUR Objectives

Properties Objective D: Use the definition and properties of slope.

1. Consider a line with slope -3. Describe the change in the height of the line when it moves one unit to the right.
Sample: The line moves 3 units down.

2. a. Suppose points A and B lie on the same horizontal line and $A = (4, 2)$. Give possible coordinates of B.
Sample: (6, 2)

b. Give the slope of $\overleftrightarrow{AB}$ and explain why the line must have this slope.
Slope is zero; slope $= \frac{2-2}{6-4} = \frac{0}{2} = 0$.

3. a. Suppose points A and C lie on the same vertical line and $A = (4, 2)$. Give possible coordinates of C.
Sample: (4, 5)

b. Give the slope of $\overleftrightarrow{AC}$ and explain why the line must have this slope.
Slope is undefined; slope $= \frac{5-2}{4-4} = \frac{3}{0}$, which is undefined.

In 4–9, tell if the slope of the line is *positive*, *negative*, *zero*, or *undefined*.

4. line l negative
5. line m zero
6. line n positive
7. line p undefined
8. x-axis zero
9. y-axis undefined

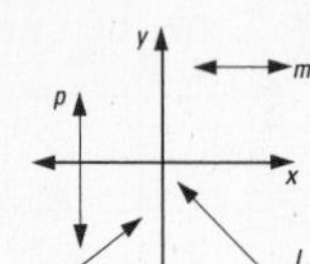

Name

In 10–12, consider a line which goes through the point (-7, 5) and has the given slope. Give another point with integer coefficients that lies on the line.

Samples are given.

10. $\frac{5}{2}$ (-5, 10) 11. -4 (-6, 1) 12. 1 (-6, 6)

Uses Objective E: Calculate rates of change from real data.

13. The cost of upholstering a sofa is given in the table below.

YARDS OF FABRIC	COST
8	$560
9	$585
10	$610
11	$635
12	$660

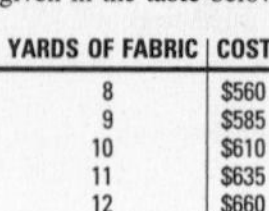

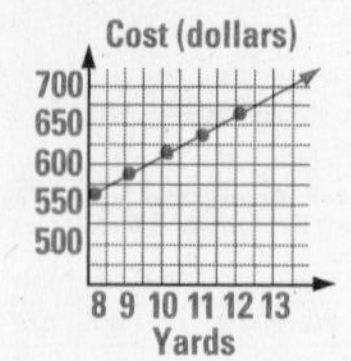

a. What is the rate of change in cost from 8 yards to 12 yards? $25/yd

b. Graph the data in the table and draw a line through the points.

c. Find the slope of the line from Part b. 25

d. How is the slope related to the rate of change in Part a?
The slope equals the rate of change.

Representations Objective H: Graph a straight line given a point and the slope.

In 14 and 15, graph the line described.

14. The line passes through (-2, 5) and has slope -3.

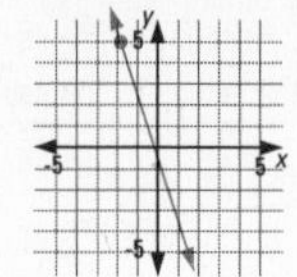

15. The line passes through (1, 0) and has slope $\frac{3}{4}$.

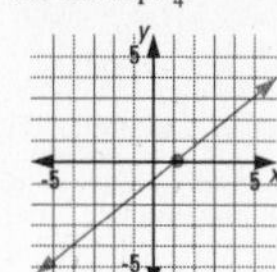

Name

LESSON MASTER 7-4 B Questions on SPUR Objectives

Vocabulary

1. What is the *y-intercept* of a line?
The point where the line crosses the y-axis.

2. Write the *slope-intercept* form for the equation of a line and tell what m and b represent.
$y = mx + b$; m is the slope and b is the y-intercept.

Skills Objective B: Find an equation for a line given its slope and one point on it.

In 3–9, a line is described. Write its equation in slope-intercept form.

3. slope $\frac{5}{6}$, y-intercept 2 $y = \frac{5}{6}x + 2$
4. slope -8, y-intercept -1 $y = -8x - 1$
5. slope -1, y-intercept 0 $y = -x$
6. slope 3, x-intercept 4 $y = 3x - 12$
7. passes through (-1, 1), slope $\frac{1}{2}$ $y = \frac{1}{2}x + \frac{3}{2}$
8. passes through (-8, -4), slope -2 $y = -2x - 20$
9. passes through (3, 5), slope 0 $y = 5$

In 10 and 11, a line is graphed. a. Give the slope of the line. b. Give the y-intercept. c. Write an equation for the line.

10.

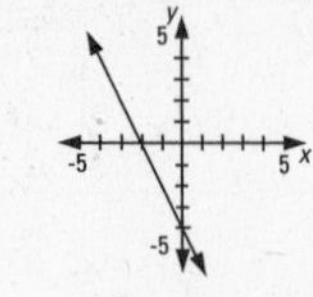

a. -2 b. -4
c. $y = -2x - 4$

11.

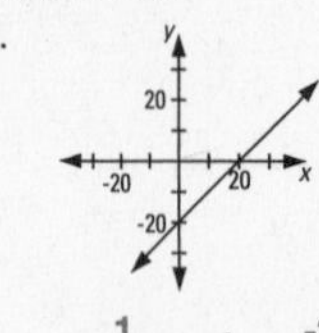

a. 1 b. -20
c. $y = x - 20$

Name

Skills Objective C: Write an equation for a line in slope-intercept form, and find its slope and y-intercept.

In 12–14, an equation of a line is given. a. Write it in slope-intercept form. b. Give the slope. c. Give the y-intercept.

12. $3x + y = 36$
a. $y = -3x + 36$
b. -3
c. 36

13. $-5x + 2y = -8$
a. $y = \frac{5}{2}x - 4$
b. $\frac{5}{2}$
c. -4

14. $x - y = 6$
a. $y = x - 6$
b. 1
c. -6

Uses Objective F: Use equations for lines to describe real situations.

In 15 and 16, a situation is given that can be described by a line. a. Give the y-intercept. b. Find the slope. c. Write an equation for the line.

15. Margie has 88 CDs. Through a club, she will purchase 3 new CDs per month.
a. 88 b. 3 c. $y = 3x + 88$

16. Engraving costs $18 plus .75 per letter.
a. 18 b. .75 c. $y = .75x + 18$

Representations Objective H: Graph a straight line given its equation, or given a point and the slope.

In 17 and 18, graph the equation.

17. slope $-\frac{3}{2}$, y-intercept -4

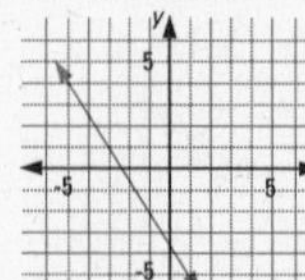

18. $-3x + y = 1$

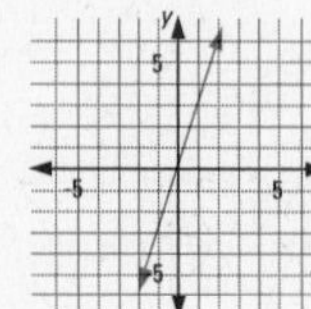

Name

LESSON MASTER 7-5 B

Questions on SPUR Objectives

Skills Objective B: Find an equation for a line given its slope and one point on it.

In 1–6, a point and slope are given. Write an equation of the line given its slope and one point.

1. slope $\frac{2}{3}$, point (3, 5) $y = \frac{2}{3}x + 3$
2. slope -6, point (1, 0) $y = -6x + 6$
3. slope -1, point (0, 3) $y = -x + 3$
4. slope 2, point (0, 0) $y = 2x$
5. slope 0, point (-3, 8) $y = 8$
6. slope -3.5, point (-4, 5) $y = -3.5x - 9$

7. **a.** Write an equation for the line graphed at the right.
   $y = -\frac{1}{2}x + 3$

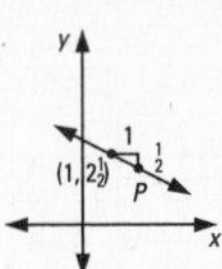

   b. What are the coordinates of point *P*?
   (2, 2)

   c. Show that the coordinates of point *P* satisfy your equation from Part **a**.
   $2 = -\frac{1}{2}(2) + 3;\ 2 = -1 + 3;\ 2 = 2$

   d. At what point will the line cross the *y*-axis? (0, 3)

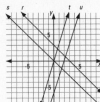

8. Match each line *r*, *s*, *t*, and *u* with its equation below.
   a. $y = -x$ s
   b. $y = -x + 3$ r
   c. $y = 3x - 6$ u
   d. $y = 3x$ t

Name

Uses Objective F: Use equations for lines to describe real situations.

9. The cost for renting a car for a day is \$36 per day plus 22¢ per mile. Let x = the number of miles and y = the cost.
   a. Give a possible point (x, y). Sample: (10, 38.20)
   b. Write an equation for a line which relates x and y. $y = .22x + 36$
   c. Give the slope of the line. .22
   d. Use your answer to Part **b** to find the cost if you rent a car for a day and drive 180 miles. \$75.60

10. Koyi set aside \$850 he earned over the summer to use for miscellaneous expenses while he is away at college. He plans to use \$20 each week.
   a. Give a possible point (x, y) which fits this situation. Sample: (2, 810)
   b. Write an equation for a line which relates x and y. $y = -20x + 850$
   c. Give the slope of the line. -20
   d. Use your answer to Part **b** to find how long Koyi's money will last. 42.5 weeks

11. The water in a 3-foot deep pool is 6 inches deep. A hose is filling the pool at the rate of 3 inches per hour.
   a. Give a possible point (x, y) which fits this situation. Sample: (3, 15)
   b. Write an equation for a line which relates x and y. $y = 3x + 6$
   c. Give the slope of the line. 3
   d. Use your answer to Part **b** to find how long it will take to fill the pool to 34 inches deep. $9\frac{1}{3}$ hours

12. A community club has 5,500 leaflets to deliver. The club members hope to distribute 400 a day. Let x = the number of days and y = the number of leaflets still available. Write an equation relating x and y. $y = -400x + 5{,}500$

Name

LESSON MASTER 7-6 B

Questions on SPUR Objectives

Skills Objective B: Find an equation for a line given two points on it.

In 1–10, find the equation in slope-intercept form for the line containing the two points.

1. (1, 3) and (-2, 1) $y = \frac{2}{3}x + \frac{7}{3}$
2. (-6, -6) and (0, -4) $y = \frac{1}{3}x - 4$
3. (1, 4) and (-2, -5) $y = 3x + 1$
4. (-3, 13) and (-1, -1) $y = -7x - 8$
5. (3, 12) and (-4, -16) $y = 4x$
6. (-3, 7) and (6, -8) $y = -\frac{5}{3}x + 2$
7. (9, 2) and (18, 11) $y = x - 7$
8. (1, 1) and (5, 4) $y = \frac{3}{4}x + \frac{1}{4}$
9. (8, 6) and (-3, 6) $y = 6$
10. (100, -300) and (101, -299) $y = x - 400$

In 11 and 12, two points are given. a. Write an equation in slope-intercept form for the line containing the two points. b. Graph the line from Part a and check that both points are on the line.

11. (-3, 7) and (5, -1)
   a. $y = -x + 4$

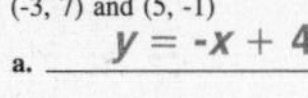

   b.

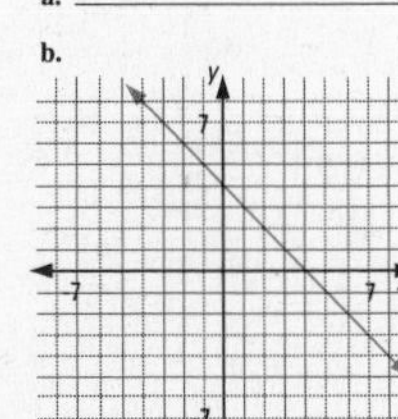

12. (6, -3) and (0, -3)
   a. $y = -3$
   b.

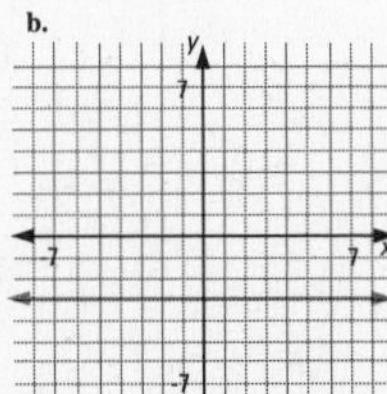

Name

Uses Objective F: Use equations for lines to describe real situations.

13. If Abby uses 2 cups of flour, she can make 24 muffins. If she uses $3\frac{1}{2}$ cups, she can make 42 muffins. Let c = number of cups of flour and m = number of muffins.
   a. Write the two ordered pairs (c, m) described. (2, 24), $(3\frac{1}{2}, 42)$
   b. Write an equation for the line through the two points. $y = 12x$
   c. If she uses 5 cups of flour, how many muffins can she make? 60 muffins

14. At Sew-n-Sew Windows, there is a linear relationship between the width of a window and the width of the fabric before it is pleated into draperies. A window 44 inches wide requires a 120-inch width of fabric. A 60-inch window requires 160 inches. Let x = the width of the window and y = the width of the drapery fabric.
   a. Write the two ordered pairs (x, y) described. (44, 120), (60, 160)
   b. Write an equation for the line through the two points. $y = 2.5x + 10$
   c. If a window is 38 inches wide, how wide should the fabric be before it is pleated? 105 inches

15. The Blueport Bus Company finds that if they lower their prices, more people will ride the bus. Right now they charge \$1.25 per ride and average 2,400 customers per day. Analysts feel that there is a linear relationship between the cost x and the number of riders y and that if the cost were dropped to \$1.00 the number of riders would increase to 2,700.
   a. Write an equation that relates the variables x and y. $y = -1{,}200x + 3{,}900$
   b. Use your answer to Part **a** to predict the number of riders if the cost of a bus ride were lowered to \$.80. 2,940 riders

Name

LESSON MASTER 7-7 B

Questions on SPUR Objectives

Uses Objective G: Given data whose graph is approximately linear, find a linear equation to fit the graph.

1. *Multiple choice.* In which of these scatterplots is the data almost linear? b

(a) (b) (c) (d)

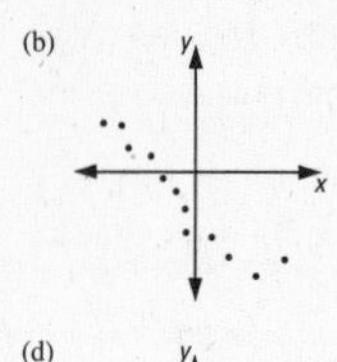

2. Based on a study of 200 dishwasher purchases, the table below shows the age of the dishwashers and the number of repairs needed by this group of dishwashers each year.

Age in Years	1	2	3	4	5	6	7	8	9	10
Number of Repairs	2	3	4	6	7	8	10	11	13	16

a. Use the grid on the next page, and carefully draw a scatterplot of points (age, number of repairs).
Sample scatterplot is given.

Name

Samples are given for b, c, d, f.

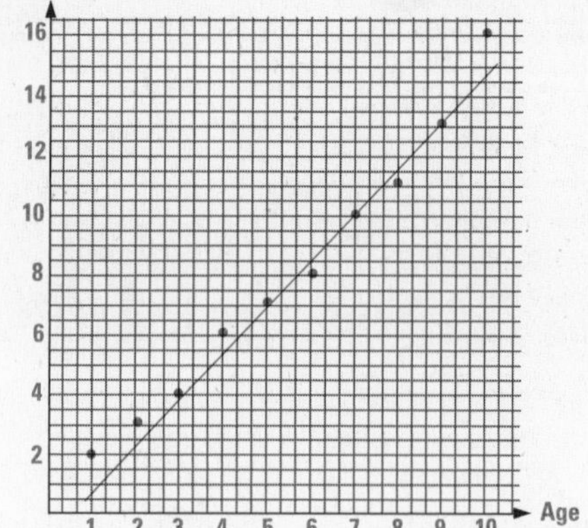

b. Fit a line to the data and draw it with a ruler.

c. Give the coordinates of two points on the line you drew. (3, 4), (5, 7)

d. Use your two points to find an equation of your line. $y = \frac{3}{2}x - \frac{1}{2}$

e. According to your equation, what happens to the number of repairs as the dishwashers get older?
The number of repairs increases.

f. Use your equation to find the number of repairs when the dishwashers are 12 years old. ≈ 18 repairs

Review Objective B, Lesson 5-6

In 3 and 4, solve each inequality and graph all solutions on the number line provided.

3. $2m + 14 \le 6m - 2$ $m \ge 4$

4. $25 - 5b < 50 - 8b$ $b < 8\frac{1}{3}$

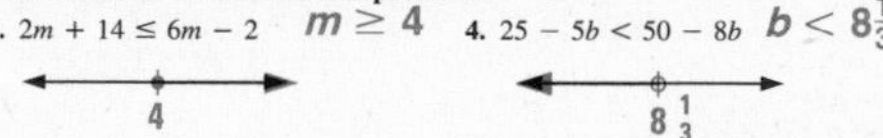

Name

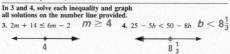

LESSON MASTER 7-8 B

Questions on SPUR Objectives

Skills Objective C: Write an equation for a line in standard form, and from that form find its slope and y-intercept.

1. Write the standard form for an equation of a line. Then identify the constants.
$Ax + By = C$; A, B, and C are constants.

2. Are there any lines that cannot be described by an equation in standard form? If so, which ones?
No; all lines can be described by an equation in standard form.

In 3–12, tell if the equation is in standard form.

3. $7y + 2x = 18$ no
4. $x + y = -8$ yes
5. $4x - 2y = 5$ yes
6. $y = 3x + 8$ no
7. $-x + 3y = -8$ yes
8. $4x + 2y + 9 = 0$ no
9. $0x - 2y = 7$ yes
10. $22x + 0y = 44$ yes
11. $y = -x + 0$ no
12. $15y - x = 19$ no

In 13–20, a. rewrite the equation in standard form with integer coefficients, and b. give the values of *A*, *B*, and *C*. Samples are given.

13. $y = -2x + 5$ a. $2x + y = 5$ b. 2, 1, 5

14. $y = \frac{4}{3}x + 1$ a. $-4x + 3y = 3$ b. -4, 3, 3

15. $y = -\frac{7}{8}x - \frac{1}{3}$ a. $21x + 24y = -8$ b. 21, 24, -8

16. $2y + 3x = 9$ a. $3x + 2y = 9$ b. 3, 2, 9

17. $y = 4x$ a. $-4x + y = 0$ b. -4, 1, 0

18. $-\frac{1}{2}x = 14$ a. $-x + 0y = 28$ b. -1, 0, 28

19. $2.1x - .8y = .6$ a. $21x - 8y = 6$ b. 21, -8, 6

20. $\frac{5}{6}y = \frac{3}{4}x$ a. $-9x + 10y = 0$ b. -9, 10, 0

Name

Uses Objective F: Use equations for lines to describe real situations.

21. In a math competition, a team gets -2 points for wrong answers and 5 points for right answers. The Acute Anglers got x wrong answers and y right answers. Their final score was 67.

a. Write an equation in standard form describing the relationship between x and y. $-2x + 5y = 67$

b. Give three solutions to your equation in Part **a**.
Samples: (-1, 13), (4, 15), (9, 17)

22. Jeff and Sally sold books for the school book sale. Some cost \$15 and some cost \$20. They forgot to keep track of the number of each type they sold, but they do know that they collected \$900. Let x = number of \$15 books and y = number of \$20 books sold.

a. Find the number of \$20 books sold if only \$20 books were sold. 45 books

b. Find the number of \$20 books sold if 24 \$15 books were sold. 27 books

c. Write an equation in standard form describing the relationship between x and y. $15x + 20y = 900$

Representations Objective H: Graph a straight line given its equation.

In 23 and 24, graph the line described.

23. $6x + 3y = 9$

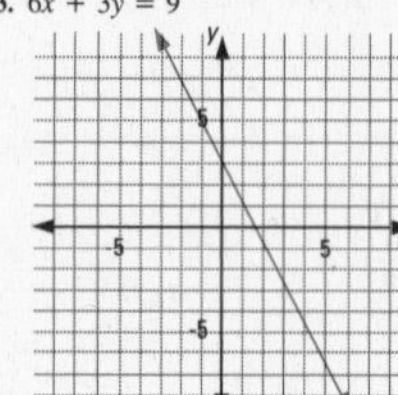

24. $5x - 2y = 8$

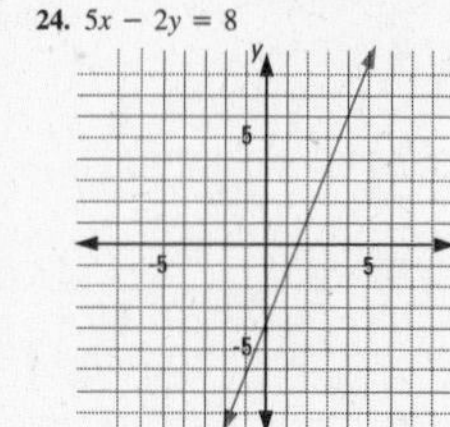

Name

LESSON MASTER 7-9 B Questions on SPUR Objectives

Representations Objective I: Graph linear inequalities.

In 1–4, write an inequality that describes the graph.

1.

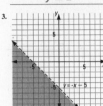

$y \le 2$

2. 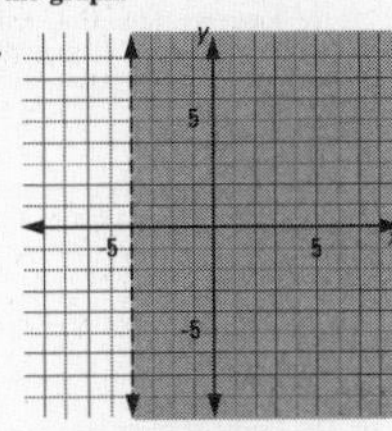
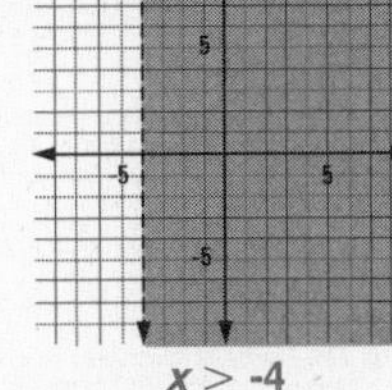

$x > -4$

3.

$y = -x - 5$

$y < -x - 5$

4. 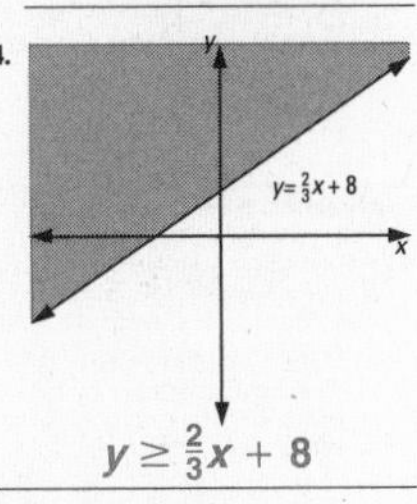

$y \ge \frac{2}{3}x + 8$

In 5 and 6, an inequality is given. a. Tell if you should shade above or below the boundary line. b. Tell if the boundary line should be solid or dashed.

5. $y < x - 11$

a. below

b. dashed

6. $y \ge 5x + 4$

a. above

b. solid

Name

In 7 and 8, graph the inequality a. on the number line and b. on the coordinate grid.

7. $y > -4$

a. -4 y

b. 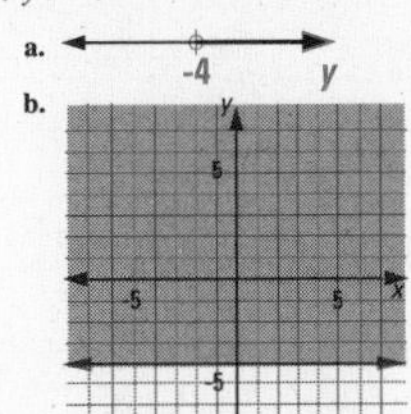

8. $x \le 5$

a. 5

b. 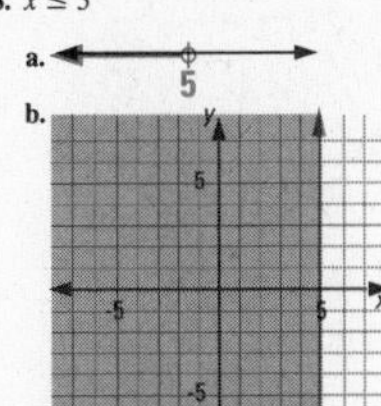

In 9–10, graph the inequality.

9. $y \le x + 4$

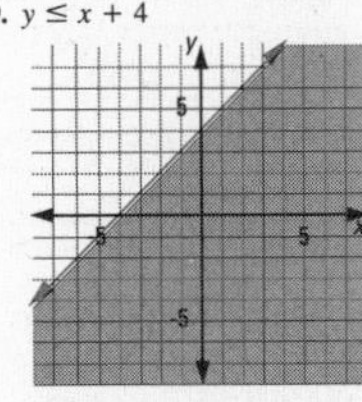

10. $y > -2x - 3$

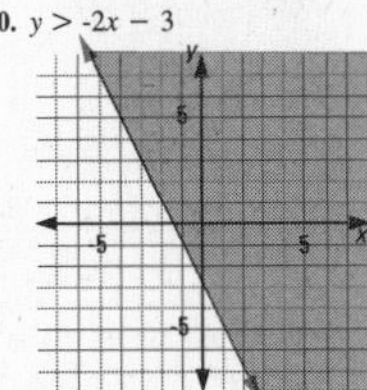

11. In World-Cup Soccer, a team gets 3 points for a win and 1 point for a tie. Let W be the number of wins and T be the number of ties.

a. If a team has more than 3 points, what inequality must W and T satisfy?

$3W + T > 3$

b. Graph all possible pairs (W, T) for a team that has played 3 games and has more than 3 points.

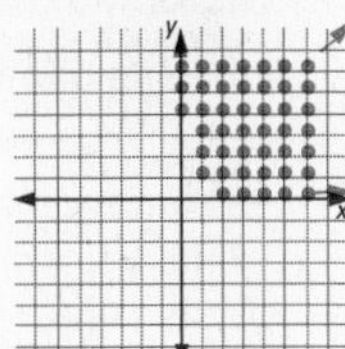

Name

LESSON MASTER  **8-1 B** Questions on SPUR Objectives

Vocabulary

1. Consider a number of the form x^n.

a. x^n is called a power.

b. x is the base.

c. n is the exponent.

In 2 and 3, an expression is given. a. Write the expression using exponents. b. Identify the *base(s)*. c. Identify the *exponent(s)*. d. Identify the *coefficient*.

2. $38 \cdot c \cdot c \cdot c \cdot c$

a. $38c^4$

b. c

c. 4

d. 38

3. $8 \cdot x \cdot x \cdot y \cdot y \cdot y \cdot y \cdot y$

a. $8x^2y^5$

b. x, y

c. 2, 5

d. 8

4. The data below show the amount of money in a bank account.

Deposit	\$500.00
End of first year	500(1.07) = \$535.00
End of second year	500(1.07)(1.07) = \$572.45

a. What is the annual yield? 7%

b. What is the principal? \$500

c. What is the interest paid during the two-year period? \$72.45

Skills Objective A: Evaluate integer powers of real numbers.

In 5–10, evaluate the expression. Give answers rounded to the nearest ten-thousandth.

5. 5^3 125

6. 19^2 361

7. 3.4^2 11.56

8. 1.06^6 1.4185

9. $(1 + .04)^7$ 1.3159

10. $200(1.085)^{12}$ 532.3372

Name

Uses Objective F: Calculate compound interest.

11. a. Write an expression for the amount in an account after 18 years if \$3,500 is invested at 7.2% annual yield.

$3{,}500(1.072)^{18}$

b. Write a key sequence to enter this on your calculator.

Sample: 3500 ⊠ 1.072 y^x 18 ⊟

c. To the nearest dollar, how much is in the account after 18 years? \$12,234

12. A bank uses the spreadsheet below to show the amount in a savings account earning 6% interest. The principal invested is \$800.

	A	B	C
1	YEAR	BALANCE	YEARLY INTEREST
2	0	800.00	
3	1	848.00	48.00
4	2	898.88	50.88
5	3	952.81	53.93
6	4		

a. What formula can be entered in cell B6? Sample: =B5*1.06

b. What number should appear in cell B6? 1009.98

c. What formula can be entered in cell C6? Sample: =B6−B5

d. What number should appear in cell C6? 57.17

e. What trend do you notice in Column C? What do you think accounts for this?

Sample: The amount of interest increases because the balance each year is greater.

13. Barb won \$5,000 in a lottery and decided to put it in the bank for an emergency. An emergency never arose. How much was in the account after 15 years if the account had an annual yield of 9%? \$18,212.41

14. A department store charges 19.6% interest per year on unpaid monthly bills. How much would you owe if you did not pay a bill of \$272 for 2 years? \$389.07

Name

LESSON MASTER 8-2 B Questions on SPUR Objectives

Skills Objective A: Evaluate integer powers of real numbers.

In 1–10, evaluate.

1. 15^0 **1**
2. 27.4^0 **1**
3. $9^2 \cdot 9^0$ **81**
4. $(4.3 + 6)^0$ **1**
5. $\left(\frac{2}{3}\right)^4$ $\frac{16}{81}$
6. $\left(\frac{3}{4}\right)^4 + \left(\frac{6}{5}\right)^0$ $1\frac{81}{256}$
7. $(y + 64)^0$ when $y = 10$ **1**
8. $4 \cdot 3^3 + 2 \cdot 8^1 + 12 \cdot 18^0$ **136**
9. $500(6^n)$ when $n = 0$ **500**
10. $133^{(7-7)}$ **1**

Properties Objective E: Use properties of exponents to explain operations with powers.

11. Suppose an investment of $300 earns 8% interest each year.
    a. What does $300(1.08)^3$ represent?
    Total value of investment after 3 years
    b. What does $300(1.08)^0$ represent?
    Value of investment at beginning
    c. Use the expression from Part b to explain why $(1.08)^0$ equals 1.
    Sample: The value of the investment at the beginning is 300(1), or $300(1.08)^0$. So, $(1.08)^0 = 1$.

Name

Uses Objective G: Solve problems involving exponential growth.

12. At the computer, Mrs. Gold enlarged a graphic 20%. She enlarged the resulting graphic 20%, and then enlarged this newest graphic another 20%. If the original graphic was 3 inches wide, how wide was the final graphic? **≈5.2 inches**

13. A greenhouse purchased a dozen ivy plants. Periodically, new plants are started by taking *cuttings* of the old plant. It is estimated that the number of plants will be multiplied by 3 each month.
    a. How many plants will there be after 6 months? **8,748 plants**
    b. How many plants will there be after n months? $12(3)^n$
    c. Do you think there will be enough space at the greenhouse for all the ivy plants if they continue the process for a year? Explain your answer.
    Sample: No; there would be more than 6 million plants.

Representations Objective I: Graph exponential relationships.

14. An analyst predicts that the number of subscribers to the *Bradley Sentinel* will increase 15% each year for the next five years. Today, there are 4,500 subscribers.
    a. Make a table of values showing the number of subscribers 0, 1, 2, 3, 4, and 5 years from now.

x	y
0	4,500
1	5,175
2	5,951
3	6,844
4	7,871
5	9,051

    b. Graph the number of subscribers for 0 through 5 years.

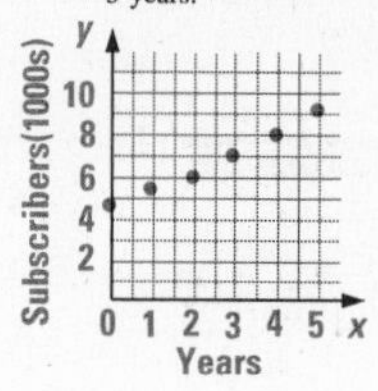

Name

LESSON MASTER 8-3 B Questions on SPUR Objectives

Uses Objective G: Solve problems involving exponential growth.
Representations Objective I: Graph exponential relationships.

1. The transportation department is studying two reports related to the predicted increase in the number of passengers at the airport. Report *A* predicts an increase of 1 million passengers each year, while Report *B* predicts that each year there will be a 6% increase. This year there are 14 million passengers at the airport. Let x = the number of years.
    a. Write an expression for the number of passengers if that number increases by 1 million per year. $14{,}000{,}000 + 1{,}000{,}000x$
    b. Write an expression for the number of passengers if that number increases by 6% per year. $14{,}000{,}000(1.06)^x$
    c. Fill in the table below.

YEAR	INCREASE BY 1,000,000	INCREASE BY 6%
0	14,000,000	14,000,000
1	15,000,000	14,840,000
2	16,000,000	15,730,400
3	17,000,000	16,674,224
4	18,000,000	17,674,677
5	19,000,000	18,735,158
6	20,000,000	19,859,267
7	21,000,000	21,050,823
8	22,000,000	22,313,873
9	23,000,000	23,652,705
10	24,000,000	25,071,867

Name

    d. Which report predicts more traffic after 3 years? **Report A**
    e. Which report predicts more traffic after 6 years? **Report A**
    f. Which report predicts more traffic after 10 years? **Report B**
    g. Make a graph showing the information in the table. Connect the points for each graph.

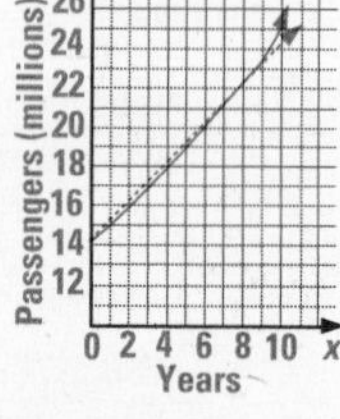

2. Sketch a possible graph below showing exponential growth.
Sample:

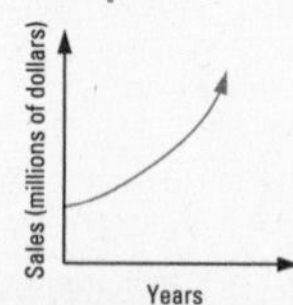

3. Sketch a possible graph below showing constant increase.
Sample:

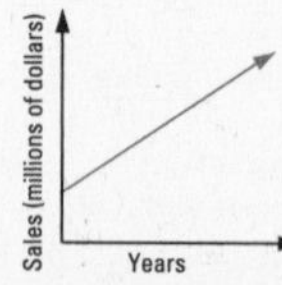

In 4–10, tell which is being described: ***constant increase*** **or** ***exponential growth.***

4. Each year the enrollment increased by 200. **constant increase**
5. Each year the enrollment increased by 4%. **exponential growth**
6. Each hour 2 more inches of snow fell. **constant increase**
7. Each month the profits increased .5%. **exponential growth**
8. $210 \cdot 1.045^x$ **exponential growth**
9. $210 + 6x$ **constant increase**
10. Each year the farm doubled its yield. **exponential growth**

Name

LESSON MASTER 8-4 B

Questions on SPUR Objectives

Uses Objective G: Solve problems involving exponential decay.

1. National Cables has launched a program to reduce its debt by 12% per year. The debt is currently $9,000,000.

YEAR	AMOUNT OF DEBT
0	$9,000,000
1	$7,920,000
2	$6,969,600
3	$6,133,248
4	≈$5,397,258
5	≈$4,749,587
6	≈$4,179,637

a. Fill in the table to show the amount of the company's debt for 0 through 6 years.

b. How much did the company reduce its debt during the first year? $1,080,000

c. How much did the company reduce its debt during the fifth year? ≈$647,671

d. Write an expression for the amount of debt remaining after x years. $9{,}000{,}000(.88)^x$

e. Use trial and error to find how long it will take to reduce the debt to less than $1,000,000. 18 years

2. A single thickness of one type of glass cuts down the emission of light by 10%. Consider a 60-watt light bulb which has an intensity of about 800 *lumens*.

a. By what number would you multiply to find the number of the light bulb's lumens emitted through a single thickness of the glass? .9

b. How many lumens are emitted through a single thickness of the glass? 720 lumens

c. How many lumens are emitted through two thicknesses of the glass? 648 lumens

d. Let t = the number of thicknesses of glass. Write an expression to describe the number of lumens that are emitted through t thicknesses of the glass. $800(.9)^t$

e. How many lumens are emitted through five thicknesses of the glass? ≈472 lumens

Name

3. Today, the Johnsville Lumber Company has 18,000 acres of trees available for lumber. They are cutting the trees at a faster rate than they are replacing them. As a result, they estimate that each year they will have 15% fewer acres of trees available for lumber.

a. Write and equation to describe this situation. $y = 18{,}000(.85)^x$

b. How many acres of trees will be available for lumber after 15 years? ≈1,572 acres

In 4–7, *multiple choice*. Tell if the situation described is (a) exponential growth, (b) exponential decay, (c) constant growth, or (d) constant decrease.

4. The water level is going down 3 inches per day. d

5. The amount of mail increases 5% per year. a

6. Each year the company increases profits by $400,000. c

7. Each month the number of accidents is reduced 2%. b

Representations Objective I: Graph exponential relationships.

In 8–11, *multiple choice*. Match the graph to the equation.

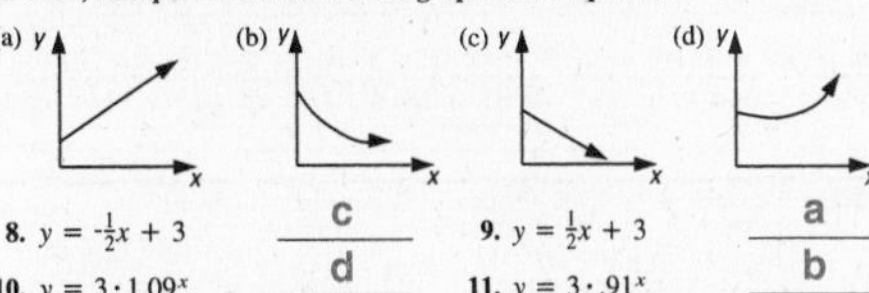

8. $y = -\frac{1}{2}x + 3$ c

9. $y = \frac{1}{2}x + 3$ a

10. $y = 3 \cdot 1.09^x$ d

11. $y = 3 \cdot .91^x$ b

12. Refer to Question 1. Graph the amount of the company's debt for 0 through 6 years. Connect the points of the graph with a smooth curve.

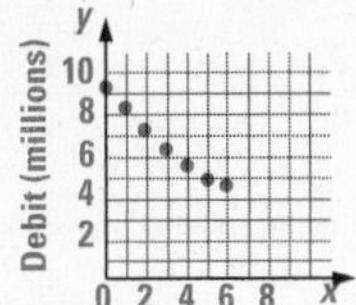

Name

LESSON MASTER 8-5 B

Questions on SPUR Objectives

Skills Objective B: Simplify products and powers of powers.

In 1–6, write each expression as a single power.

1. $8^4 \cdot 8^3$ 8^7

2. $10^2 \cdot 10^2$ 10^4

3. $5^6 \cdot 5^5 \cdot 5^2$ 5^{13}

4. $6 \cdot 6^3$ 6^4

5. $(3^4)^2$ 3^8

6. $(14^3)^5$ 14^{15}

7. a. Simplify $m^4 \cdot m^2$. m^6

b. Check your answer by letting $m = 3$. $3^4 \cdot 3^2 = 81 \cdot 9 = 729;\ 3^6 = 729$

In 8–27, simplify each expression.

8. $m^2 \cdot m^3$ m^5

9. $x^4 \cdot x^4$ x^8

10. $(g^4)^3$ g^{12}

11. $(a^5)^5$ a^{25}

12. $r^3 \cdot r^4 \cdot r^2$ r^9

13. $e \cdot e^3$ e^4

14. $w^4 \cdot w \cdot w^5$ w^{10}

15. $k^7 \cdot y^3 \cdot k \cdot y^3$ k^8y^6

16. $(n^3 \cdot n^5)^2$ n^{16}

17. $(d \cdot d^2)^4$ d^{12}

18. $4p^3 \cdot 5p^6$ $20p^9$

19. $-6x^2 \cdot 2x$ $-12x^3$

20. $x^2 \cdot y \cdot x^4 \cdot y^3 \cdot y$ x^6y^5

21. $(h^0)^3$ 1

22. $5n(n^6)^3$ $5n^{19}$

23. $x^0 \cdot 2x^3$ $2x^3$

24. $a(a^6 - a^3)$ $a^7 - a^4$

25. $5x^2(x + 2x^4)$ $5x^3+10x^6$

26. $m^2(m^3 - y^3)$ $m^5 - m^2y^3$

27. $(b^4)^3 - (b^3)^4$ 0

Name

Properties Objective E: Identify properties of exponents and use them to explain operations with powers.

28. Show how to simplify $r^2 \cdot r^4$

a. by using repeated multiplication. $r^2 \cdot r^4 = r \cdot r(r \cdot r \cdot r \cdot r) = r^6$

b. by using the Product of Powers Property. $r^2 \cdot r^4 = r^{2+4} = r^6$

29. Show how to simplify $(x^3)^4$

a. by treating x^3 as a chunk. $(x^3)^4 = x^3 \cdot x^3 \cdot x^3 \cdot x^3 = x^{12}$

b. by using the Power of a Power Property. $(x^3)^4 = x^{3 \cdot 4} = x^{12}$

30. Write a multiplication expression that uses the Product of Powers Property and has the value w^9. Sample: $w^3 \cdot w^6$

31. Write an expression that uses the Power of a Power Property and has the value m^{18}. Sample: $(m^2)^9$

In 32–37, solve for x.

32. $8^x \cdot 8^3 = 8^7$ $x = 4$

33. $4^4 \cdot 4^x = 4^5$ $x = 1$

34. $n^x \cdot n^3 = n^3$ $x = 0$

35. $(5^4)^x = 5^{12}$ $x = 3$

36. $(9^x)^5 = 9^{10}$ $x = 2$

37. $e(e^8)^x = e^{17}$ $x = 2$

Review Objective A, Lesson 3-1

38. In a magic square, each row, column, and diagonal has the same sum. Fill in the boxes at the right so each of these sums is $-6x$. Sample is given.

x	$-6x$	$-x$
$-4x$	$-2x$	0
$-3x$	$2x$	$-5x$

Name

LESSON MASTER 8-6 B

Questions on SPUR Objectives

Skills Objective A: Evaluate integer powers of real numbers.

In 1–8, evaluate the expression. Give your answers as a simple fraction.

1. 7^{-1} $\frac{1}{7}$
2. 11^{-2} $\frac{1}{121}$
3. $\left(\frac{1}{5}\right)^{-1}$ 5
4. 6^{-3} $\frac{1}{216}$
5. $2 \cdot 3^{-4}$ $\frac{2}{81}$
6. $20^{-8} \cdot 20^{8}$ 1
7. $\left(\frac{2}{3}\right)^{-2}$ $\frac{9}{4}$
8. $3^{-2} \cdot 3^{-3}$ $\frac{1}{243}$

In 9–16, evaluate the expression. Give your answer as a decimal.

9. 10^{-1} 0.1
10. 10^{-4} 0.0001
11. 10^{-2} 0.01
12. 10^{-10} 0.0000000001
13. $6 \cdot 10^{-1}$ 0.6
14. $5 \cdot 10^{-3}$ 0.005
15. $2 \cdot 10^3 + 8 \cdot 10^2 + 6 \cdot 10^1 + 6 \cdot 10^0 + 3 \cdot 10^{-1} + 4 \cdot 10^{-2} + 5 \cdot 10^{-3}$ 2866.345
16. $9 \cdot 10^5 + 4 \cdot 10^4 + 3 \cdot 10^2 + 8 \cdot 10^0 + 2 \cdot 10^{-1} + 7 \cdot 10^{-4} + 1 \cdot 10^{-5}$ 940,308.20071

Skills Objective B: Simplify products of and powers of powers.

17. $m^{-3} \cdot m^5$ m^2
18. $x^2 \cdot x^{-8}$ x^{-6}
19. $a^{-2} \cdot a^{-6}$ a^{-8}
20. $(a^{-3})^4$ a^{-12}
21. $x^3 \cdot x^{-9} \cdot x^2$ x^{-4}
22. $n \cdot n^{-6}$ n^{-5}
23. $uw^4 \cdot u^{-2}w^{-8}$ $u^{-1}w^{-4}$
24. $(g^{-1})^{-5}$ g^5

In 25–28, write each expression without negative exponents.

25. 4^{-x} $\frac{1}{4^x}$
26. x^{-3} $\frac{1}{x^3}$
27. $m^{-2}n^5$ $\frac{n^5}{m^2}$
28. $7a^{-1}b^{-5}$ $\frac{7}{ab^5}$

Name

In 29–33, give examples of three different pairs of values of a and b that satisfy the equation. Samples are given.

29. $4^a \cdot 4^b = 4^3$ $a = 1, b = 2$ $a = 5, b = -2$ $a = 0, b = 3$
30. $3^a \cdot 3^b = 3^1$ $a = 1, b = 0$ $a = -1, b = 2$ $a = 5, b = -4$
31. $x^a \cdot x^b = x^2$ $a = 1, b = 1$ $a = 0, b = 2$ $a = 3, b = -1$
32. $(5^a)^b = 5^6$ $a = 2, b = 3$ $a = -3, b = -2$ $a = 6, b = 1$
33. $(y^a)^b = y^{-8}$ $a = 4, b = -2$ $a = 1, b = -8$ $a = -2, b = 4$

Properties Objective E: Identify the Negative Exponent Property and use it to explain operations with powers.

34. Explain the relationship between b^n and b^{-n}.
Sample: They are reciprocals of each other.

35. Show how to simplify $m^{-4} \cdot m^4$
   a. by first applying the Negative Exponent Property.
   $m^{-4} \cdot m^4 = \frac{1}{m^4} \cdot m^4 = \frac{m^4}{m^4} = 1$
   b. by first applying the Product of Powers Property.
   $m^{-4} \cdot m^4 = m^{-4+4} = m^0 = 1$

Uses Objective G: Solve problems involving exponential decay.

36. Carl has \$3276.99 in a saving account that earns 7% annually. Assuming no withdrawals or deposits were made, how much did he have in the account 4 years ago? \$2500

37. Crestburg's population doubled each of the last five decades. Today there are p people in Crestburg. How many people were there 50 years ago? $p(.5)^5$ people

Uses Objective H: Use and simplify expressions with powers in everyday situations.

38. A test has 20 multiple-choice questions, each with 4 options. What is the probability of guessing all the correct answers? Express your answer using a negative exponent. 4^{-20}

Name

LESSON MASTER 8-7 B

Questions on SPUR Objectives

Skills Objective A: Evaluate quotients of integer powers of real numbers.

In 1–8, write as a single power.

1. $\frac{3^6}{3^4}$ 3^2
2. $\frac{6^5}{6^9}$ 6^{-4}
3. $\frac{8^{-7}}{8^4}$ 8^{-11}
4. $\frac{12^6}{12^{-8}}$ 12^{14}
5. $\frac{5^{-8}}{5^{-2}}$ 5^{-6}
6. $\frac{4^6}{4^6}$ 4^0
7. $\frac{7^5 \cdot 7^2}{7^3}$ 7^4
8. $\frac{2^8 \cdot 2^{-4}}{2^7}$ 2^{-3}

In 9 and 10, rewrite each equation using powers of 2.

9. $\frac{32}{8} = 4$ $\frac{2^5}{2^3} = 2^2$
10. $\frac{16}{64} = \frac{1}{4}$ $\frac{2^4}{2^6} = 2^{-2}$

In 11–18, evaluate. Write the answer as a decimal.

11. $\frac{5^4}{5^2}$ 25
12. $\frac{3^5}{3}$ 81
13. $\frac{4^5}{4^7}$ 0.0625
14. $\frac{10^5}{10^{11}}$ 0.000001
15. $\frac{48 \cdot 10^5}{6 \cdot 10^2}$ 8000
16. $\frac{6.6 \cdot 10^7}{1.1 \cdot 10^{12}}$ 0.00006
17. $\frac{3 \cdot 10^6}{12 \cdot 10^4}$ 25
18. $\frac{4.06 \cdot 10^9}{2 \cdot 10^2}$ 20,300,000

Skills Objective B: Simplify quotients of powers.

19. Simplify $\frac{x^5}{x^{12}}$. Give your answer
   a. as a fraction. $\frac{1}{x^7}$
   b. using a negative exponent. x^{-7}

Name

In 20–31, simplify. Write your answers without negative exponents.

20. $\frac{a^7}{a^2}$ a^5
21. $\frac{x^5}{x^8}$ $\frac{1}{x^3}$
22. $\frac{u^{-6}}{u^{-2}}$ $\frac{1}{u^4}$
23. $\frac{a^4b^8}{ab^2}$ a^3b^6
24. $\frac{m^6n^8}{m^2n^{10}}$ $\frac{m^4}{n^2}$
25. $\frac{15a^7}{3a^2}$ $5a^5$
26. $\frac{16d^4e^{11}}{20d^6e^4}$ $\frac{4e^7}{5d^2}$
27. $\frac{-18cb^8}{6c^8b^2}$ $\frac{-3b^6}{c^7}$
28. $\frac{9u^6}{4u^{-2}v^5}$ $\frac{9u^8}{4v^5}$
29. $\frac{(y-5)^3}{(y-5)^4}$ $\frac{1}{y-5}$
30. $\frac{(3v)^4}{(3v)^8}$ $\frac{1}{81v^4}$
31. $\frac{14c^3}{3x} \cdot \frac{6x^3}{c^{12}}$ $\frac{28x^2}{c^9}$

Properties Objective E: Identify the Quotient of Powers Property and use it to explain operations with powers.

32. Write an algebraic fraction that the Quotient of Powers Property can be used to simplify to b^5. Sample: $\frac{b^8}{b^3}$

33. Explain how to use the Quotient of Powers Property to find the value of x in $\frac{6^x}{6^3} = 6^8$.
Sample: $\frac{6^x}{6^3} = 6^{x-3} = 6^8$; so $x - 3 = 8$ and $x = 11$.

Uses Objective H: Use and simplify expressions with powers in everyday situations.

34. Pluto's average distance from the sun is $3.66 \cdot 10^9$ miles. Earth is about $9.3 \cdot 10^7$ miles from the sun. Pluto's distance from the sun is how many times Earth's distance? ≈39 times

35. In 1992, Colorado produced $7.26 \cdot 10^7$ bushels of wheat. What percent is this of that year's total U.S. wheat production of $2.46 \cdot 10^9$ bushels? ≈3%

Name

LESSON MASTER 8-8 B **Questions on SPUR Objectives**

Skills Objective A: Evaluate integer powers of real number products and quotients.

In 1–6, tell if the number is *positive* or *negative*.

1. -13^5 Negative
2. -11^6 Negative
3. $(-8)^4$ Positive
4. $\left(-\frac{4}{5}\right)^7$ Negative
5. 17^3 Positive
6. $(-2.6)^{87}$ Negative

In 7–20, evaluate each expression.

7. -8^2 -64
8. $(-9)^2$ 81
9. -3^2 -9
10. $(-6)^3$ -216
11. -7^3 -343
12. $(-4)^4$ 256
13. $\left(\frac{1}{2}\right)^5$ $\frac{1}{32}$
14. $\left(-\frac{3}{10}\right)^4$ $\frac{81}{10{,}000}$
15. $-\left(\frac{4}{3}\right)^2$ $-\frac{16}{9}$
16. $(-5.1)^2$ 26.01
17. $(3 \cdot 4)^2$ 144
18. $(3^{-2})^3$ $\frac{1}{729}$
19. $(1.8 \cdot 10^4)^2$ 324,000,000
20. $(-7.66 \cdot 10^3)^2$ 58,675,600

Skills Objective C: Rewrite powers of products and quotient.

In 21–28, simplify each expression.

21. $(4x)^2$ $16x^2$
22. $(3a^5)^3$ $27a^{15}$
23. $(3xyz)^0$ 1
24. $\left(\frac{1}{6}a^4b\right)^4$ $\frac{1}{1296}a^{16}b^4$
25. $4n(8n^5)^3$ $2048n^{16}$
26. $(5r^2)^4(-2r^3)^5$ $-20{,}000r^{23}$
27. $-\left(\frac{3a^2}{b}\right)^4$ $-\frac{81x^8}{b^4}$
28. $\left(\frac{3}{4}m\right)^2 \cdot (8m)^2$ $36m^4$

Name

Properties Objective E: Identify the Product of a Power and Power of a Quotient Properties and use them to explain operations with powers.

29. Show how to simplify $(mx^{-3})^4$
   a. by rewriting using repeated multiplication.
   $(mx^{-3})^4 = mx^{-3} \cdot mx^{-3} \cdot mx^{-3} \cdot mx^{-3} = m^4x^{-12}$
   b. by rewriting using the Power of a Product Property.
   $(mx^{-3})^4 = m^4(x^{-3})^4 = m^4 \cdot x^{-3 \cdot 4} = m^4x^{-12}$

30. Show how to simplify $\left(\frac{3}{u^e}\right)^4$
   a. by rewriting using repeated multiplication.
   $\left(\frac{3}{u^e}\right)^4 = \left(\frac{3}{u^e}\right)\left(\frac{3}{u^e}\right)\left(\frac{3}{u^e}\right)\left(\frac{3}{u^e}\right) = \frac{81}{u^{4e}}$
   b. by rewriting using the Power of a Quotient Property.
   $\left(\frac{3}{u^e}\right)^4 = \frac{3^4}{(u^e)^4} = \frac{81}{u^{4e}}$

In 31–34, *multiple choice*. Identify the property that is illustrated.

(a) Power of a Power (b) Power of a Product
(c) Product of Powers (d) Power of a Quotient
(e) Quotient of Powers

31. $\left(\frac{a}{3}\right)^4 = \frac{a^4}{81}$ d
33. $m^3 \cdot m^6 = m^9$ c
33. $(e^5)^2 = e^{10}$ a
34. $\frac{x^3}{x^8} = x^{-5}$ e

Uses Objective H: Use and simplify expressions with powers in everyday situations.

35. Find the volume of each cube.
   a. n^3 cm^3
   b. $27n^3$ cm^3
   c. k^3n^3 cm^3

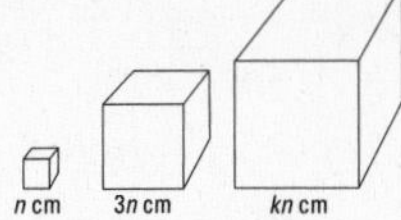

Name

LESSON MASTER 

Questions on SPUR Objectives

Skills Objective A: Evaluate integer powers of real numbers.

In 1–6, simplify, giving the answer as a simple fraction.

1. $\left(\frac{3}{14}\right)^{-1}$ $\frac{14}{3}$
2. $\left(\frac{2}{7}\right)^{-2}$ $\frac{49}{4}$
3. $\left(\frac{4}{3}\right)^{-3}$ $\frac{27}{64}$
4. $(-3)^{-4}$ $\frac{1}{81}$
5. -3^{-4} $-\frac{1}{81}$
6. $\left(-\frac{1}{10}\right)^{-4}$ 10,000

7. *Multiple choice.* Which of the following equals $(3m^{-3})^{-4}$? Explain your reasoning.
   (a) $81m^{12}$ (b) $\frac{m^{12}}{81}$ (c) $\frac{81}{m^{12}}$ (d) $\frac{1}{81m^{12}}$
   b; $(3m^{-3})^{-4} = 3^{-4}(m^{-3})^{-4} = \frac{1}{81}m^{12} = \frac{m^{12}}{81}$

Properties Objective D: Test a special case to determine whether a pattern is true.

8. Give a counterexample to the pattern $a^3 \cdot a^2 = a^6$.
   Sample: $3^3 \cdot 3^2 = 27 \cdot 9 = 243$; $3^6 = 729$

9. For each value of a, tell if $\frac{a^3}{a^2} = a^4$ is *true* or *false*.
   a. $a = 2$ false
   b. $a = 1$ true
   c. $a = .1$ false
   d. $a = 0$ false

10. For each value of x, tell if $(-x)^5 = -(x)^5$ is *true* or *false*.
   a. $x = 1$ true
   b. $x = 0$ true
   c. $x = -1$ true
   d. $x = 2$ true

Name

In 11–14, *multiple choice*. Choose the simplified form of the given expression. Check your answer by testing a special case. Sample checks are given.

11. $(4x^3)^2$ (a) $16x^5$ (b) $16x^6$ (c) $4x^5$ (d) $16x^5$ b
   $x = 2$: $(4 \cdot 2^3)^2 = (4 \cdot 8)^2 = 32^2 = 1024$; $16 \cdot 2^6 = 16 \cdot 64 = 1024$
   check

12. $5x^4 \cdot 3x^3$ (a) $15x^7$ (b) $8x^7$ (c) $15x^{12}$ (d) $16{,}875^{14}x^7$ a
   $x = 2$: $(5 \cdot 2^4) \cdot (3 \cdot 2^3) = 80 \cdot 24 = 1920$; $15 \cdot 2^7 = 15 \cdot 128 = 1920$
   check

13. $\frac{x^{12}}{x^6}$ (a) x^2 (b) $\frac{1}{x^6}$ (c) x^6 (d) $\frac{1}{x^2}$ c
   $x = 3$: $\frac{3^{12}}{3^6} = \frac{531{,}441}{729} = 729$; $3^6 = 729$
   check

14. $\left(\frac{2}{x^2}\right)^{-3}$ (a) $\frac{x^6}{8}$ (b) $\frac{x^6}{6}$ (c) $-\frac{x^6}{8}$ (d) $\frac{1}{8x}$ a
   $x = 3$: $\left(\frac{2}{3^2}\right)^{-3} = \frac{2^{-3}}{(3^2)^{-3}} = \frac{2^{-3}}{3^{-6}} = \frac{3^6}{2^3} = \frac{729}{8}$; $\frac{3^6}{8} = \frac{729}{8}$
   check

15. Show two different ways to simplify $\left(\frac{x}{y}\right)^3\left(\frac{x}{y}\right)^{-1}$.
   Sample: $\left(\frac{x}{y}\right)^3\left(\frac{x}{y}\right)^{-1} = \left(\frac{x}{y}\right)^{3-1} = \left(\frac{x}{y}\right)^2 = \frac{x^2}{y^2}$;
   $\left(\frac{x}{y}\right)^3\left(\frac{x}{y}\right)^{-1} = \frac{x^3}{y^3} \cdot \frac{x^{-1}}{y^{-1}} = \frac{x^{3-1}}{y^{3-1}} = \frac{x^2}{y^2}$

16. Consider the pattern $\sqrt{x^2 + y^2} = x + y$.
   a. Test the case with four different pairs of numbers for x and y.
   Sample: $\sqrt{1^2 + 2^2} = \sqrt{5} \neq 1 + 2$; $\sqrt{1^2 + 3^2} = \sqrt{10} \neq 1 + 3$; $\sqrt{0^2 + 4^2} = \sqrt{16} = 4 = 0 + 4$; $\sqrt{2^2 + 4^2} = \sqrt{20} \neq 2 + 4$
   b. Do you think the pattern is true? Why or why not?
   No; there exists at least one counterexample.

Name

LESSON MASTER 9-1 B

Questions on SPUR Objectives

Vocabulary

In 1–6, use the graphs of parabolas A and B pictured at the right.

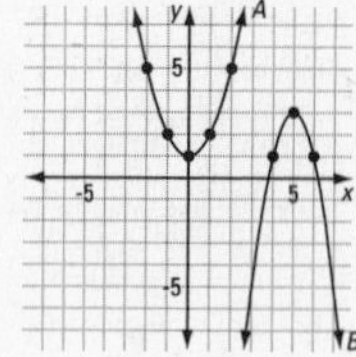

1. What seems to be the vertex of
   a. parabola A? (0, 1)
   b. parabola B? (5, 3)

2. What is the axis of symmetry of parabola A? y-axis, $x = 0$

3. Give an equation for the axis of symmetry of parabola B. $x = 5$

4. Which parabola opens
   a. up? A

   b. down? B

5. Which parabola has a
   a. maximum? B
   b. minimum? A

6. Give the coordinates of the point that is the reflection image of the given point over the parabola's axis of symmetry.
   a. (-2, 5) on parabola A (2, 5)
   b. (6, 1) on parabola B (4, 1)

Skills Objective A: Solve quadratic equations of the form $ax^2 = k$.

In 7–10, find both values of x. If answers are not integers, round to the nearest hundredth.

7. $5x^2 = 180$ $x = 6$, or $x = -6$

8. $\frac{1}{4}x^2 = 36$ $x = 12$, or $x = -12$

9. $\frac{7}{6}x^2 = 14$ $x = 3.46$, or $x = -3.46$

10. $4.8x^2 = 912$ $x = 13.78$, or $x = -13.78$

Name

Uses Objective E: Use quadratic equations to solve problems about paths of projectiles.

In 11–13, use $d = 16t^2$, Galileo's formula relating the time t in seconds an object falls a distance d in feet.

11. How far does an object fall in 8 seconds? 1,024 feet

12. How far does an object fall in $3t$ seconds? $144t^2$ feet

13. How long does it take a stone to fall from the top of 676-foot skyscraper to the ground below? 6.5 seconds

Representations Objective F: Graph equations of the form $y = ax^2$ and interpret these graphs.

In 14 and 15, an equation is given. Make a table of values using x-values -3, -2, -1, 0, 1, 2, and 3. Graph the equation.

14. $y = \frac{3}{2}x^2$

15. $y = -2x^2$

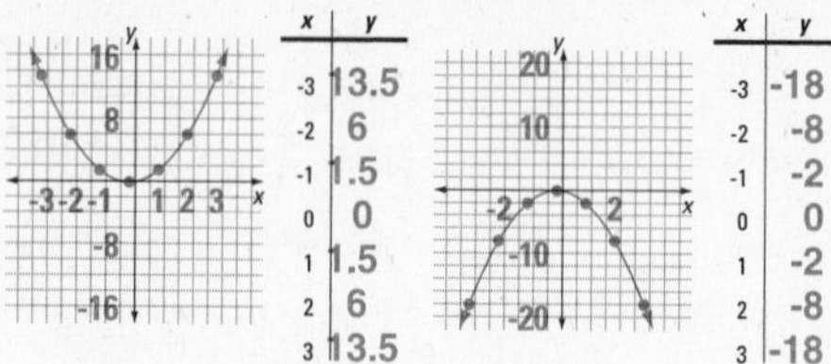

x	y
-3	13.5
-2	6
-1	1.5
0	0
1	1.5
2	6
3	13.5

x	y
-3	-18
-2	-8
-1	-2
0	0
1	-2
2	-8
3	-18

In 16 and 17, an equation is given. a. Tell if its graph opens *up* or *down*. b. Tell if it has a *maximum* or a *minimum*.

16. $y = \frac{2}{3}x^2$
   a. up b. minimum

17. $y = -5x^2$
   a. down b. maximum

Name

LESSON MASTER 9-2 B

Questions on SPUR Objectives

Representations Objective F: Graph equations of the form $y = ax^2 + bx + c$ and interpret these graphs.

In 1 and 2, tell if the graph of the equation opens *up* or *down*.

1. $y = 3x^2 - 4x - 1$ up

2. $y = -2x^2 + 3$ down

In 3 and 4, the graph of a parabola is shown. a. Give the coordinates of the vertex. b. Give the y-intercept. c. Write an equation for the axis of symmetry.

3.

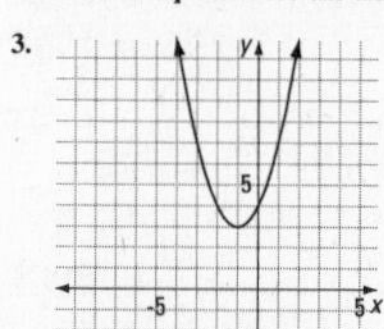

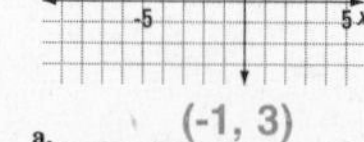

a. (-1, 3)
b. 4
c. $x = -1$

4.

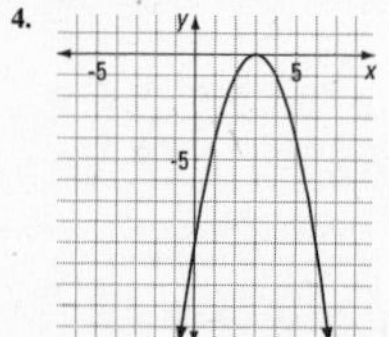

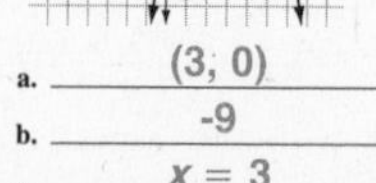

a. (3, 0)
b. -9
c. $x = 3$

5. The table of values below is for a parabola.

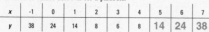

x	-1	0	1	2	3	4	5	6	7
y	38	24	14	8	6	8	14	24	38

a. Fill in the missing values.

b. What are the coordinates of its vertex? (3, 6)

c. What is its y-intercept? 24

d. Does this parabola open up? yes

e. Does the parabola have a minimum value? yes

Name

In 6 and 7, an equation is given. a. Make a table of values using x-values -3, -2, -1, 0, 1, 2, and 3. b. Graph the equation. c. Give the coordinates of the vertex. d. Give the y-intercept. e. Write an equation for the axis of symmetry.

6. $y = x^2 - 4x + 5$

a.

x	y
-3	26
-2	17
-1	10
0	5
1	2
2	1
3	2

b.

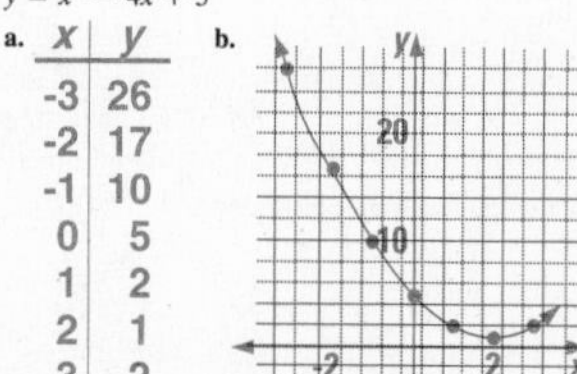

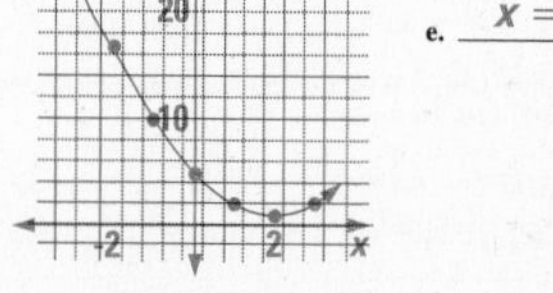

c. (2, 1)
d. 5
e. $x = 2$

7. $y = -3x^2 + 1$

a.

x	y
-3	-26
-2	-11
-1	-2
0	1
1	-2
2	-11
3	-26

b.

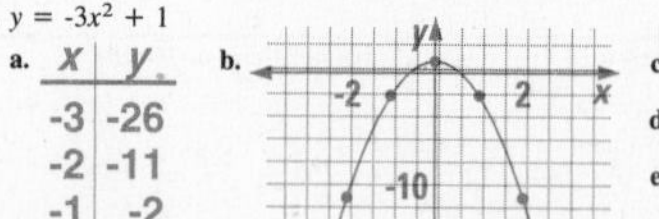

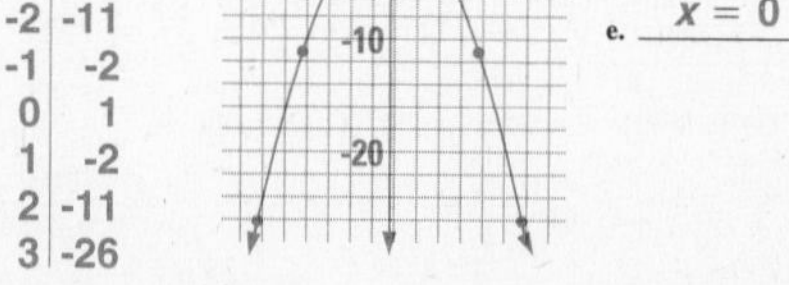

c. (0, 1)
d. 1
e. $x = 0$

8. a. Use symmetry to complete the graph at the right.
   b. Name its y-intercept. 3
   c. Name its x-intercepts. 1, 3

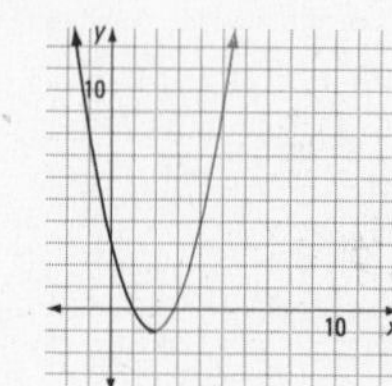

Name

LESSON MASTER 9-3 B Questions on SPUR Objectives

Representations Objective F: Graph equations of the form $y = ax^2 + bx + c$ and interpret these graphs.

1. 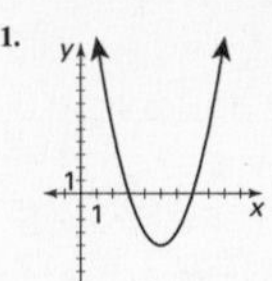

In the graph of the equation $x^2 - 10x + 21$ shown at the left, the x-intercepts are 3 and 7.

a. What is the x-coordinate of the vertex? **5**

b. Use your answer to Part **a** to find the y-coordinate of the vertex. **-4**

c. Write an equation for the axis of symmetry. **$x = 5$**

2. a. On the default window of an automatic grapher, graph the four parabolas given. Then sketch them in the window at the right.

$y = -x^2 - 1$
$y = -2x^2 - 2$
$y = -3x^2 - 3$
$y = -4x^2 - 4$

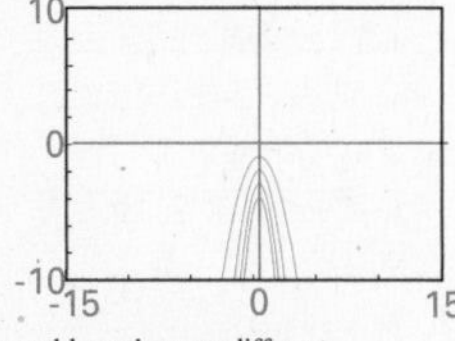

b. Describe how the graphs are similar and how they are different.

Sample: They all open down and have the y-axis for their axis of symmetry. The vertices are at different points, and the graphs appear to get "narrower."

c. Describe the graph of $-10x^2 - 10$.

Sample: It opens down and has the y-axis for its axis of symmetry. The vertex is at (0, -10). It is quite "narrow."

Name

In 3 and 4, the graph of a parabola is given. Identify a different window that shows the vertex, the y-intercept, and both x-intercepts. **Samples are given.**

3. $y = x^2 - 8x - 22$

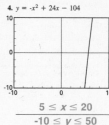

$-5 \le x \le 15$
$-40 \le y \le 10$

4. $y = -x^2 + 24x - 104$

$5 \le x \le 20$
$-10 \le y \le 50$

5. Identify a window for the graph of $y = -x^2 + 5$ so the graph will look like the graph at the right.

Sample: $0 \le x \le 3$; $0 \le y \le 5$

6. Graph $y = 2x^2 + 40x + 156$ on a window that shows the vertex and x-intercepts.

a. Estimate the coordinates of the vertex. **(-10, -44)**

b. Write an equation for the axis of symmetry. **$x = -10$**

c. Estimate the x-intercepts. **-14.7, -5.3**

7. a. Use an automatic grapher and graph $y = x^2 + 1$ and $y = 2x + 4$ on the same set of axes.

b. Estimate the coordinates of the points where the two graphs intersect. **(-1, 2), (3, 10)**

Name

LESSON MASTER 9-4 B Questions on SPUR Objectives

Uses Objective E: Use quadratic equations to solve problems about paths of projectiles.

In 1–6, use the graph at the right. It shows the height h in feet of a small rocket t seconds after it is launched.

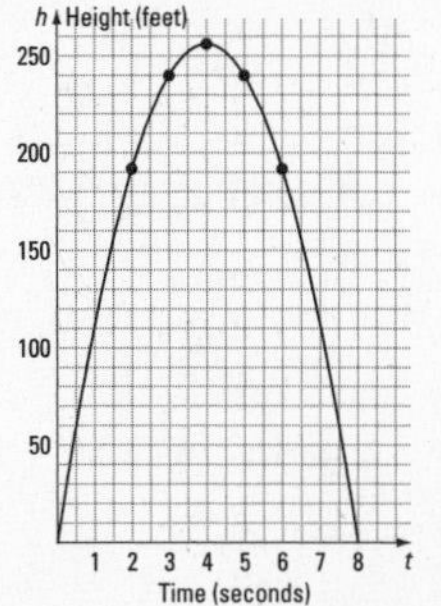

1. How long is the rocket in the air? **8 seconds**

2. What is the greatest height the rocket reaches? **≈256 feet**

3. About how high is the rocket after 1 second? **≈112 feet**

4. After 2 seconds,

a. about how high is the rocket? **≈192 feet**

b. is the rocket *going up* or *coming down*? **going up**

5. After 6 seconds,

a. about how high is the rocket? **≈192 feet**

b. is the rocket *going up* or *coming down*? **coming down**

6. Do you think the rocket is traveling faster from 0 to 1 second or from 3 to 4 seconds? Explain your thinking.

Sample: From 0 to 1 second, the rocket ascends 112 feet; from 3 to 4 seconds, it ascends only 16 feet.

Name

In 7–10, use this information. Theresa jumps off a diving platform into the swimming pool below. Theresa's path is described by the following equation: $y = -2x^2 + 2x + 15$. In this equation, x is Theresa's horizontal distance in meters from the edge of the platform, and y is her height in meters above the surface of the water. The graph of the equation is shown at the right.

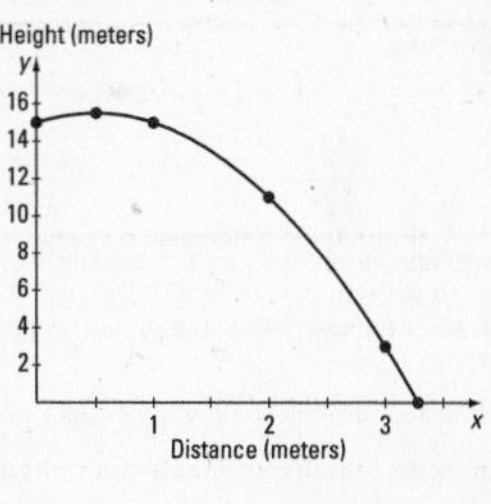

7. What is the greatest height above the water that Theresa reaches? **15.5 meters**

8. How high is the diving platform? **15 meters**

9. What is Theresa's height when she has traveled 2 meters horizontally from the edge of the platform? **11 meters**

10. Use the equation to find Theresa's height when she has traveled 1.5 meters from the edge of the platform. **13.5 meters**

Review Objective D, Lesson 1-6

In 11 and 12, a. give the exact square roots of the given number. b. Then approximate the square roots to the nearest hundred-thousandth.

11. 6 a. **$\sqrt{6}, -\sqrt{6}$** b. **2.4495, -2.4495**

12. 342 a. **$\sqrt{342}, -\sqrt{342}$** b. **18.4932, -18.4932**

In 13–16, evaluate without a calculator.

13. $-\sqrt{16}$ **-4**

14. $3\sqrt{25}$ **15**

15. $\sqrt{36} + \sqrt{64}$ **14**

16. $\sqrt{36 + 64}$ **10**

Name

LESSON MASTER 9-5 B **Questions on SPUR Objectives**

Skills Objective A: Solve quadratic equations using the Quadratic Formula.

1. Write the *quadratic formula* and explain what a, b, and c represent.

$x = \frac{-b \pm \sqrt{b^2 - 4ac}}{2a}$; a, b, and c are the coefficients a, b, and c in the equation $ax^2 + bx + c = 0$.

In 2–7, find the two values of the expression. Round answers that are *not* integers to the nearest tenth.

2. $\frac{-2 \pm 8}{2}$ 3, -5

3. $\frac{9 \pm 5}{4}$ 3.5, 1

4. $\frac{-6 \pm 15}{-6}$ 3.5, -1.5

5. $\frac{0 \pm \sqrt{81}}{3}$ 3, -3

6. $\frac{-4 \pm \sqrt{24 - -120}}{2}$ 4, -8

7. $\frac{-2 \pm \sqrt{4 - -10}}{2 \cdot 15}$ 0.1, -0.2

In 8–13, write each equation in standard form.

8. $x^2 + 40 + 4x = 0$ $x^2 + 4x + 40 = 0$

9. $3t^2 + 9t = 2$ $3t^2 + 9t - 2 = 0$

10. $4v^2 = 80 + 6v^2 - 14v$ $2v^2 - 14x + 80 = 0$

11. $3w^2 - 4w - 18 = -w^2 + w + 1$ $4w^2 - 5w - 19 = 0$

12. $12y - y^2 = 0$ $y^2 - 12y = 0$

13. $16x - x^2 + 3 = 16x$ $x^2 - 3 = 0$

Name

In 14–17, an equation in standard form is given. a. Identify *a*, *b*, and *c*. b. Give the solutions rounded to the nearest hundredth.

14. $x^2 - 10x + 16 = 0$
a. $a = 1$ $b = -10$ $c = 16$
b. $x = 8$ or $x = 2$

15. $-v^2 + 14v + 33 = 0$
a. $a = -1$ $b = 14$ $c = 33$
b. $v = 16.06$ or $v = -2.06$

16. $2s^2 + 5s - 3 = 0$
a. $a = 2$ $b = 5$ $c = -3$
b. $s = 0.5$ or $s = -3$

17. $y^2 + 12y = 0$
a. $a = 1$ $b = 12$ $c = 0$
b. $y = 0$ or $y = -12$

In 18–21, an equation is given. a. Rewrite the equation in standard form. b. Give the solutions rounded to the nearest hundredth.

18. $a^2 - 9a = 18$
a. $a^2 - 9a - 18 = 0$
b. $a = 10.68$ or $a = -1.68$

19. $-2d^2 = 3d - 15$
a. $-2d^2 - 3d + 15 = 0$
b. $d = 2.09$ or $d = -3.59$

20. $x^2 + 36 = 12x$
a. $x^2 - 12x + 36 = 0$
b. $x = 6$

21. $4(n^2 + 2n) + 3 = 10$
a. $4n^2 + 8n - 7 = 0$
b. $n = .66$ or $n = -2.66$

22. Write a check for your solutions to Question 16.
$2(0.5)^2 + 5(0.5) - 3 = 0.5 + 2.5 - 3 = 0$
$2(-3)^2 + 5(-3) - 3 = 18 - 15 - 3 = 0$

Uses Objective E: Use quadratic equations to solve problems about paths of projectiles.

In 23–25, use this information: A rocket is launched from a cliff 30 feet above the ground. Its height *h* in feet above the ground *t* seconds after it is launched is given by the equation $h = -16t^2 + 192t + 30$.

23. At what two times is the rocket 100 feet above the ground? ≈ 11.6 sec, $\approx .4$ sec

24. When is the rocket 606 feet above the ground? after 6 sec

25. When does the rocket hit the ground? in ≈ 12.2 sec

Name

LESSON MASTER 9-6 B **Questions on SPUR Objectives**

Vocabulary

1. What is the *discriminant* of the quadratic equation $ax^2 + bx + c = 0$? $b^2 - 4ac$

Properties Objective D: Identify and use the discriminant of a quadratic equation.

In 2–4, tell if the discriminant is *positive*, *negative*, or *zero*.

2. A quadratic equation has exactly one real solution. zero

3. A quadratic equation has exactly two real solutions. positive

4. A quadratic equation has no real solutions. negative

In 5–7, use the graph at the right. It shows the height *y* of a rocket in meters when it has been launched from a cliff and has been in the air for *t* seconds, where $y = 55 + 33t - 5t^2$. In 5–7, a height is given.

a. **Write a quadratic equation that could be used to find the time when the rocket reaches that height.**

b. **Use the graph to predict whether the discriminant of the equation is *positive*, *negative*, or *zero*.**

c. **Check your answer to Part b by finding the value of the discriminant.**

y
100
80
60
40
20
Height (meters)
1 2 3 4 5 6 7 8 t
Time (seconds)

5. 80 feet
a. $-5t^2 + 30t - 25 = 0$ b. positive c. 400

6. 100 feet
a. $-5t^2 + 30t - 45 = 0$ b. zero c. 0

7. 110 feet
a. $-5t^2 + 30t - 55 = 0$ b. negative c. -200

Name

In 8–15, a quadratic equation is given. a. Find the value of the discriminant. b. Give the number of real solutions. c. Find the real solutions, rounded to the nearest hundredth. If there are none, write "no solution."

8. $r^2 + 6r + 4 = 0$
a. 20
b. 2
c. $r = -5.24$ or $r = -.76$

9. $u^2 + 4u + 20 = 0$
a. -64
b. 0
c. no solution

10. $-w^2 + 22w - 121 = 0$
a. 0
b. 1
c. $w = 11$

11. $-2x^2 - 8x + 12 = 0$
a. 160
b. 2
c. $x = 1.16$ or $x = -5.16$

12. $y^2 + 3y = 0$
a. 9
b. 2
c. $y = 0$ or $y = -3$

13. $-4z^2 - 4z = 21$
a. -320
b. 0
c. no solution

14. $b^2 + 38 = 0$
a. -152
b. 0
c. no solution

15. $3(n^2 - 7n) = -30$
a. 81
b. 2
c. $n = 5$ or $n = 2$

16. For what value of h does $x^2 + 6x + h$ have exactly one solution? 9

17. Find a value of h such that $x^2 + 6x + h$ has no real solutions. $h > 9$

18. Find a value of h such that $x^2 + 6x + h$ has exactly two real solutions. $h < 9$

Name

LESSON MASTER 9-7 B

Questions on SPUR Objectives

Skills Objective B: Simplify square roots.

1. Use the drawing at the right.

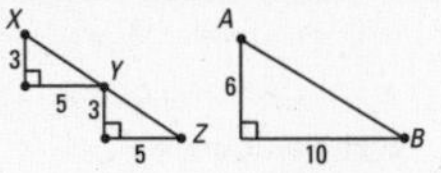

a. Calculate XY. $\sqrt{34}$

b. Express XZ as $2 \cdot XY$. $2\sqrt{34}$

c. Find AB. $\sqrt{136}$

d. Use decimal approximations to show that your answers to Parts **b** and **c** are equal. $2\sqrt{34} \approx 11.66 \approx \sqrt{136}$

2. Which property states that if a and b are non-negative real numbers, then $\sqrt{a} \cdot \sqrt{b} = \sqrt{a \cdot b}$?
Product of Square Roots Property

3. *Multiple choice.* Which of the expressions below equal $\sqrt{30}$? b, d

(a) $2\sqrt{15}$ (b) $\sqrt{2} \cdot \sqrt{15}$ (c) $5\sqrt{6}$ (d) $\sqrt{5} \cdot \sqrt{6}$

4. *Multiple choice.* Which of the expressions below equal $\sqrt{32}$? a, c

(a) $2\sqrt{8}$ (b) $16\sqrt{2}$ (c) $4\sqrt{2}$ (d) $2\sqrt{16}$

In 5–8, find the exact value of the variable in simplified form.

5.
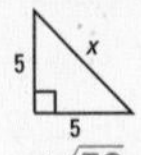

$\sqrt{50}$, or $5\sqrt{2}$

6.
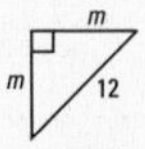

$\sqrt{72}$, or $6\sqrt{2}$

7.
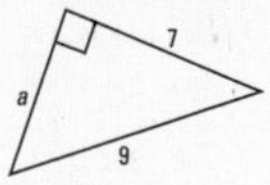

$\sqrt{32}$, or $4\sqrt{2}$

8.
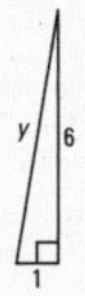

$\sqrt{37}$

Name

9.
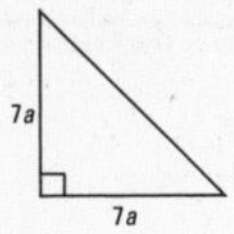

a. Use the Pythagorean Theorem to write an expression for the length of the hypotenuse of the triangle at the left. $\sqrt{98a^2}$

b. Simplify your answer to Part **a**. $7a\sqrt{2}$

In 10–20, simplify. Do not use a calculator.

10. $\sqrt{2} \cdot \sqrt{18}$ 6

11. $\sqrt{4} \cdot \sqrt{16}$ 8

12. $\sqrt{14^2}$ 14

13. $\sqrt{3^2 \cdot 7^2}$ 21

14. $\sqrt{2a} \cdot \sqrt{5}$ where a is positive $\sqrt{10a}$

15. $\sqrt{2n} \cdot \sqrt{3n}$ where n is positive $n\sqrt{6}$

16. $2\sqrt{27}$ $6\sqrt{3}$

17. $\sqrt{200}$ $10\sqrt{2}$

18. $2\sqrt{75}$ $10\sqrt{3}$

19. $2\sqrt{6} \cdot 5\sqrt{24}$ 120

20. a. $\sqrt{20}$ $2\sqrt{5}$

b. $\sqrt{45}$ $3\sqrt{5}$

c. $\sqrt{20} + \sqrt{45}$ $5\sqrt{5}$

In 21–24, give the exact solution in simplified form.

21. $x^2 = 300$
$x = 10\sqrt{3}$ or $x = -10\sqrt{3}$

22. $(2y)^2 = 432$
$y = 6\sqrt{3}$ or $y = -6\sqrt{3}$

23. $3x^2 + 18 = 165$
$x = 7$ or $x = -7$

24. $\frac{6}{u} = \frac{u}{20}$
$u = 2\sqrt{30}$ or $u = -2\sqrt{30}$

Name

LESSON MASTER 9-8 B

Questions on SPUR Objectives

Vocabulary

1. In terms of a number line, what is the *absolute value* of a number?
Sample: the distance from the number's location on a number line to the origin

Skills Objective C: Evaluate expressions and solve equations using absolute value.

In 2–18, evaluate the expression.

2. $|-8|$ 8

3. $|19|$ 19

4. $|\frac{2}{3}|$ $\frac{2}{3}$

5. $|-0.72|$ 0.72

6. $-|51|$ -51

7. $|4^2|$ 16

8. $|(-3)^2|$ 9

9. $|-9^2|$ 81

10. $-|\frac{4}{5}|$ $-\frac{4}{5}$

11. $-|-\frac{7}{16}|$ $-\frac{7}{16}$

12. ABS (0) 0

13. ABS (-5 · 7) 35

14. $|4 - 12|$ 8

15. $|4| - |12|$ -8

16. $\sqrt{12^2}$ 12

17. $\sqrt{(-12)^2}$ 12

18. Give all values of m for which $|m|$ is *not* positive. $m = 0$

In 19–24, solve and check the equation.

19. $|x| = 20$
$x = 20$ or $x = -20$
$|20| = 20$, $|-20| = 20$

20. $|x + 4| = 13$
$x = 9$ or $x = -17$
$|9 + 4| = |13| = 13$
$|-17 + 4| = |-13| = 13$

21. $|n - 8| = 5$
$n = 13$ or $n = 3$
$|13 - 8| = |5| = 5$
$|3 - 8| = |-5| = 5$

22. $|60 - x| = 14$
$x = 46$ or $x = 74$
$|60 - 46| = |14| = 14$
$|60 - 74| = |-14| = 14$

Name

23. $|8n + 4| = 32$
$n = 3.5$ or $n = -4.5$
$|8(3.5) + 4| = |32| = 32$
$|8(-4.5) + 4| = |-32| = 32$

24. $|-\frac{1}{2}x| = 28$
$x = 56$ or $x = -56$
$|-\frac{1}{2}(56)| = |-28| = 28$
$|-\frac{1}{2}(-56)| = |28| = 28$

25. A carnival prize is given if someone guesses the number of marbles in a jar. There are actually 347 marbles and a guess is g. Write an expression for how far off the guess is

a. if the guess is too high. $g - 347$

b. if the guess is too low. $347 - g$

c. if you don't know whether the guess is too high or too low. $|g - 347|$ or $|347 - g|$

Representations Objective G: Calculate and represent distances on the number line.

In 26–28, find the distance between the given points.

26.

38

27.
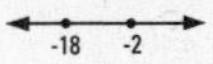

16

28.
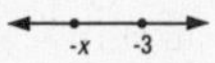

$|-x + 3|$

29. Give the coordinates of the two points on a number line that are 18 units from the point with coordinate 6. 24, -12

30. Give the coordinates of the two points on a number line that are 40 units from the point with coordinate -65. -105, -25

31. A manufacturer makes golf balls with a diameter of 1.68 inches and a tolerance of .05 in. This means they reject any balls they make whose diameter is outside the interval 1.68 ± .05 in.

a. What are the least and greatest acceptable diameters? 1.63 in., 1.73 in.

b. Is 1.677 an acceptable diameter? yes

c. Graph all acceptable diameters on a number line.

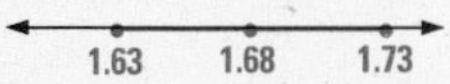

d. Let d be the diameter of an acceptable golf ball. Write an inequality relating $|d - 1.68|$ and .05 $|d - 1.68| \leq 0.05$

Name

LESSON MASTER 9-9 B **Questions on SPUR Objectives**

Representations Objective G: Calculate and represent distances in the plane.

In 1 and 2, each square represents a city block. Find how many blocks it take to travel from *P* to *Q*, a. if you travel on the streets and go by way of *R*, or b. if you travel as the crow flies.

1.

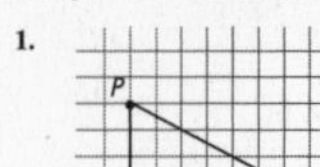

a. 9 blocks

b. ≈6.7 blocks

2.

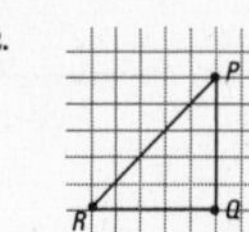

a. 10 blocks

b. ≈7.1 blocks

In 3–6, use the diagram at the right to find each length.

3. *AB* 5

4. *CD* 6

5. *EF* 8

6. *GH* 5

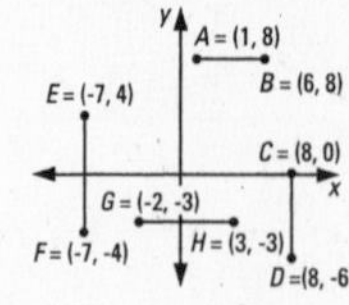

7. In the diagram at the right, $P = (-2, 1)$. Points *Q*, *R*, *S*, and *T* are each 4 units from *P* on the horizontal or vertical line through *P*. Find the coordinates of each point.

Q (2, 1) *R* (-2, 5)

S (-6, 1) *T* (-2, -3)

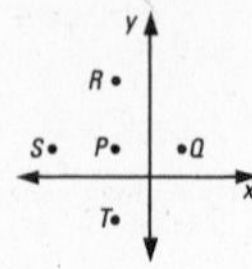

8. Find the coordinates of *M* in the diagram at the right.

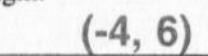

(-4, 6)

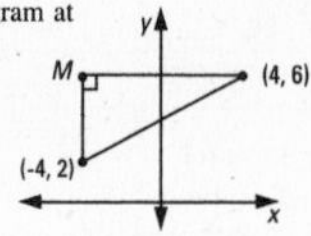

Name

9. a. Find the coordinates of *C*.

(-9, -2)

b. Find the length of $\overline{AC}$.

7

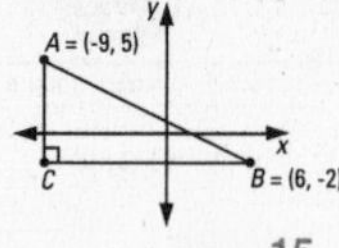

c. Find the length of $\overline{BC}$. 15

d. Use the Pythagorean Theorem to find the length of $\overline{AB}$. $\sqrt{247} \approx 16.6$

10. Write a formula for the distance between (m, n) and (r, s).

Sample: $d = \sqrt{(r-m)^2 + (s-n)^2}$

In 11–14, use the distance formula to find the distance between the two points. Round answers to the nearest hundredth.

11. (5, 6) and (12, 14) $\sqrt{113} \approx 10.63$

12. (2, -7) and (-8, 9) $\sqrt{356} \approx 18.87$

13. (-1, -5) and (3, -1) $\sqrt{32} \approx 5.66$

14. (-12, 0) and (5, -19) $\sqrt{650} \approx 25.50$

In 15–19, use the map at the right, which shows the streets and locations of three buildings in a town. The streets are 1 block apart.

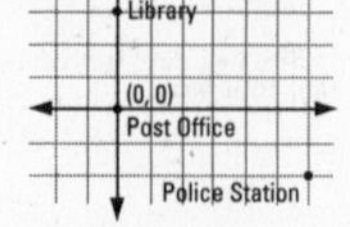

15. If the coordinates of the post office are (0, 0), what are the coordinates of the library and the police station?

(0, 3), (6, -2)

16. How far is it from the library to the post office? 3 blocks

17. How far it is from the police station to the post office "as the crow flies"? $\sqrt{40}$, or ≈6.3 blocks

18. How far is it from the police station to the library "as the crow flies"? $\sqrt{61}$, or ≈7.8 blocks

19. How far is it to drive from the police staton to the library? 11 blocks

Name

LESSON MASTER 10-1 B **Questions on SPUR Objectives**

Properties Objective E: Classify polynomials by their degree or number of terms.

In 1–8, tell whether the expression is a *monomial* (M), *binomial* (B), *trinomial* (T), *polynomial* (P), or none of these (N). List all the terms that apply.

1. fgh M, P

2. -7.2 M, P

3. $3y^{-3}$ N

4. $\frac{3}{2} + 22ab$ B, P

5. $11x^2 - x - 12$ T, P

6. $\sqrt{5}$ M, P

7. $a^2 + ab - ab^2 + b^3$ P

8. 100π M, P

In 9–12, tell which of these expressions, after being simplified, are binomials. Write *yes* or *no*.

9. $4a + 5a$ no

10. $2(b^2 + 6)$ yes

11. $5h + 12u - 8h$ yes

12. $77x^2$ no

13. a. What is the degree of $3m^5$? 5

b. What is the degree of m^3n^7? 10

14. Give an example of a monomial of degree 8 if

a. the only variable is *a*. Sample: $3a^8$

b. the monomial has two variables, *a* and *b*. Sample: a^2b^6

In 15–20, give the degree of the polynomial.

15. $3xy + 2x$ 2

16. $3r^5 + 6.9$ 5

17. $5m^8 - m^3$ 8

18. $3e^5 - 2e^5 + 4e^7$ 7

19. $a^4 + a^3 - ab^2 + ab^4$ 5

20. $w^3 + 2w^2v^2 - 6$ 4

Name

Properties Objective F: Write whole numbers as polynomials in base 10.

In 21–24, write as a polynomial in base 10.

21. 3,945 $3 \cdot 10^3 + 9 \cdot 10^2 + 4 \cdot 10^1 + 5$

22. 6,500,004 $6 \cdot 10^6 + 5 \cdot 10^5 + 4$

23. 58,257 $5 \cdot 10^4 + 8 \cdot 10^3 + 2 \cdot 10^2 + 5 \cdot 10^1 + 7$

24. 431,006,090 $4 \cdot 10^8 + 3 \cdot 10^7 + 1 \cdot 10^6 + 6 \cdot 10^3 + 9 \cdot 10^1$

In 25–28, simplify each polynomial.

25. $2 \cdot 10^4 + 3 \cdot 10^2 + 10^1$ 20,310

26. $7 \cdot 10^8 + 2 \cdot 10^4 + 10^3 + 5 \cdot 10^2$ 700,021,500

27. $4 \cdot 10^6 + 3 \cdot 10^5 + 10^4 + 7 \cdot 10^3$ 4,317,000

28. $9 \cdot 10^7 + 6 \cdot 10^6 + 8 \cdot 10^2 + 5 \cdot 10^1$ 96,000,850

Representations Objective I: Represent areas of figures in terms of polynomials.

In 29 and 30, give the area of the figure as a polynomial.

29.

x^2	x^2
x	x
x	x
x	x

$2x^2 + 6x$

30.

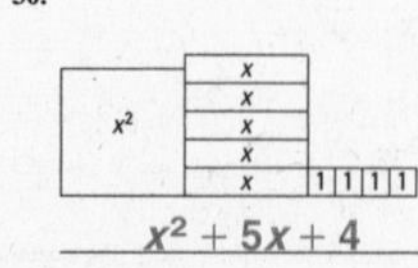

$x^2 + 5x + 4$

In 31 and 32, make a drawing to represent the polynomial using algebra tiles. Arrange the tiles to form a rectangle.

31. $3x + 12$

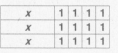

x	1	1	1	1
x	1	1	1	1
x	1	1	1	1

32. $x^2 + 4x + 3$

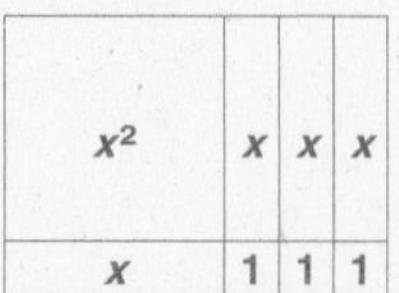

Name

LESSON MASTER 10-2 B

Questions on SPUR Objectives

Skills Objective A: Add and subtract polynomials.

In 1–6, simplify the expression.

1. $(3x^2 - 7x + 1) + (2x^2 + x - 8)$ $5x^2 - 6x - 7$
2. $(9b^2 - 3b - 2) - (b^2 + 4b - 6)$ $8b^2 - 7b + 4$
3. $(16 - 4m^2 + 2m) + (5m^2 - 3m - 10)$ $m^2 - m + 6$
4. $(a^2 - 12) - (a^2 - 4a + 2)$ $4a - 14$
5. $(2x^2 + 3x - 18) - (4x - 5)$ $2x^2 - x - 13$
6. $(p^3 + 2p^2 + 4) + (p^3 + 8p^2 + 7p)$ $2p^3 + 10p^2 + 7p + 4$

In 7 and 8, fill in the missing polynomial.

7. $(4x^2 - 7x + 11) + (\underline{x^2 + 2x + 4}) = 5x^2 - 5x + 15$
8. $(5e^2 + 12e - 3) - (\underline{-3e^2 + 12e - 4}) = 8e^2 + 1$

Uses Objective G: Translate investment situations into polynomials.

9. Jimmy has enrolled in a retirement plan in which he invests \$2,000 at the beginning of each year.
   a. Suppose the money is invested in an account with a yearly scale factor x. Complete the chart to show how much Jimmy would have in his retirement account at the end of each year.

Year	Amount at End of Year
1	$2{,}000x$
2	$2{,}000x^2 + 2{,}000x$
3	$2{,}000x^3 + 2{,}000x^2 + 2{,}000x$
4	$2{,}000x^4 + 2{,}000x^3 + 2{,}000x^2 + 2{,}000x$
5	$2{,}000x^5 + 2{,}000x^4 + 2{,}000x^3 + 2{,}000x^2 + 2{,}000x$

   b. Calculate how much would be in the account after 5 years if the interest rate were 4%. \$11,265.95
   c. Calculate how much would be in the account after 5 years if the interest rate were 10%. \$13,431.22

Name

▶ **LESSON MASTER 10-2 B** *page 2*

Suppose Jimmy's employer adds \$1,000 to Jimmy's retirement account each year.

d. Write a polynomial showing the portion of the account balance after 5 years due to the employer's contributions. Let the yearly scale factor be x.
$1{,}000x^5 + 1{,}000x^4 + 1{,}000x^3 + 1{,}000x^2 + 1{,}000x$

e. Write a polynomial showing the total amount in the account after 5 years with a yearly scale factor x. Give your answer in simplified form.
$3{,}000x^5 + 3{,}000x^4 + 3{,}000x^3 + 3{,}000x^2 + 3{,}000x$

In 10–12, Yuko will be ready for college in 6 years. Her mother is examining two plans for college savings. Each plan earns 6.5% interest compounded annually. Here are the plans.

Plan I: Deposit \$4,000 at the beginning of the 1st, 2nd, and 3rd years.

Plan II: Wait and deposit \$5,000 at the beginning of the 4th, 5th, and 6th years.

10. Fill in the spreadsheet below.

	A	B	C	D	E
1	Year	Plan I Deposit	Plan I End of Year Balance	Plan II Deposit	Plan II End of Year Balance
2	1	4,000	4,260	0	0
3	2	4,000	8,796.90	0	0
4	3	4,000	13,628.70	0	0
5	4	0	14,514.56	5,000	5,325
6	5	0	15,458.01	5,000	10,996.13
7	6	0	16,462.78	5,000	17,035.87

11. What formula can be used to calculate the value in
   a. cell C7? Samples: $=4000*(1.065^6+1.065^5+1.065^4)$; $1.065*C6$
   b. cell E7? Samples: $=5000*(1.065^3+1.065^2+1.065)$; $1.065*(E6+5000)$

12. Which plan yields more money after 6 years? How much more?
Plan II; \$573.09

Name

LESSON MASTER 10-3 B

Questions on SPUR Objectives

Skills Objective C: Multiply a polynomial by a monomial.

In 1–14, simplify.

1. $7(2x)$ $14x$
2. $8a(6a)$ $48a^2$
3. $3m^2(4m^3)$ $12m^5$
4. $-r^3(12r^4)$ $-12r^7$
5. $5(e + 14)$ $5e + 70$
6. $6(d - 9)$ $6d - 54$
7. $3y(y^2 - 2y + 1)$ $3y^3 - 6y^2 + 3y$
8. $11b^3(2ab^2 + 7a)$ $22ab^5 + 77ab^3$
9. $9r(-3r^4 - 8)$ $-27r^5 - 72r$
10. $2bc(-4b^2c)$ $-8b^3c^2$
11. $-7mn(m^2 + 2mn - 3n)$ $-7m^3n - 14m^2n^2 + 21mn^2$
12. $2(x + 6) + 5(x - 4)$ $7x - 8$
13. $10(x^2 + 3x + 2) - 4x(x + 8)$ $6x^2 - 2x + 20$
14. $a^2(a^3 + 4a - 7) + a^3(-a^2 - a + 4)$ $-a^4 + 8a^3 - 7a^2$

In 15–20, fill in the blank.

15. $6abc(\underline{-2abc^2}) = -12a^2b^2c^3$
16. $3(x + \underline{7}) = 3x + 21$
17. $5m(\underline{3m} + 3) = 15m^2 + 15m$
18. $a^2(a^3 + \underline{5a^2}) = a^5 + 5a^4$
19. $(\underline{-3})(4y + 6) = -12y - 18$
20. $(\underline{xy^2})(x^2 - x) = x^3y^2 - x^2y^2$

Name

▶ **LESSON MASTER 10-3 B** *page 2*

Representations Objective I: Represent areas of figures in terms of polynomials.

In 21–24, a rectangle is shown.
a. Express the area as length • width.
b. Express the area as the sum of smaller areas.
c. Combine the two expressions from Parts a and b to write an equation for the area of the rectangle.

21.

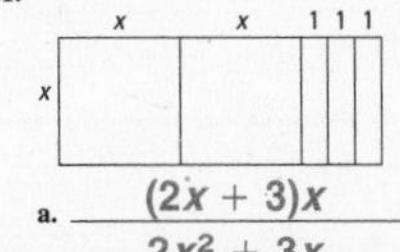

a. $(2x + 3)x$
b. $2x^2 + 3x$
c. $(2x + 3)x = 2x^2 + 3x$

22.

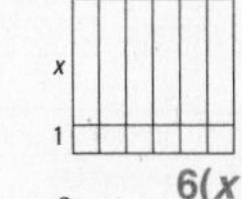

a. $6(x + 1)$
b. $6x + 6$
c. $6(x + 1) = 6x + 6$

23. 24.

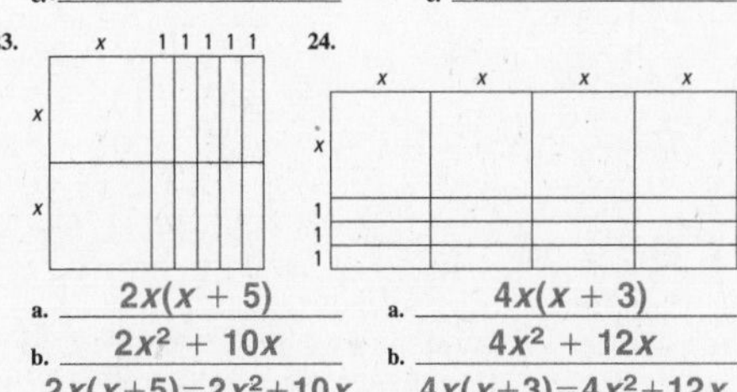

23.
a. $2x(x + 5)$
b. $2x^2 + 10x$
c. $2x(x+5) = 2x^2 + 10x$

24.
a. $4x(x + 3)$
b. $4x^2 + 12x$
c. $4x(x+3) = 4x^2 + 12x$

25. The length ℓ of a rectangle is 2 more than 3 times its width w.
   a. Write an expression for ℓ in terms of w. $3w + 2$
   b. Express the area as length · width in terms of w. $(3w + 2)w$
   c. Multiply to express your answer to Part **b** as a polynomial. $3w^2 + 2w$
   d. Check that your answers to Parts **b** and **c** are equal by substituting $\ell = 10$.
   $(3 \cdot 10 + 2)10 = 320;\ 3 \cdot 10^2 + 2 \cdot 10 = 320$

Name

LESSON MASTER 10-4 B

Questions on SPUR Objectives

Skills Objective B: Multiply polynomials.

In 1–11, multiply and simplify.

1. $(a + 4)(a^2 + 4a - 3)$ $a^3 + 8a^2 + 13a - 12$
2. $(m - 1)(m^2 - 4m + 5)$ $m^3 - 5m^2 + 9m - 5$
3. $(a + b)(2a - 8b)$ $2a^2 - 6ab - 8b^2$
4. $(x^2 + 6x + 9)(x^2 - 1)$ $x^4 + 6x^3 + 8x^2 - 6x - 9$
5. $(2y^2 + 3y + 4)(y^2 - y + 2)$ $2y^4 + y^3 + 5y^2 + 2y + 8$
6. $(-a^2 + 3a - 2)(a^2 + 3a - 2)$ $-a^4 + 9a^2 - 12a + 4$
7. $(2a + 4b - 7)(3a - b + 1)$ $6a^2 + 10ab - 4b^2 - 19a + 11b - 7$
8. $(3m + 4)(2m - 2) - (3m)^2$ $-3m^2 + 2m - 8$
9. $4(3e^2 + 6e - 9) - (e + 1)(e - 1)$ $11e^2 + 24e - 35$
10. $(p + q + r)(p - q - r) + r(r + q)$ $p^2 - qr - q^2$
11. $(y + 6)(y + 2)(y - 3)$ $y^3 + 5y^2 - 12y - 36$

Representations Objective I: Represent areas and volumes of figures with polynomials.

12. a. Express the area of the largest rectangle as length • width. $(x + y + 2)(x + y + 1)$

	x	y	2
y			
x			
1			

b. Express this area as the sum of nine smaller rectangles. $xy + y^2 + 2y + x^2 + xy + 2x + x + y + 2$

c. Simplify your answer to Part b. $x^2 + 2xy + y^2 + 3x + 3y + 2$

Name

13. A cube has edges of length 8 inches. Suppose a larger cube has edges that are x inches longer.

a. What is the volume of the first cube? 512 in^3

b. Write an expression for the volume of the larger cube. $(x^3 + 24x^2 + 192x + 512) \text{ in}^3$

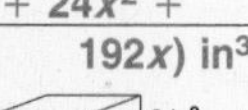

c. How much greater is the volume of the larger cube than the volume of the smaller cube? $(x^3 + 24x^2 + 192x) \text{ in}^3$

14. a. Write two expressions for the volume of the box at the right.

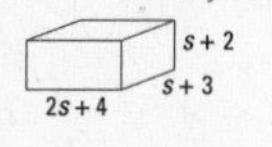

$(2s + 4)(s + 3)(s + 2)$

$2s^3 + 14s^2 + 32s + 24$

b. Check your answer by substituting 3 for x.

$(2 \cdot 3 + 4)(3 + 3)(3 + 2) = 10 \cdot 6 \cdot 5 = 300$

$2 \cdot 3^3 + 14 \cdot 3^2 + 32 \cdot 3 + 24 = 54 + 126 + 96 + 24 = 300$

Review Objective F, Lesson 9-2

15. Use the equation $y = x^2 - 2x - 8$.

a. Make a table of values using x-values -3, -2, -1, 0, 1, 2, and 3.

b. Graph the equation.

c. Give the coordinates of the vertex.

d. Give the y-intercept.

e. Give the equation of the axis of symmetry.

b.

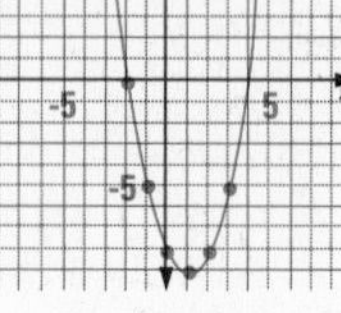

a.

x	-3	-2	-1	0	1	2	3
y	7	0	-5	-8	-9	-8	-5

c. (1, -9) d. -8 e. $x = 1$

Name

LESSON MASTER 10-5 B

Questions on SPUR Objectives

Vocabulary

1. In the FOIL algorithm, explain what the letters F-O-I-L represent.

F: product of FIRST terms

O: product of OUTSIDE terms

I: product of INSIDE terms

L: product of LAST terms

Skills Objective C: Multiply two binomials.

In 2–14, multiply and simplify.

2. $(u + 3)(u + 10)$ $u^2 + 13u + 30$
3. $(x - 4)(x - 5)$ $x^2 - 9x + 20$
4. $(e - 2)(e + 1)$ $e^2 - e - 2$
5. $(y + 6)(y - 4)$ $y^2 + 2y - 24$
6. $(2a + 1)(a - 7)$ $2a^2 - 13a - 7$
7. $(3b + 6)(4b + 2)$ $12b^2 + 30b + 12$
8. $(x - 7)(x + 7)$ $x^2 - 49$
9. $(r^2 + 3r)(r + 4)$ $r^3 + 7r^2 + 12r$
10. $(4m + 7)(4m - 7)$ $16m^2 - 49$
11. $(3a + b)(2a - 8b)$ $6a^2 - 22ab - 8b^2$
12. $(2u^2 - 3uv)(6u - 2v)$ $12u^3 - 22u^2v + 6uv^2$
13. $(p + 3q)^2$ $p^2 + 6pq + 9q^2$
14. $(2 + \sqrt{3})(8 - \sqrt{3})$ $13 + 6\sqrt{3}$

In 15 and 16, fill in the blanks.

15. $(x + 5)(x + \underline{3}) = x^2 + 8x + 15$
16. $(y - \underline{1})(y + 4) = y^2 + 3y - 4$

Name

17. Complete the table for each equation, and graph the points for both equations on the grid at the right.

a. $y = (x - 1)(x - 3)$

x	-2	-1	0	1	2	3	4	5
y	15	8	3	0	-1	0	3	8

b. $y = x^2 - 4x + 3$

x	-2	-1	0	1	2	3	4	5
y	15	8	3	0	-1	0	3	8

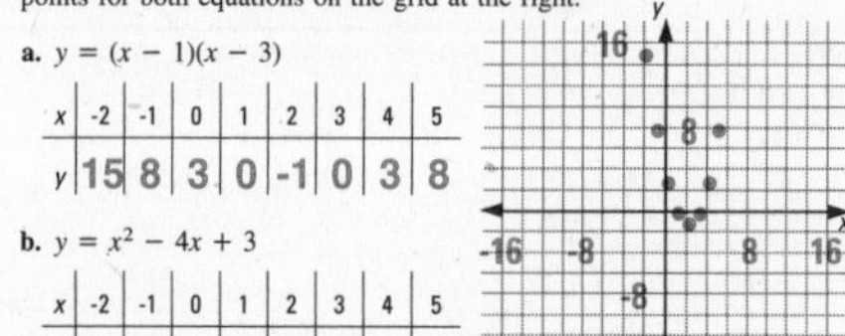

18. What is true of the points you graphed for the equations above? Explain why this relationship exists.

Sample: The two sets are the same; $x^2 - 4x + 3$ is the expanded form of $(x - 1)(x - 3)$.

Representations Objective I: Represent the product of two binomials as an area.

In 19 and 20, an area representation is shown. a. Express the area as length · width. b. Multiply and simplify the expression you wrote for Part a.

19.

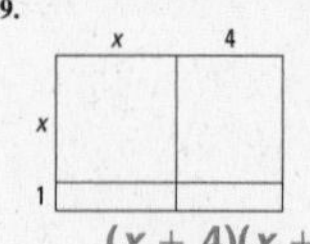

a. $(x + 4)(x + 1)$

b. $x^2 + 5x + 4$

20.

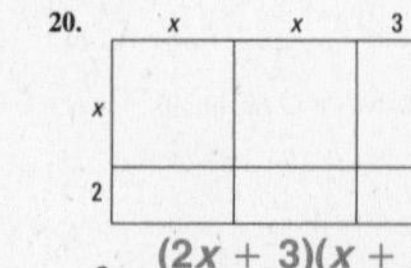

a. $(2x + 3)(x + 2)$

b. $2x^2 + 7x + 6$

21. a. Multiply $(x + 3)(2x + 1)$. $2x^2 + 7x + 3$

b. At the right, draw an area diagram to represent the multiplication.

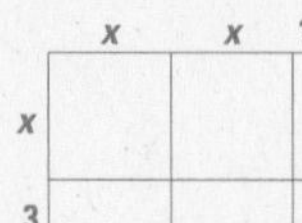

22. An oil painting that measures 14 in. by 20 in. is surrounded by a frame f in. wide. Write a polynomial for the total area of the painting and frame. $(4f^2 + 68f + 280) \text{ in}^2$

Name

LESSON MASTER 10-6 B **Questions on SPUR Objectives**

Skills Objective C: Multiply two binomials.
Objective D: Expand squares of binomials.

In 1–4, match equivalent expressions.

1. $a^2 + 2ab + b^2$ ___c___ a. $(a - b)^2$
2. $a^2 + b^2$ ___d___ b. $(a + b)(a - b)$
3. $a^2 - 2ab + b^2$ ___a___ c. $(a + b)^2$
4. $a^2 - b^2$ ___b___ d. none of these

5. Expand $(m + 8)^2$ by
   a. using the FOIL algorithm. $(m + 8)(m + 8) = m^2 + 8m + 8m + 64 = m^2 + 16m + 64$
   b. using the Perfect Square Patterns. $(m + 8)^2 = m^2 + 2 \cdot m \cdot 8 + 8^2 = m^2 + 16m + 64$

In 6–10, expand.

6. $(d + 5)^2$ $d^2 + 10d + 25$
7. $(b - 6)^2$ $b^2 - 12b + 36$
8. $(2x - 7)^2$ $4x^2 - 28x + 49$
9. $(3e + 1)^2$ $9e^2 + 6e + 1$
10. $(4a + 7)^2$ $16a^2 + 56a + 49$

In 11–15, tell if the expression is the difference of two squares. Write *yes* or *no*. If you write *no*, explain your answer.

11. $d^2 - 17$ No; 17 is not a square.
12. $m^2 - 25$ yes
13. $r^2 + 36$ No; $r^2 + 36 = r^2 - (-36)$; -36 is not a square
14. $4x^2y^2 - 81$ yes
15. $(u - 4)^2$ no; $(u - 4)^2 = u^2 - 8u + 16$

Name

In 16–22, multiply and simplify.

16. $(b + 7)(b - 7)$ $b^2 - 49$
17. $(3m + 2)(3m - 2)$ $9m^2 - 4$
18. $(4b - 5)^2$ $16b^2 - 40b + 25$
19. $(8a + 2e)(8a - 2e)$ $64a^2 - 4e^2$
20. $(x - y)^2 - (x + y)(x - y)$ $2y^2 - 2xy$
21. $(2 + \sqrt{5})(2 - \sqrt{5})$ -1
22. $(2 + \sqrt{5})^2$ $9 + 4\sqrt{5}$

23. Explain how you could use the Difference of Two Squares Pattern to calculate $21 \cdot 19$ mentally.
$21 \cdot 19 = (20 + 1)(20 - 1) = 20^2 - 1^2 = 400 - 1 = 399$

Representations Objective I: Represent the square of a binomial as an area.

24. a. Express the area of the figure at the right as the square of a binomial. $(x + 4)^2$

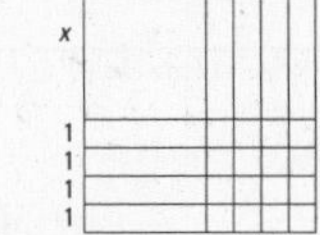

b. Express the area as the sum of smaller areas. $x^2 + 8x + 16$

In 25 and 26, an expression is given. a. Make an algebra-tile drawing to illustrate the expression. b. Write the expanded polynomial expression represented by your drawing.

25. $(x + 2)^2$

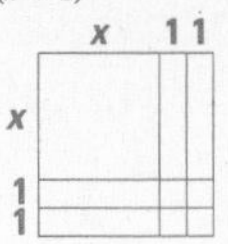

b. $x^2 + 4x + 4$

26. $(2x + 3)^2$

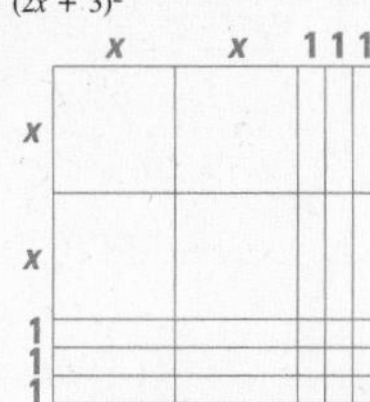

b. $4x^2 + 12x + 9$

Name

LESSON MASTER 10-7 B **Questions on SPUR Objectives**

Uses Objective H: Use the chi-square statistic to determine whether or not an event is likely.

In 1–3, use the following information and the chi-square critical value table given below.

A market researcher wanted to know if a new cereal, Oat-Toasties, would be more appealing to people than the four leading sellers in a particular city. A taste test in a local shopping center gave the following results.

Cereal	Percent of People Choosing Cereal
Oat-Toasties	26%
Munch Mates	21%
Sun-Risers	20%
Wheat Cracklers	18%
A.M. Crispies	15%

1. Suppose 200 people had been asked their choices.
   a. Find the number of people choosing each cereal.
   Oat-Toasties 52 Munch Mates 42
   Sun-Risers 40 Wheat Cracklers 36
   A.M. Crispies 30
   b. Before recommending that Oat-Toasties be manufactured for national distribution, the market researcher must decide whether the test results show a special support for Oat-Toasties. To do this, he first considers the situation in which it is equally likely that a person would choose any of the five cereals. In such a case, how many people would be expected to choose each cereal?
   Oat-Toasties 40 Munch Mates 40
   Sun-Risers 40 Wheat Cracklers 40
   A.M. Crispies 40
   c. Find the chi-square statistic for this experiment using the actual test results and the expected values from Part b. 6.6

Name

Critical Chi-Square Values

$n - 1$	.10	.05	.01	.001
1	2.71	3.84	6.63	10.8
2	4.61	5.99	9.21	13.8
3	6.25	7.81	11.34	16.3
4	7.78	9.49	13.28	18.5
5	9.24	11.07	15.09	20.5
6	10.6	12.6	16.8	22.5
7	12.0	14.1	18.5	24.3
8	13.4	15.5	20.1	26.1
9	14.7	16.9	21.7	27.9
10	16.0	18.3	23.2	29.6

d. Refer to the Critical Chi-Square Values Table above. Using your answer to Part c, do you think the researcher should recommend that the cereal be manufactured for national distribution? Explain your thinking.
Sample: No; there is a greater than 10% chance the results would occur in the equally-likely cases.

2. Suppose 1,000 people had been asked their opinion, and their percents were those given in the table on page 179.
   a. Calculate the chi-square statistic for these test results. (Follow the steps suggested by Parts **a** and **b** in Question 1.) 33
   b. Refer to the Critical Chi-Square Values Table above. Using your answer to Part **a**, do you think the researcher should recommend that the cereal be manufactured for national distribution? Explain your thinking.
   Sample: Yes; there is less than .1% chance the results would occur in the equally-likely cases.

3. From your answers to Questions 1 and 2, what can you say about the relationship between sample size and the conclusions reached by the market researcher?
Sample: When the sample size is greater, there is more support for Oat-Toasties and the researcher's conclusion is correct.

Name

LESSON MASTER 11-1 B Questions on SPUR Objectives

Representations Objective H: Find solutions to systems of equations by graphing.

1. a. Use a brace { to write the system shown on this graph. $\begin{cases} x - 2y = 0 \\ 2x - y = 6 \end{cases}$

b. What is the solution to the system? (4, 2)

c. Write a check to show that your answer to Part **b** is a solution to the system from Part **a**.
$4 - 2(2) = 0;\ 2(4) - 2 = 6$

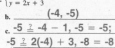

In 2–4, a system of equations is given. a. Graph the equations. b. Give the solution. c. If there is a solution, check it.

2. $\begin{cases} y = x - 1 \\ y = 2x + 3 \end{cases}$ a.

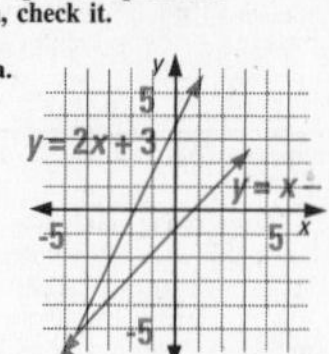

b. (-4, -5)

c. $-5 \overset{?}{=} -4 - 1, -5 = -5;$
$-5 \overset{?}{=} 2(-4) + 3, -8 = -8$

3. $\begin{cases} x - 2y = 5 \\ 4x - y = -1 \end{cases}$ a.

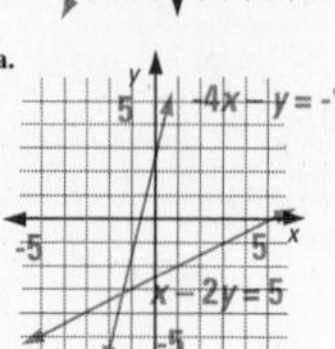

b. (-1, -3)

c. $-1 - 2(-3) \overset{?}{=} 5, 5 = 5;$
$4(-1) - (-3) \overset{?}{=} -1, -1 = -1$

4. $\begin{cases} y = 3x - 2 \\ 6x - 2y = 6 \end{cases}$ a.

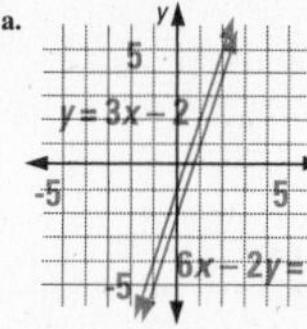

b. No solution

c.

Name

5. a. Graph the system below for $-5 \le x \le 5$.

$\begin{cases} y = 2x - 5 \\ y = x^2 - 4x + 3 \end{cases}$

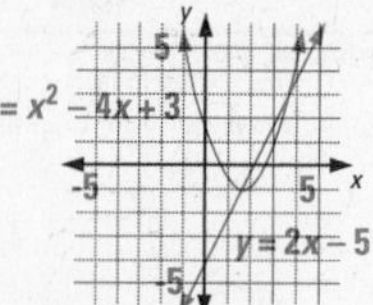

b. Give the two solutions.
(2, -1), (4, 3)

In 6–10, use the graph which shows the percent of U.S. households that had color or black-and-white television sets in various years. A line has been fitted to each set of data and the coordinates of the darkened points have been given.

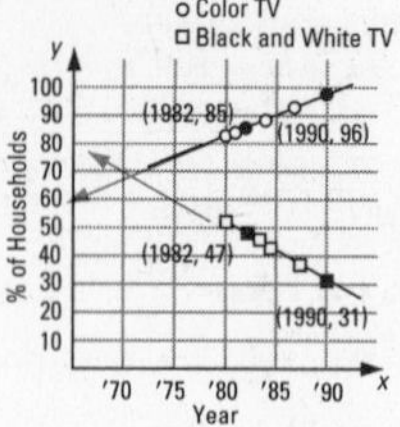

6. In what year were there about twice as many households with color sets as there were with black-and-white sets?
1984

7. Write the equation for the line fitted to data for color TVs.
$y = 1.375x - 2640.25$

8. Write the equation for the line fitted to data for black-and-white TVs.
$y = -2x + 4011$

9. Extend the lines in the graph to find an estimate of the year in which there were an equal number of households with color and with black-and-white TVs. 1971

10. Check your answer to Question 9 in the equations for Questions 7 and 8.
$1.375(1971) - 2640.25 = 69.875;$
$-2(1971) + 4011 = 69$

Name

LESSON MASTER 11-2 B Questions on SPUR Objectives

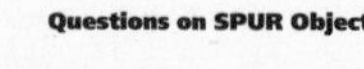

Skills Objective A: Solve systems of linear equations using substitution.

In 1 and 2, tell if the given point is the solution of the system.

1. (3, 8) $\begin{cases} y = 4x - 4 \\ y = \frac{2}{3}x + 6 \end{cases}$ yes

2. (-2, 12) $\begin{cases} y = -5x + 2 \\ y = 2x - 8 \end{cases}$ no

In 3–10, solve the system using substitution and check your results.

3. $\begin{cases} a = b - 5 \\ a = -2b + 7 \end{cases}$
(4, -1)
$-1 \overset{?}{=} 4 - 5, -1 = -1;$
$-1 \overset{?}{=} -2(4) + 7; -1 = -1$

4. $\begin{cases} y = 3x + 23 \\ y = x + 11 \end{cases}$
(-6, 5)
$5 \overset{?}{=} 3(-6) + 23, 5 = 5;$
$5 \overset{?}{=} -6 + 11, 5 = 5$

5. $\begin{cases} y = \frac{3}{2}x + 12 \\ y = x + 8 \end{cases}$
(-8, 0)
$0 \overset{?}{=} \frac{3}{2}(-8) + 12, 0 = 0;$
$0 \overset{?}{=} -8 + 8, 0 = 0$

6. $\begin{cases} m = 8n - 3 \\ m = -4n + 6 \end{cases}$
$\left(\frac{3}{4}, 3\right)$
$3 \overset{?}{=} 8\left(\frac{3}{4}\right) - 3, 3 = 3;$
$3 \overset{?}{=} -4\left(\frac{3}{4}\right) + 6, 3 = 3$

7. $\begin{cases} d = 2e + 1 \\ d = 5e - 8 \end{cases}$
(3, 7)
$7 \overset{?}{=} 2(3) + 1, 7 = 7;$
$7 \overset{?}{=} 5(3) - 8, 7 = 7$

8. $\begin{cases} y = 6x - 7 \\ y = -2x - 9 \end{cases}$
$\left(-\frac{1}{4}, -\frac{17}{2}\right)$
$-\frac{17}{2} \overset{?}{=} 6\left(-\frac{1}{4}\right) - 7, -\frac{17}{2} = -\frac{17}{2};$
$-\frac{17}{2} \overset{?}{=} -2\left(-\frac{1}{4}\right) - 9, -\frac{17}{2} = -\frac{17}{2}$

9. $\begin{cases} y = x \\ y = 3x - 20 \end{cases}$
(10, 10)
$10 = 10;$
$10 \overset{?}{=} 3(10) - 20, 10 = 10$

10. $\begin{cases} r = \frac{1}{2}s + 1 \\ r = -\frac{2}{3}s + 15 \end{cases}$
(12, 7)
$7 \overset{?}{=} \frac{1}{2}(12) + 1, 7 = 7;$
$7 \overset{?}{=} -\frac{2}{3}(12) + 15, 7 = 7$

Name

Uses Objective F: Use systems of linear equations to solve real-world problems.

11. A cellular telephone company offers two plans to customers who use their mobile phone service. The monthly charges are given below.

Basic Plan: \$20 service fee plus \$.30 per minute of use
Frequent-Caller Plan: \$45 service fee plus \$.20 per minute of use

Let x = minutes of phone use and y = cost.

a. Write an equation describing the basic plan. $y = .3x + 20$

b. Write an equation describing the frequent-caller plan. $y = .2x + 45$

c. Solve a system of equations to find the number of minutes of phone use that would cost the same under the two plans. 250 minutes

d. If you estimate that you will use a cellular telephone for 100 minutes per month, which plan is better? Explain your reasoning.
Basic Plan; The basic plan would cost \$50, while the frequent-caller plan would cost \$65.

12. CD Showcase Club charges a membership fee of \$15 and then \$10.50 for each CD purchased. CD Budget Club charges a membership fee of \$5 and then \$11.75 for each CD.

a. Describe these charges with a system of equations. $\begin{cases} y = 10.5x + 15 \\ y = 11.75x + 5 \end{cases}$

b. Solve the system to find the number of CDs purchased for which the total charges at each club are the same. 8 CDs

c. If you think you will be buying many, many CDs, which club is less expensive? Explain your reasoning.
CD Showcase Club; After 8 CDs, the charges at Showcase Club will be less than charges at Budget Club.

Name

LESSON MASTER 11-3 B

Questions on SPUR Objectives

Skills Objective A: Solve systems of linear equations using substitution.

In 1–8, solve and check the system of equations.

1. $\begin{cases} y = x + 5 \\ 3x + y = 17 \end{cases}$

   (3, 8)
   $8 \overset{?}{=} 3 + 5, 8 = 8;$
   $3(3) + 8 \overset{?}{=} 17, 17 = 17$

2. $\begin{cases} y = 3x \\ 3x - 2y = 12 \end{cases}$

   (-4, -12)
   $-12 \overset{?}{=} 3(-4), -12 = -12;$
   $3(-4) - 2(-12) \overset{?}{=} 12, 12 = 12$

3. $\begin{cases} m = 10n - 2 \\ m - 2n = 2 \end{cases}$

   $\left(3, \frac{1}{2}\right)$
   $3 \overset{?}{=} 10\left(\frac{1}{2}\right) - 2, 3 = 3;$
   $3 - 2\left(\frac{1}{2}\right) \overset{?}{=} 2, 2 = 2$

4. $\begin{cases} x = y - 6 \\ 2x + 10y = 0 \end{cases}$

   (-5, 1)
   $-5 \overset{?}{=} 1 - 6, -5 = -5;$
   $2(-5) + 10(1) \overset{?}{=} 0, 0 = 0$

5. $\begin{cases} x = \frac{1}{2}y \\ 4x + y = 30 \end{cases}$

   (5, 10)
   $5 \overset{?}{=} \frac{1}{2}(10), 5 = 5;$
   $4(5) + 10 \overset{?}{=} 30, 30 = 30$

6. $\begin{cases} a = 3b - 3 \\ 7a - 2b = 17 \end{cases}$

   (3, 2)
   $3 \overset{?}{=} 3(2) - 3, 3 = 3;$
   $7(3) - 2(2) \overset{?}{=} 17, 17 = 17$

7. $\begin{cases} x + y = 8 \\ x - y = 4 \end{cases}$

   (6, 2)
   $6 + 2 \overset{?}{=} 8, 8 = 8;$
   $6 - 2 \overset{?}{=} 4, 4 = 4$

8. $\begin{cases} x - y = 3 \\ 4x - 3y = 19 \end{cases}$

   (10, 7)
   $10 - 7 \overset{?}{=} 3, 3 = 3;$
   $4(10) - 3(7) \overset{?}{=} 19, 19 = 19$

In 9 and 10, two lines have the given equations. Find the point of intersection.

9. Line ℓ: $y = -2x - 6$
   Line m: $y = 5x + 15$

   (-3, 0)

10. Line p: $y = -x + 3$
    Line q: $y = -5x - 2$

    $\left(-\frac{5}{4}, \frac{17}{4}\right)$

Name

11. Solve the system below.

    $\begin{cases} A = B + 2 \\ B = 2C + 9 \\ A + C = -1 \end{cases}$

    $A = 3, B = 1, C = -4$

Uses Objective F: Use systems of linear equations to solve real-world problems.

12. A concession stand sells hot dogs for $2 and hamburgers for $3. One day 486 sandwiches worth $1,218 were sold. How many hot dogs and how many hamburgers were sold?

    hotdogs, 240; hamburgers, 246

13. One newspaper reported that the mayor received a salary increase of 5%. Another paper reported that the mayor's salary went up $2000. What was the mayor's salary before the increase?

    $40,000

14. A garden with a perimeter of 75 meters is to be 1.5 times as long as it is wide. What will be the dimensions of the garden?

    length, 22.5 m; width, 15 m

Review Objective A, Lesson 10-2

In 15–17, simplify the expression.

15. $(5x^2 - 12x + 3) + (2x^2 + x - 10) - (x^2 + 3)$ $\quad 6x^2 - 11x - 10$

16. $-(3c^2 - 5c - 8) - (c^2 + 4c - 7)$ $\quad 2c^2 - 9c - 1$

17. $(22 - 5a^2 + 4a) + (2a^2 - 4a - 15)$ $\quad -3a^2 + 7$

Name

LESSON MASTER 11-4 B

Questions on SPUR Objectives

Skills Objective B: Solve systems of linear equations by addition.

In 1 and 2, write the equation that results when you add the left and right sides of the two equations.

1. $\begin{cases} 3x + 5y = 13 \\ x - 5y = 3 \end{cases}$ $\quad 4x = 16$

2. $\begin{cases} -4x + 2y = 15 \\ 4x - 8y = 10 \end{cases}$ $\quad -6y = 25$

In 3–10, solve the system. Check your solution.

3. $\begin{cases} c + d = 1 \\ c - d = -11 \end{cases}$

   (-5, 6)
   $-5 + 6 \overset{?}{=} 1, 1 = 1;$
   $-5 - 6 \overset{?}{=} -11, -11 = -11$

4. $\begin{cases} -8x + 2y = 2 \\ 8x + 5y = -23 \end{cases}$

   (-1, -3)
   $-8(-1) + 2(-3) \overset{?}{=} 2, 2 = 2;$
   $8(-1) + 5(-3) \overset{?}{=} -23,$
   $-23 = -23$

5. $\begin{cases} -6x + 4y = 28 \\ 6x + 10y = 28 \end{cases}$

   (-2, 4)
   $-6(-2) + 4(4) \overset{?}{=} 28,$
   $28 = 28;$
   $6(-2) + 10(4) \overset{?}{=} 28,$
   $28 = 28$

6. $\begin{cases} 5r + 3s = 24 \\ 5r + 8s = 39 \end{cases}$

   (3, 3)
   $5(3) + 3(3) \overset{?}{=} 24,$
   $24 = 24;$
   $5(3) + 8(3) \overset{?}{=} 39,$
   $39 = 39$

7. $\begin{cases} 2u + 3w = 26 \\ 5w - 2u = 22 \end{cases}$

   (4, 6)
   $2(4) + 3(6) \overset{?}{=} 26,$
   $26 = 26;$
   $5(6) - 2(4) \overset{?}{=} 22,$
   $22 = 22$

8. $\begin{cases} 2m + n = 9 \\ -2m - 3n = -21 \end{cases}$

   $\left(\frac{3}{2}, 6\right)$
   $2\left(\frac{3}{2}\right) + 6 \overset{?}{=} 9, 9 = 9;$
   $-2\left(\frac{3}{2}\right) - 3(6) \overset{?}{=} -21,$
   $-21 = -21$

9. $\begin{cases} \frac{3}{4}x + y = 8 \\ \frac{1}{4}x - y = 0 \end{cases}$

   (8, 2)
   $\frac{3}{4}(8) + 2 \overset{?}{=} 8, 8 = 8;$
   $\frac{1}{4}(8) - 2 \overset{?}{=} 0, 0 = 0$

10. $\begin{cases} 5e - 2f = 30 \\ 9e - 2f = 54 \end{cases}$

    (6, 0)
    $5(6) - 2(0) \overset{?}{=} 30,$
    $30 = 30;$
    $9(6) - 2(0) \overset{?}{=} 54,$
    $54 = 54$

Name

Uses Objective F: Use systems of linear equations to solve real-world problems.

11. In the school bookstore, four pencils and an eraser cost 65¢. Two pencils and an eraser cost 45¢. Find the cost of each item.

    pencil, 10¢; eraser, 25¢

12. Joanie weighs 8 pounds more than Jennie does. Together they weigh 212 pounds. Find the weight of each girl.

    Joanie, 110 lb; Jennie, 102 lb

13. When Brad flew from Indianapolis to St. Louis, he had the wind with him and was traveling at 260 mph. However, on the return trip, he was going against the wind and traveled only 170 mph. What was the plane's speed (without wind)? What was the average speed of the wind?

    215 mph; 45 mph

14. Mark has one less than twice the number of tapes as Felipe has. Together they have 65 tapes. How many tapes does each boy have?

    Mark, 43 tapes; Felipe, 22 tapes

15. On Saturday, Katie earned $51 for mowing 3 lawns and weeding 3 gardens. On Sunday, she earned $25 for mowing 1 lawn and weeding 3 gardens. How much does she earn for each lawn she mows and for each garden she weeds?

    lawn, $13; weed, $4

16. At the university dormitory, two plans are offered.

    Plan 1: Room and board and 13 meals per week for $5,110
    Plan 2: Room and board and 19 meals per week for $5,146

    At these rates what is the cost for room and board alone? What is the cost per meal?

    $5032; $6

17. A sandwich with 2 slices of bread and 4 slices of ham has 350 calories. A sandwich with 2 slices of bread and 2 slices of ham has 240 calories. How many calories are in each slice of bread and in each slice of ham?

    ham, 55 cal; bread, 65 cal

Name

LESSON MASTER 11-5 B **Questions on SPUR Objectives**

Skills Objective C: Solve systems of linear equations by multiplying.

1. Consider the system $\begin{cases} 9x - y = -4 \\ 3x + 5y = 10 \end{cases}$.

a. What is the result if the two equations are added? $12x + 4y = 6$

b. What is the result if the first equation is multiplied by five and then the two equations are added? $48x = -10$

c. What is the result if the second equation is multiplied by -3 and then the two equations are added? $-16y = -34$

2. Solve the system $\begin{cases} a - 3b = 7 \\ 5a + b = 19 \end{cases}$

a. by multiplying and adding to eliminate b. (4, -1)

b. by multiplying and adding to eliminate a. (4, -1)

3. Consider the system $\begin{cases} 4x + 5y = 2 \\ 2x - 3y = 34 \end{cases}$.

a. Would you plan to eliminate x or y to solve the system? Explain your choice.
Sample: x, because only one equation would need to be multiplied

b. Solve the system. (8, -6)

c. Check your solution to Part **c**.
$4(8) + 5(-6) = 2$, $2 = 2$;
$2(8) - 3(-6) = 34$, $34 = 34$

Name

In 4–9, solve the system. Check your solution. Checks are not given.

4. $\begin{cases} 3t + 2u = -1 \\ 6t - u = 8 \end{cases}$ (1, -2)

5. $\begin{cases} -y + 4x = 12 \\ 5y + 5x = 40 \end{cases}$ (4, 4)

6. $\begin{cases} 5x + 2y = -19 \\ 2x - 10y = 14 \end{cases}$ (-3, -2)

7. $\begin{cases} 10x + 3y = 34 \\ 5x + 4y = 37 \end{cases}$ (1, 8)

8. $\begin{cases} 2c - 9d = 15 \\ \frac{1}{4}c - 2d = 1 \end{cases}$ (12, 1)

9. $\begin{cases} -6x - 9y = 42 \\ 8x + 42y = -36 \end{cases}$ $\left(-8, \frac{2}{3}\right)$

Uses Objective F: Use systems of linear equations to solve real-world problems.

10. At Clucker's Chicken, a bucket of 4 pieces of dark meat and 5 pieces of white meat costs $7.05. A bucket of 3 pieces of dark meat and 8 pieces of white meat costs $8.90. Find the cost of a piece of dark meat and of a piece of white meat. d., $.70; w., $.85

11. At Curly's Copies, Chad made 56 copies costing $16. Color copies cost $.75 each and black-and-white copies cost $.10 each. How many copies of each type did Chad make? 16 color; 40 b.w.

12. Ann has 30 straws of length a and 24 straws of length b. How many triangles of each type drawn at the right can she make using all the straws?

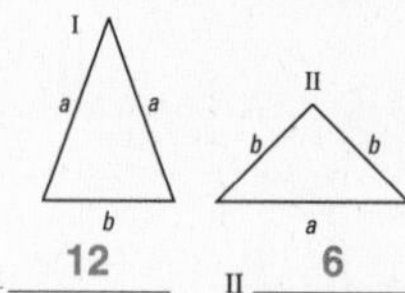

I. 12 II. 6

Name

LESSON MASTER 11-6 B **Questions on SPUR Objectives**

Properties Objective E: Determine whether a system has no solutions, one solution, or infinitely many solutions.

In 1–4, match equations whose graphs are parallel lines.

1. $y = 2x + 7$	c	**a.** $y = 3x - 6$
2. $y = -3x - 9$	b	**b.** $3x + y = 40$
3. $4x + 3y = 18$	d	**c.** $y = 2x + 12$
4. $6x - 2y = 12$	a	**d.** $8x + 6y = 22$

5. Consider the system $\begin{cases} y = 5x + 1 \\ 10x - 2y = -2 \end{cases}$.

a. Find three ordered pairs that are solutions to $y = 5x + 1$.
Sample: (0, 1), (1, 6), (2, 11)

b. Show that each ordered pair from Part **a** is also a solution to $10x - 2y = -2$.
$10(0) - 2(1) = -2$; $10(1) - 2(6) = -2$;
$10(2) - 2(11) = -2$

c. How many solutions does this system have? infinitely many

In 6–9, tell if the system has *no solutions, one solution,* or *infinitely many solutions.*

6. $\begin{cases} 3x + 2y = -4 \\ 6x + 4y = 7 \end{cases}$ no solution

7. $\begin{cases} 5a + b = 18 \\ 10a + b = 36 \end{cases}$ one solution

8. $\begin{cases} 8r + 2s = -18 \\ s = -4r - 9 \end{cases}$ infinitely many

9. $\begin{cases} 2(x + 3) = y \\ 5x - y = 1 \end{cases}$ one solution

Name

Uses Objective F: Use systems of linear equations to solve real-world problems.

10. At a movie theater, the Ohira family bought 2 adult tickets and 4 children's tickets for $26. The Teasdale family bought 3 adult tickets and 6 children's tickets for $42. How much does an adult ticket cost?

a. Write a system of equations to answer the question. $\begin{cases} 2a + 4c = 26 \\ 3a + 6c = 42 \end{cases}$

b. How many solutions does this system have? no solutions

c. What does your answer to Part **b** suggest about the situation?
Sample: The families did not pay the same prices for their tickets.

Representations Objective H: Find solutions to systems of equations by graphing.

11. Describe the graph of a system of linear equations that has

a. no solutions. parallel lines

b. one solution. lines intersecting at one point

c. infinitely many solutions. the same line

In 12 and 13, a system of equations is given.
a. Graph each system. b. Give the solution.

12. $\begin{cases} 4x + 2y = -8 \\ 6x + 3y = 4 \end{cases}$

a.

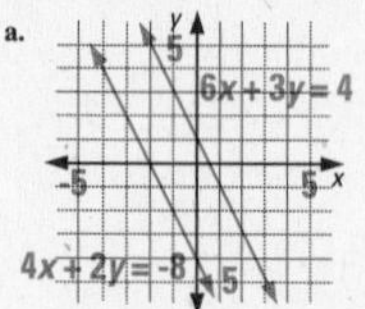

b. no solution

13. $\begin{cases} -3x + y = 2 \\ 6x - 2y = -4 \end{cases}$

a.

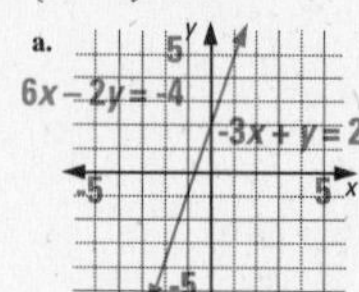

b. infinitely many solutions

Name

LESSON MASTER 11-7 B Questions on SPUR Objectives

Properties Objective D: Recognize sentences with no solutions, one solution, or all real numbers as solutions.

1. a. Add $6x$ to both sides of $10 - 6(x + 1) = 4 - 6x$. What sentence results? $4 = 4$
   b. Describe the solutions to $10 - 6(x + 1) = 4 - 6x$. all real numbers

2. a. Add $-7x$ to both sides of $7x + 9 < 7 + 7x$. What sentence results? $9 < 7$
   b. Describe the solutions to $7x + 9 < 7 + 7x$. no solutions

In 3–12, *multiple choice*. Tell if the sentence is
(a) *sometimes true.* (b) *always true.* (c) *never true.*

3. $h + 4 > h + 1$ b
4. $2x + 8 = 2(x + 8)$ c
5. $-7a = 6 - 7a$ c
6. $2x + 9 + 7x \geq 9(1 + x)$ b
7. $m + 17 = -m - 1$ a
8. $-3u + 12 < 8u - 10$ a
9. $2(b + 7) = 6b + 14$ a
10. $-4(x + 8) + 20 = 3x - (12 + 7x)$ b
11. $-12a + 19 < 4a - 16a + 15$ c
12. $7n + 16 \leq 3(n + 5) + 1$ a

In 13–15, write an inequality that — Samples are given.

13. has no solutions. $x + 5 < x + 4$
14. has $x > 0$ as its solution. $2x + 10 > x + 10$
15. is true for all real numbers. $x + 8 > x + 7$

Name

▶ **LESSON MASTER 11-7 B** *page 2*

In 16–19, solve.

16. $8 + 13m = 8 + 10m$ $m = 0$
17. $5(x - 2) = 2x + 10 + 3x$ no solution
18. $7y + 14 \geq 7(y + 2)$ y = all real numbers
19. $\frac{2}{3}(x - 9) < x - \frac{1}{3}x$ x = all real numbers

Uses Objective F: Use systems of linear equations to solve real-world problems.

20. The printing charges for business cards at four different companies are given below.

Company A: $20 plus $.02 per card
Company B: $15 plus $.03 per card
Company C: $20 plus $.03 per card
Company D: $16 plus $.02 per card plus $4 delivery (already included in the charges at the other companies)

a. Let x = number of cards. Write an expression for the cost of x business cards from each company.
A $.02x + 20$ B $.03x + 15$
C $.03x + 20$ D $.02x + 16 + 4$

b. When does Company A charge more than Company B? for less than 500 cards

c. When does Company B charge more than Company C? never

d. When are the charges at Company A and Company D the same? always

Name

LESSON MASTER 11-8 B Questions on SPUR Objectives

Uses Objective G: Use systems of linear inequalities to solve real-world problems.

1. A craft company sells kits for sewing banners and wind socks. They fill boxes with either 15 banner kits or 10 wind sock kits. They want to bring between 200 and 300 items to sell at an upcoming flea market. Let b = the number of boxes containing banner kits and w = the number of boxes containing wind sock kits.

a. Find two different combinations of boxes of banner kits and boxes of wind sock kits that satisfy the company's plans.
Sample: 10 banner boxes, 10 wind sock kits; 8 banner boxes, 16 wind sock kits

b. Describe this situation with a system of four inequalities.
$b \geq 0$
$w \geq 0$
$15b + 10w < 300$
$15b + 10w > 200$

c. Graph the system.

Representations Objective I: Graphically represent solutions to systems of linear inequalities.

2. *Multiple choice.* Which point is a solution to $\begin{cases} y < 3x + 1 \\ y > x - 3 \end{cases}$? c

(a) (2, 7) (b) (-2, -5) (c) (2, 0) (d) (5, 1)

3. Write a system of inequalities to describe the points in Quadrant IV. $\begin{cases} x > 0 \\ y < 0 \end{cases}$

4. Describe the graph of $x = 0, y > 0$. positive part of the y-axis

Name

▶ **LESSON MASTER 11-8 B** *page 2*

In 5–7, consider the system $\begin{cases} x > 0 \\ y > -x \\ y < x - 4 \end{cases}$.

Tell if each point below is a solution of the system. If not, tell which inequality it fails to satisfy.

5. (6, 1) yes
6. (1, 1) no; $y < x - 4$
7. (2, -5) no; $y > -x$

In 8 and 9, graph the system of inequalities.

8. $\begin{cases} x > 0 \\ y > 0 \\ 3x + y < 7 \end{cases}$
9. $\begin{cases} x \leq 0 \\ y \geq 0 \\ y \geq 2x + 5 \end{cases}$

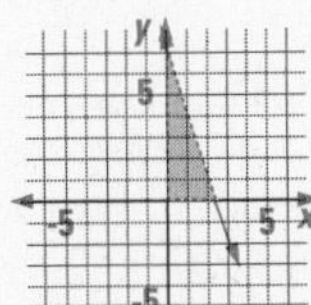

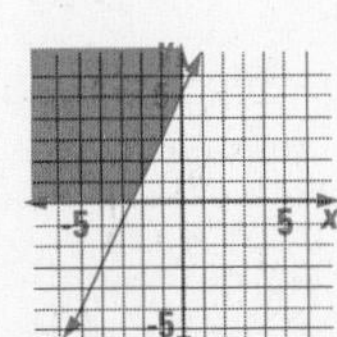

In 10 and 11, write a system of inequalities to describe the graph.

10.

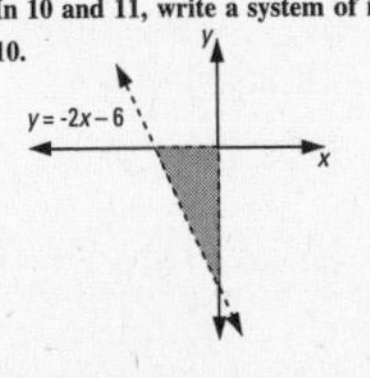

11.

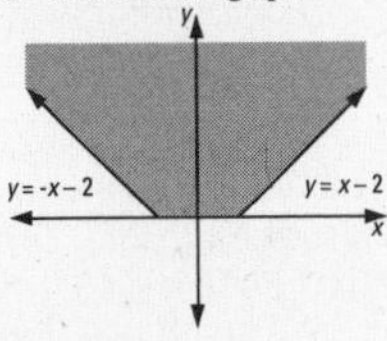

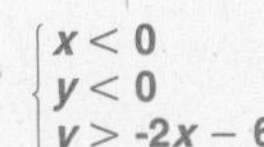
$\begin{cases} x < 0 \\ y < 0 \\ y > -2x - 6 \end{cases}$

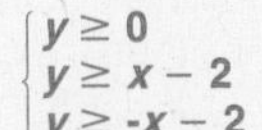
$\begin{cases} y \geq 0 \\ y \geq x - 2 \\ y \geq -x - 2 \end{cases}$

Name

LESSON MASTER 12-1 B Questions on SPUR Objectives

Skills Objective A: Factor positive integers into primes.

In 1–4, list all the pairs of integers whose product is the given integer.

1. 42 — 1, 42; -1, -42; 2, 21; -2, -21; 3, 14; -3, -14; 6, 7; -6, -7
2. 67 — 1, 67; -1, -67
3. -32 — 1, -32; -1, 32; 2, -16; -2, 16; 4, -8; -4, 8
4. -55 — 1, -55; -1, 55; 5, -11; -5, 11

In 5–7, list all the common factors of the given pair of integers.

5. 12 and 20 — 1, 2, 4
6. 6 and 27 — 1, 3
7. 8 and 25 — 1

In 8–12, write the prime factorization of the given integer in standard form.

8. 72 — $2^3 \cdot 3^2$
9. 177 — $3 \cdot 59$
10. 540 — $2^2 \cdot 3^3 \cdot 5$
11. 4653 — $3^2 \cdot 11 \cdot 47$
12. 5775 — $3 \cdot 5^2 \cdot 7 \cdot 11$

In 13–18, determine if the given number is prime.

13. 71 — yes
14. 91 — no
15. 131 — yes
16. 1149 — no
17. 2001 — no
18. 5537 — no

19. Show with an array that 30 is a composite number.

Sample:

• • • • • •
• • • • • •
• • • • • •
• • • • • •
• • • • • •

Name

► **LESSON MASTER 12-1 B** *page 2*

In 20–23, the product and sum of a pair of integers is given. Find the numbers.

20. product = 12, sum = 8 — 2 and 6
21. product = 36, sum = 37 — 1 and 36
22. product = -16, sum = 6 — 8 and -2
23. product = -24, sum = -2 — -6 and 4

In 24–27, rewrite the fraction in lowest terms.

24. $\frac{168}{196}$ — $\frac{6}{7}$
25. $\frac{484}{1331}$ — $\frac{4}{11}$
26. $\frac{3528}{140}$ — $\frac{126}{5}$
27. $\frac{4455}{189}$ — $\frac{165}{7}$

Properties Objective E: Apply the definitions and properties of primes and factors.

In 28–30, give the number of factors in the prime factorization.

28. 5^3 — 3
29. 27^4 — 12
30. $2^3 \cdot 25^2$ — 7

31. Explain why the number $11^4 + 11^{15} + 11^{23}$ could not be prime.

Sample: $11^4 + 11^{15} + 11^{23} = 11^4(1 + 11^{11} + 11^{19})$, so 11^4 is a factor of the number.

Review Objective B, Lesson 8-5

In 32–39, simplify.

32. $y^2 \cdot y^5$ — y^7
33. $x^7 \cdot x^7$ — x^{14}
34. $(m^5)^3$ — m^{15}
35. $(e^5)^5$ — e^{25}
36. $a^2 \cdot a^4 \cdot a^4$ — a^{10}
37. $c \cdot c^5$ — c^6
38. $(m^2 \cdot m^6)^3$ — m^{24}
39. $x^4 \cdot y \cdot x^3 \cdot y^3$ — x^7y^4

Name

LESSON MASTER 12-2 B Questions on SPUR Objectives

Skills Objective B: Find common monomial factors of polynomials.

In 1 and 2, list all the factors of the given monomial.

1. $5x^2$ — $1, 5, x, x^2, 5x, 5x^2$
2. $49ax^2$ — $1, 7, 49, a, x, ax, x^2, ax^2, 7a, 7x, 7ax, 7x^2, 7ax^2, 49a, 49x, 49ax, 49x^2, 49ax^2$

In 3–8, tell if the polynomial is prime.

3. $4x + 8$ — no
4. $3n + 10$ — yes
5. $x^2 + 7x$ — no
6. $pq + 2y$ — yes
7. $2m + 3mn$ — no
8. $2x^2y + bx^2$ — no

In 9–14, find the greatest common factor of the given monomials.

9. $20x$ and 5 — 5
10. $12x^2$ and $18x^3$ — $6x^2$
11. y^5 and y^3 — y^3
12. $5t$ and 32 — 1
13. $5x^3$, $12x^2$, and $20x^2y$ — x^2
14. $15ab^2$, $21a^2b^2$, and $6a^2b$ — $3ab$

In 15–19, fill in the blanks.

15. $16x + 24 = 8(\underline{2x} + \underline{3})$
16. $7b^5 - 12b^2 = b^2(\underline{7b^3} - \underline{12})$
17. $20uv^2 + 28u^2v = 4uv(\underline{5v} + \underline{7u})$
18. $12x^4 + 18x^3 - 30x^2 = 6x^2(\underline{2x^2} + \underline{3x} - \underline{5})$
19. $3m^2n + 6m^2n^2 = \underline{3m^2n}(1 + 2n)$

Name

► **LESSON MASTER 12-2 B** *page 2*

In 20–25, factor the polynomial completely.

20. $45x + 50$ — $5(9x + 10)$
21. $32x^2 - 16x$ — $16x(2x - 1)$
22. $10ax^2 - 2a^2x$ — $2ax(5x - a)$
23. $9r^2 - 3r$ — $3r(3r - 1)$
24. $11 + 4x + 1$ — $4(x + 3)$
25. $30m^4 + 11m^3y - 5m^2$ — $m^2(30m^2 + 11my - 5)$

In 26 and 27, a fraction is given. a. Factor the numerator. b. Simplify the fraction.

26. $\frac{2x^3 + 5x}{x}$, $(x \neq 0)$
a. $x(2x^2 + 5)$
b. $2x^2 + 5$

27. $\frac{24r - 16}{80}$
a. $8(3r - 2)$
b. $\frac{3r - 2}{10}$

Representations Objective J: Represent quadratic expressions and their factorization with areas.

In 28 and 29, make a drawing of algebra tiles showing a rectangle that has the given area.

28. $x^2 + 5x$

	x	1	1	1	1	1
x	x^2	x	x	x	x	x

29. $4x + 2$

	x	x	1
1	x	x	1
1	x	x	1

30. a. Use algebra-tile diagrams to show two different rectangles each with area $4x^2 + 8x$.

	x	x	x	x
x	x^2	x^2	x^2	x^2
1	x	x	x	x
1	x	x	x	x

	x	x	1	1	1	1
x	x^2	x^2	x	x	x	x
x	x^2	x^2	x	x	x	x

b. What is the complete factorization of $4x^2 + 8x$? — $4x(x + 2)$

Name

LESSON MASTER 12-3 B

Questions on SPUR Objectives

Skills Objective C: Factor quadratic expressions.

In 1–16, factor the expression.

1. $b^2 + 7b + 12$ — $(b + 4)(b + 3)$	2. $a^2 - 2a - 15$ — $(a + 3)(a - 5)$
3. $h^2 + 10h - 24$ — $(h + 12)(h - 2)$	4. $x^2 - 12x + 27$ — $(x - 3)(x - 9)$
5. $y^2 - 16y + 64$ — $(y - 8)^2$	6. $12 + 13w + w^2$ — $(w + 12)(w + 1)$
7. $8 + n^2 + 6n$ — $(n + 4)(n + 2)$	8. $x^2 - 81$ — $(x + 9)(x - 9)$
9. $y^2 + 17 + 18y$ — $(y + 17)(y + 1)$	10. $2x^2 - 14x$ — $2x(x - 7)$
11. $10a^2 + 50a + 60$ — $10(a + 3)(a + 2)$	12. $x^3 - 10x^2 + 9x$ — $x(x - 9)(x - 1)$
13. $m^3 - 16m$ — $m(m + 4)(m - 4)$	14. $6y^2 + 18y - 60$ — $6(y + 5)(y - 2)$
15. $2a^2 - 20a + 50$ — $2(a - 5)^2$	16. $-140 + 4x^2 - 8x$ — $4(x + 5)(x - 7)$

Properties Objective G: Determine whether a quadratic polynomial can be factored over the integers.

In 17–21, tell whether the expression is factorable over the integers. If so, give the factorization.

17. $a^2 + 17a + 12$ — no

18. $c^2 - 144$ — yes; $(c + 12)(c - 12)$

19. $x^2 + 9x - 10$ — yes; $(x + 10)(x - 1)$

20. $y^2 + 15y + 56$ — yes; $(y + 8)(y + 7)$

21. $b^2 + 8b + 20$ — no

Name

Representations Objective J: Represent quadratic expressions and their factorization with areas.

22. An algebra-tile diagram is shown at the right.

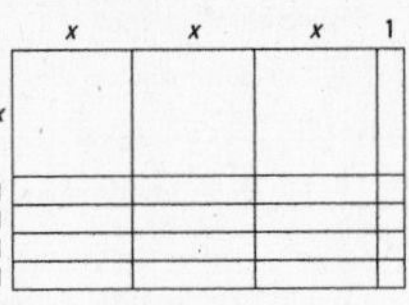

a. Give the area of the figure as a polynomial. $3x^2 + 13x + 4$

b. Give the area in factored form. $(3x + 1)(x + 4)$

In 23 and 24, show that the polynomial can be factored by drawing a rectangular algebra-tile diagram.

23. $x^2 + 6x + 8$

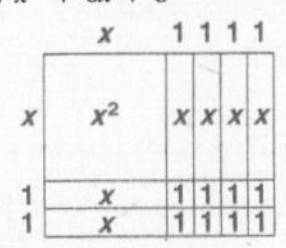

24. $x^2 + 5x + 4$

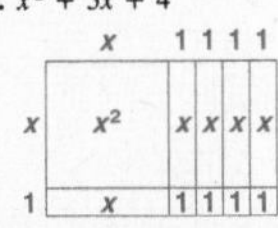

Review Objective A, Lesson 9-5

In 25–28, an equation in standard form is given. a. Use the quadratic formula to give the values of *a*, *b*, and *c*. b. Give the solutions rounded to the nearest hundredth.

25. $x^2 - 12x + 20 = 0$
a. $a =$ 1 $b =$ -12 $c =$ 20
b. $x = 10$ or $x = 2$

26. $x^2 + 8x + 10 = 0$
a. $a =$ 1 $b =$ 8 $c =$ 10
b. $x = -1.55$ or $x = -6.45$

27. $2x^2 + 6x - 1 = 0$
a. $a =$ 2 $b =$ 6 $c =$ -1
b. $x = .16$ or $x = -3.16$

28. $-x^2 + 9x = 0$
a. $a =$ -1 $b =$ 9 $c =$ 0
b. $x = 9$ or $x = 0$

Name

LESSON MASTER 12-4 B

Questions on SPUR Objectives

Skills Objective D: Solve quadratic equations by factoring.

In 1–12, solve by factoring.

1. $x^2 + 7x + 6 = 0$ — $x = -1$ or $x = -6$	2. $x^2 - 9x + 18 = 0$ — $x = 6$ or $x = 3$
3. $x^2 + 5x - 24 = 0$ — $x = 3$ or $x = -8$	4. $0 = x^2 - x - 20$ — $x = 5$ or $x = -4$
5. $y^2 = 14y - 49$ — $y = 7$	6. $a^2 + a = 56$ — $a = 7$ or $a = -8$
7. $45 + n^2 + 14n = 0$ — $n = -9$ or $n = -5$	8. $a^2 - 144 = 0$ — $a = 12$ or $a = -12$
9. $3x^2 - 27x = 0$ — $x = 0$ or $x = 9$	10. $x^2 + 10x + 25 = 0$ — $x = -5$
11. $2x^2 = 12x$ — $x = 0$ or $x = 6$	12. $\frac{x^2 + 5x}{2} = -2$ — $x = -1$ or $x = -4$

Properties Objective F: Recognize and use the Zero Product Property.

In 13 and 14, tell what equations result from applying the Zero Product Property.

13. $(x + 3)(x - 8) = 0$ — $x + 3 = 0,\ x - 8 = 0$

14. $a(a - 4) = 0$ — $a = 0,\ a - 4 = 0$

15. $(n + 5)(n + 6)(n - 4) = 0$ — $n = -5$ or $n = -6$ or $n = 4$

Name

16. a. Give four pairs of numbers whose product is 12. Sample: 1, 12; 2, 6; 3, 4; -3, -4

b. Give four pairs of numbers whose product is 0. Sample: 1, 0; 8, 0; -6, 0; 100, 0

c. Explain why there is a Zero Product Property but there is no Twelve Product Property.
Sample: To get a product of zero, zero must be a factor; to get a product of 12, 12 does not have to be a factor.

In 17–20, if the polynomial is factorable over the integers, factor and solve the equation using the Zero Product Property. If it is not factorable, use the Quadratic Formula.

17. $x^2 + 9x + 12 = 0$ — $x = -1.63$ or $x = -7.37$

18. $x^2 - 8x - 20 = 0$ — $x = 10$ or $x = -2$

19. $t^2 + 9t + 14 = 0$ — $t = -2$ or $t = -7$

20. $x^2 - 12x = 0$ — $x = 0$ or $x = 12$

Uses Objective I: Solve quadratic equations in real situations.

21. A rectangular park is 3 blocks longer than it is wide. Its area is 40 square blocks. Let w = width.

a. Write an expression for the length of the rectangle. $w + 3$

b. Write an equation of the form length · width = area. $(w + 3)w = 40$

c. Find the length and width of the park. 8 blocks, 5 blocks

22. At a party with n guests, every guest shook hands with every other guest once, for $\frac{n^2 - n}{2}$ handshakes. If there were 66 handshakes, how many guests were there? 12 guests

Name

LESSON MASTER 12-5 B Questions on SPUR Objectives

Skills Objective C: Factor quadratic expressions.

1. Consider factoring the polynomial $4x^2 + 4x - 3$ into two binomials $(ax + b)(cx + d)$.

a. List all the possible pairs of numbers for a and c.
1, 4; 2, 2

b. List all the possible pairs of numbers for b and d.
3, -1; -3, 1

c. List all the possible binomials $(ax + b)(cx + d)$.
$(4x + 3)(x - 1)$; $(x - 3)(4x + 1)$;
$(4x - 3)(x + 1)$; $(x + 3)(4x - 1)$;
$(2x + 1)(2x - 3)$; $(2x - 1)(2x + 3)$

d. Factor $4x^2 + 4x - 3$. $(2x + 3)(2x - 1)$

In 2–15, factor.

2. $2x^2 + 9x + 9$ — $(2x + 3)(x + 3)$
3. $3x^2 - 14x - 5$ — $(3x + 1)(x - 5)$
4. $5x^2 + 6 - 17x$ — $(5x - 2)(x - 3)$
5. $6x^2 + 5x + 1$ — $(3x + 1)(2x + 1)$
6. $6x^2 + 13x + 2$ — $(6x + 1)(x + 2)$
7. $4n^2 - 3n - 7$ — $(n + 1)(4n - 7)$
8. $10a^2 + 11a - 6$ — $(2a + 3)(5a - 2)$
9. $20x + 4 + 9x^2$ — $(9x + 2)(x + 2)$
10. $3x^2 + 14x - 49$ — $(x + 7)(3x - 7)$
11. $4y^2 + 4y + 1$ — $(2y + 1)^2$

Name

12. $4a^2 + 10a + 4$ — $2(2a + 1)(a + 2)$
13. $3x^3 - 7x^2 + 4x$ — $x(3x - 4)(x - 1)$
14. $27m^2 - 36m + 12$ — $3(3m - 2)^2$
15. $30y^3 - 2y^2 - 4y$ — $2y(3y + 1)(5y - 2)$

Skills Objective D: Solve quadratic equations by factoring.

In 16–21, solve the equation.

16. $(2z - 1)(z + 4) = 0$ — $z = \frac{1}{2}$ or $z = -4$
17. $t(3t - 7) = 0$ — $t = 0$ or $t = \frac{7}{3}$
18. $3s(2s + 5) = 0$ — $s = 0$ or $s = -\frac{5}{2}$
19. $2m^2 + m - 3 = 0$ — $m = -\frac{3}{2}$ or $m = 1$
20. $-12y = -4 - 5y^2$ — $y = 2$ or $y = \frac{2}{5}$
21. $0 = 9x^2 - 12x + 4$ — $x = \frac{2}{3}$

Name

LESSON MASTER 12-6 B Questions on SPUR Objectives

Uses Objective I: Solve quadratic equations in real situations.

In 1 and 2, use this information: The area of a rectangular parking lot is 9,600 square meters and its perimeter is 400 meters.

1. Use the Babylonian method to find the dimensions of the parking lot. Show your work.

$\ell + w = 200$, so let $\ell = 100 + x$ and $w = 100 - x$.
$(100 + x)(100 - x) = 9{,}600$ $\quad \ell = 100 + 20 = 120$
$10{,}000 - x^2 = 9{,}600$ $\quad w = 100 - 20 = 80$
$x^2 = 400$ $\quad$ length, 120 m;
$x = 20$ $\quad$ width, 80 m

2. Use a modern method to find the dimensions of the parking lot. Show your work.

$2\ell + 2w = 400$ $\quad \ell w = 9{,}600$
$2w = 400 - 2\ell$ $\quad \ell(200 - \ell) = 9{,}600$
$w = 200 - \ell$ $\quad \ell^2 - 200\ell + 9{,}600 = 0$
$(\ell - 120)(\ell - 80) = 0$
$\ell = 120$ or $\ell = 80$
length, 120 m; width, 80 m

In 3 and 4, use this information: The serving area of a restaurant is 4000 square feet, while its perimeter is 260 feet.

3. Use the Babylonian method to find the dimensions of the restaurant. Show your work.

$\ell + w = 130$, so let $\ell = 65 + x$ and $w = 65 - x$.
$(65 + x)(65 - x) = 4000$ $\quad \ell = 65 + 15 = 80$
$4225 - x^2 = 4000$ $\quad w = 65 - 15 = 50$
$x^2 = 225$
$x = 15$ $\quad$ length, 80 ft; width, 50 ft

Name

4. Use a modern method to find the dimensions of the restaurant. Show your work.

$2\ell + 2w = 260$ $\quad \ell w = 4000$
$2w = 260 - 2\ell$ $\quad \ell(130 - \ell) = 4000$
$w = 130 - \ell$ $\quad \ell^2 - 130\ell + 4000 = 0$
$(\ell - 80)(\ell - 50) = 0$
$\ell = 80$ or $\ell = 50$
length, 80 ft; width, 50 ft

5. One of Lisa's sisters is 7 years older than she is, and the other is 7 years younger. The product of the two sisters' ages is 51. How old is Lisa?

10 years

6. The square and rectangle pictured at the right have the same area.

36

a. What is the area of each figure?
1296 square units

b. What are the dimensions of the rectangle?
54 units, 24 units

$x + 15$

$x - 15$

Review Objective E, Lesson 1-2

In 7–20, tell if the number is a *whole number* (W), an *integer* (I), or a *real number* (R). List all terms that apply.

7. 17 — W, I, R
8. 23.9 — R
9. $\sqrt{121}$ — W, I, R
10. $\frac{3}{2}$ — R
11. $\sqrt{10}$ — R
12. $\frac{1}{3}$ — R
13. $-\pi$ — R
14. $-\frac{40}{20}$ — I, R
15. -.5% — R
16. -443 — I, R
17. $2.\overline{88}$ — R
18. $-\sqrt{32}$ — R
19. 0 — W, I, R
20. 0.001 — R

Name

LESSON MASTER 12-7 B

Questions on SPUR Objectives

Vocabulary

1. a. Explain what a *simple fraction* is.
Sample: a fraction with an integer in both the numerator and the denominator

b. List any three simple fractions. Sample: $\frac{4}{5}, \frac{100}{3}, -\frac{7}{2}$

c. List any three fractions that are *not* simple fractions. Sample: $2\frac{1}{4}, -3\frac{1}{3}, \frac{\sqrt{2}}{2}$

2. a. Explain what a *rational number* is.
Sample: a number that is a simple fraction or that equals a simple fraction

b. List any three rational numbers. Sample: $5, \frac{2}{3}, .\overline{6}$

c. List any three numbers that are *not* rational numbers. Sample: $\pi, \sqrt{3}, -\sqrt{10}$

Properties Objective H: Apply the definitions and properties of rational and irrational numbers.

In 3–14, tell whether the number is *rational* or *irrational*.

3. $\frac{4}{5}$ rational
4. $\sqrt{3}$ irrational
5. 8.7 rational
6. $6\frac{1}{2}$ rational
7. $2.\overline{6}$ rational
8. -0.4 rational
9. $\frac{8}{9}$ rational
10. 0 rational
11. $-\sqrt{81}$ rational
12. $\sqrt{50}$ irrational
13. $\sqrt{36}$ rational
14. $9.\overline{83}$ rational

Name

In 15–22, find a simple fraction for the number.

15. $8\frac{1}{3}$ $\frac{25}{3}$
16. 1.025 $\frac{41}{40}$
17. $16\frac{12}{31}$ $\frac{508}{31}$
18. $.\overline{7}$ $\frac{7}{9}$
19. 56% $\frac{14}{25}$
20. $9.\overline{45}$ $\frac{104}{11}$
21. $.\overline{541}$ $\frac{541}{999}$
22. $6.84\overline{8}$ $\frac{1541}{225}$

In 23 and 24, determine whether the solutions are *rational* or *irrational*.

23. $4x^2 - 9 = 0$ rational
24. $x^2 - 4x - 1 = 0$ irrational

25. A tire has a diameter of 24 inches. Find its circumference and tell if the circumference is *rational* or *irrational*.
24π in.; irrational

26. A square window has a side of length of 18. Find the length of a diagonal and tell if the length is *rational* or *irrational*.
$18\sqrt{2}$; irrational

27. A square picture has a side of length $12\sqrt{2}$. Find the length of a diagonal and tell if the length is *rational* or *irrational*.
24; rational

Name

LESSON MASTER 12-8 B

Questions on SPUR Objectives

Properties Objective G: Determine whether a quadratic polynomial can be factored over the integers.

In 1 and 2, consider the polynomial $ax^2 + bx + c$.

1. Suppose $b^2 - 4ac$ is a perfect square.
a. What must be true about the solutions to $ax^2 + bx + c = 0$? They are rational.
b. Is $ax^2 + bx + c$ factorable over the set of polynomials with integer coefficients? yes

2. Suppose $b^2 - 4ac$ is not a perfect square.
a. What must be true about the solutions to $ax^2 + bx + c = 0$? They are irrational.
b. Is $ax^2 + bx + c$ factorable over the set of polynomials with integer coefficients? no

In 3–10, a polynomial is given. a. Calculate the discriminant of the polynomial. b. Use the discriminant to determine whether the expression can be factored over the integers. c. If possible, factor the polynomial.

3. $x^2 + 3x + 1$
a. 5
b. not factorable
c.

4. $3x^2 + 8x + 4$
a. 16
b. factorable
c. $(3x+2)(x+2)$

5. $2w^2 - 10w + 8$
a. 36
b. factorable
c. $2(w-4)(w-1)$

6. $5y^2 + 4y - 3$
a. 76
b. not factorable
c.

Name

7. $6x^2 + 12x - 5$
a. 264
b. not factorable
c.

8. $7a^2 - 25a - 12$
a. 961
b. factorable
c. $(7a + 3)(a - 4)$

9. $8x^2 - 15$
a. 480
b. not factorable
c.

10. $2 + 9x^2 - 16x$
a. 184
b. not factorable
c.

11. The equation $y = 2x^2 - 20x + 41$ is graphed at the right. Are the x-intercepts rational? Explain your thinking.
No; the discriminant, 72, is not a perfect square.

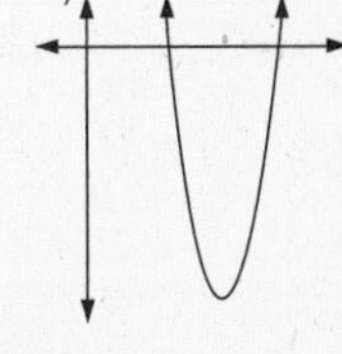

12. Consider the polynomial $ax^2 + 12x + 5$. For what value(s) of a from 1 to 7 is the polynomial factorable?
4, 7

13. The polynomial $x^2 - 6$ can be factored into $(x + \sqrt{6})(x - \sqrt{6})$.
a. Show that $(x + \sqrt{6})(x - \sqrt{6}) = x^2 - 6$.
$(x+\sqrt{6})(x-\sqrt{6}) = x^2 - \sqrt{6}x + \sqrt{6}x - 6 = x^2 - 6$
b. Calculate the discriminant of $x^2 - 6$. 24
c. Does the situation in Parts a and b violate the Discriminant Theorem? Explain your answer.
No; The discriminant, 24, is not a perfect square, so $x^2 - 6$ cannot be factored over the integers; $\sqrt{6}$ is not an integer.

Name

LESSON MASTER 13-1 B Questions on SPUR Objectives

Vocabulary

1. Give a definition for *function*.
Sample: A function is a correspondence between two variables in which each value of the first variable is paired with exactly one value of the second variable.

Properties Objective C: Determine whether a set of ordered pairs is a function.

In 2–11, decide if the equation, inequality, or set of points represents a function. If it is *not* a function, give two ordered pairs that show why a function is not described.

2. {(4, 3), (5, 4), (6, 5), (7, 6), (8, 7)}
a function

3. $y = 7x$
a function

4. {(9, 3), (6, -3), (8, 10), (4, -3), (9, 18)}
Not a function; (9, 3), (9, 18)

5. $y = \pm\sqrt{x}$
Not a function; sample: (4, 2), (4, -2)

6. {(9, 5), (6, 5), (12, 5), (2, 5), (-17, 5), (0, 5)}
a function

7. $y < x + 4$
Not a function; sample: (5, 8), (5, 7)

8. $3x + 5y = 16$
a function

9. $y = \lfloor x + 1 \rfloor$
a function

Name

▶ LESSON MASTER 13-1 B *page 2*

10. $y = 2x^2$
a function

11. $x = 2y^2$
Not a function; Sample: (8, 2), (8, -2)

12. Give an example of a relation that is *not* a function.
Sample: $x = y^2$

Representations Objective H: Determine whether or not a graph represents a function.

In 13–15, tell if the graph represents a function.

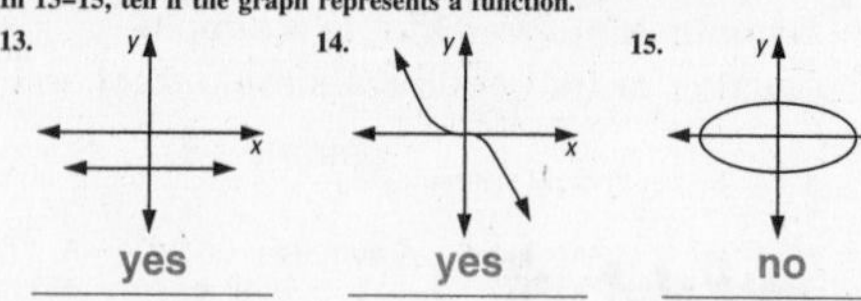

13. yes 14. yes 15. no

Representations Objective I: Graph functions.

In 16 and 17, a. graph the equation, and b. tell if the equation describes a function.

16. $x + y = 7$
a.

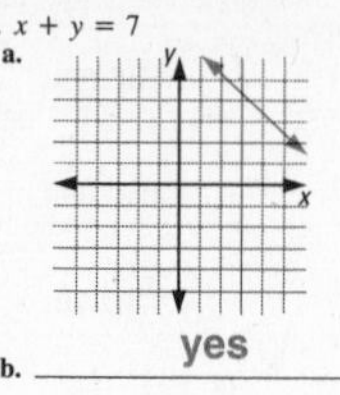

b. yes

17. $x = -4$
a.

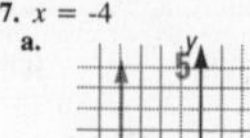

b. no

Name

LESSON MASTER 13-2 B Questions on SPUR Objectives

Skills Objective A: Evaluate functions and solve equations involving function notation.

In 1–3, tell how the expression or equation should be read.

1. SQR(8) — the square root of eight
2. $f(x) = 6x$ — *f* of *x* equals six *x*
3. ABS(-1) — the absolute value of negative one

In 4–9, evaluate.

4. SQR(121) — 11
5. $f(8)$ if $f(x) = 7x$ — 56
6. ABS(13) — 13
7. SQR(25) + 14 — 19
8. $g(10)$ if $g(x) = x + 13.8$ — 23.8
9. $f(-3)$ if $f(x) = x^2 + 2x + 1$ — 4

In 10–13, an equation for a function is given. Find $f(-5)$.

10. $f(x) = -x$ — 5
11. $f(t) = t^3$ — -125
12. $f(x) = 2^x$ — $\frac{1}{32}$
13. $f(x) = \frac{x}{10} + \frac{4x}{5}$ — $-\frac{9}{2}$

14. Let $f(x) = -4x + 2$. Calculate.
a. $f(3)$ — -10
b. $f(6)$ — -22
c. $\frac{f(3) - f(6)}{3(6)}$ — $\frac{2}{3}$

15. Suppose $f(x) = 6x + 14$. For what value of x is $f(x) = -34$? — -8

Name

▶ LESSON MASTER 13-2 B *page 2*

Uses Objective E: Use function notation and language in real situations.

16. Let $c(x)$ = the number of children in classroom x.
Let $a(x)$ = the number of adults in classroom x.
a. If your classroom is classroom x, find $c(x)$ and $a(x)$.
Answers will vary.
b. Find $c(x) + a(x)$ and tell what it represents.
Answers will vary; the number of people in the classroom.

17. During the first 6 decades of the 1900s, Crestview's population during decade d could be approximated by $p(d) = 2{,}500 \cdot (1.15)^d$.
a. Evaluate $p(5) - p(4)$.
≈656 people
b. What does $p(5) - p(4)$ stand for?
the increase in population from the 4th to the 5th decades

Representations Objective I: Graph functions.

In 18 and 19, the equation of a function is given. a. Graph the function. b. Give the *y*-intercept.

18. $f(x) = 3x - 5$
a.

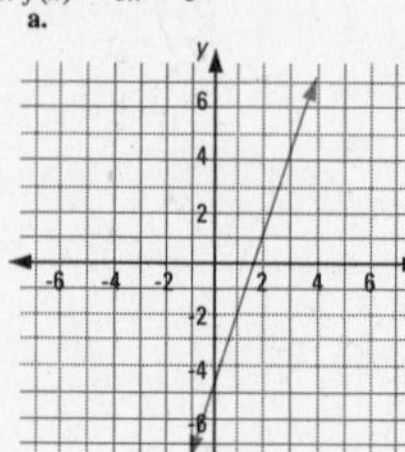

b. -5

19. $g(x) = x^2 + 3$
a.

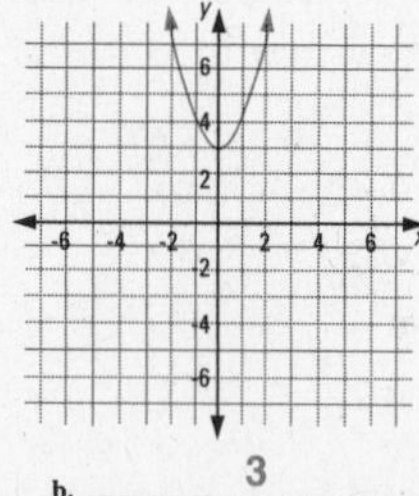

b. 3

Name

LESSON MASTER 13-3 B

Questions on SPUR Objectives

Skills Objective A: Evaluate functions and solve equations involving absolute-value notation.

In 1–4, let $A(x) = |x|$. Calculate.

1. $A(-12)$ 12
2. $A(8)$ 8
3. $A(-5.9)$ 5.9
4. $A(\frac{6}{5})$ $\frac{6}{5}$

In 5–8, let $g(x) = |3x - 4|$. Calculate.

5. $g(6)$ 14
6. $g(1)$ 1
7. $g(\frac{4}{3})$ 0
8. $g(-5)$ 19

In 9–12, let $f(x) = -|2x|$. Calculate.

9. $f(-4)$ -8
10. $f(\frac{1}{2})$ -1
11. $f(-11)$ -22
12. $f(-0.05)$ -0.1

In 13–16, solve.

13. $|x + 3| = 5$ $x = 2$ or $x = -8$
14. $|y - 4| + 1 = 3$ $y = 6$ or $y = 2$
15. $3|2z| = 30$ $z = 5$ or $z = -5$
16. $-4|5a + 2| = -28$ $a = 1$ or $a = -\frac{9}{5}$

Uses Objective E: Use function notation and language in real situations.

17. *Multiple choice.* When 2-inch nails are manufactured, the actual length is usually slightly more or less than 2 inches. Let $f(x)$ = the error in a nail with length x. Which equation relates $f(x)$ and x? b

(a) $f(x) = \frac{|2 + x|}{2}$ (b) $f(x) = |2 - x|$
(c) $f(x) = |x|$ (d) $f(x) = -|x + 2|$

Name

18. *Multiple choice.* Suppose you start at home and walk along Kinzer Street to the library. Let $f(b)$ = the distance from home to the school after you have walked b blocks. Which equation relates $f(b)$ and b? c

(a) $f(b) = |b|$ (b) $f(b) = |10 - b|$
(c) $f(b) = |6 - b|$ (d) $f(b) = |b - 10|$

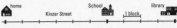

home — Kinzer Street — School — 1 block — library

Representations Objective I: Graph absolute-value functions.

In 19 and 20, graph the function.

19. $f(x) = |\frac{1}{2}x|$

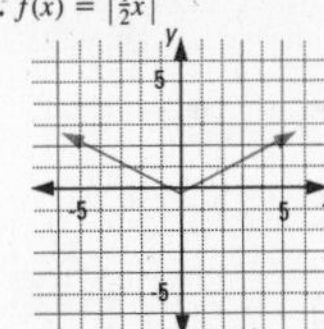

20. $f(x) = -|x - 4| + 1$

Review Objective F, Lesson 9-2

In 21 and 22, an equation is given. a. Graph the equation. b. Give the coordinates of the vertex. c. Give the *y*-intercept.

21. $y = -\frac{1}{2}x^2 + 5$

a.

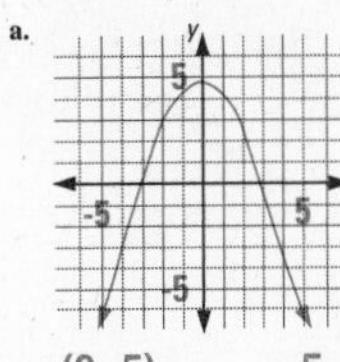

b. (0, 5) c. 5

22. $y = x^2 - 2x + 3$

a.

b. (1, 2) c. 3

Name

LESSON MASTER 13-4 B

Questions on SPUR Objectives

Properties Objective D: Find the domain and the range of a function from its formula, graph, or rule.

1. Explain how to find the range of f when $f(x) = 2x^2 + 1$.
Sample: Graph the function; think about what values are possible for $f(x)$.

2. a. Give the domain of f when $f(x) = \frac{3}{9 - x}$. all reals except 9

b. Give the domain of g when $g(x) = \frac{x + 2}{5 + x}$. all reals except -5

c. Give an example of a function whose domain is the set of all real numbers but 7. Sample: $f(x) = \frac{2}{x - 7}$

In 3–12, a function is described. a. Give its domain. b. Give its range.

3. $\{(-4, 9), (7, 7), (0, 3), (2, -8), (5, 3)\}$
a. $\{-4, 7, 0, 2, 5\}$
b. $\{9, 7, 3, -8\}$

4. $\{(-9, 3), (6, 3), (0, 3), (11, 3)\}$
a. $\{-9, 6, 0, 11\}$
b. $\{3\}$

5. $g(x) = \sqrt{x} + 4$
a. $\{x: x \geq 0\}$
b. $\{y: y \geq 4\}$

6. $f(x) = -|x| - 3$
a. all real numbers
b. $\{y: y \leq -3\}$

7. $f(x) = \frac{2x}{x}$
a. all reals except 0
b. $\{2\}$

8. $g(x) = 5x^2$
a. all real numbers
b. $\{y: y \geq 0\}$

9.
a. $\{x: -3 \leq x \leq 0\}$
b. $\{y: -3 \leq y \leq 0\}$

10.
a. $\{x: x \geq 0\}$
b. $\{y: y \geq 0\}$

Name

11.
a. all real numbers
b. all real numbers

12.
a. all integers
b. all integers

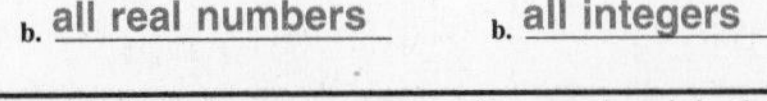

Uses Objective E: Use function notation and language in real situations.

13. The set of ordered pairs below associates a year with the population of New York City (rounded to the nearest million) in that year.
$\{(1860, 1.2), (1880, 1.9), (1900, 2.4), (1920, 5.6)\}$

a. Give the domain. $\{1860, 1880, 1900, 1920\}$

b. Give the range. $\{1.2, 1.9, 2.4, 5.6\}$

14. Let $s(x)$ = a student's test grade when the percent of correct answers is x. The chart at the right gives the values of this function.

Percent Correct	Grade
88–100	5
75–87	4
62–74	3
50–61	2
0–49	1

a. Give the domain. whole numbers ≤ 100

b. Give the range. $\{1, 2, 3, 4, 5\}$

c. Is the set of all possible ordered pairs (grade, percent correct) a function? Why or why not?
No; any grade can have more than one percent-correct value.

Name

LESSON MASTER 13-5 B

Questions on SPUR Objectives

Uses Objective F: Determine values of probability functions.

1. *Multiple choice.* Let x be a value in the range of a probability function. Tell which inequality must be true. **C**

   (a) $x \geq 0$ (b) $0 < x < 1$ (c) $0 \leq x \leq 1$ (d) $x < 1$

2. A bag contains cherry, lemon, and grape candies. $P(\text{cherry}) = \frac{2}{5}$, and $P(\text{lemon}) = \frac{1}{5}$, where $P(\text{flavor})$ means the probability that a candy drawn at random is flavor x.

   a. Find $P(\text{grape})$. $\frac{2}{5}$

   b. What is the range of this function? $\{\frac{1}{5}, \frac{2}{5}\}$

3. During the holiday season, the student council has a lottery to give away gift certificates to the school store. This year, $P(\text{freshman}) = \frac{3}{16}$, $P(\text{sophomore}) = \frac{1}{4}$, and $P(\text{junior}) = \frac{3}{16}$, where $P(\text{class})$ means the probability that the name drawn is a member of class x.

   a. Find $P(\text{senior})$. $\frac{3}{8}$

   b. What is the range of this function? $\{\frac{3}{8}, \frac{1}{4}, \frac{3}{16}\}$

4. Let $P(n)$ = the probability of getting a *product* of n when two fair dice are thrown.

   a. Find $P(6)$. $\frac{1}{9}$

   b. List 3 numbers that *cannot* be values for n. **Sample: -1, 27,100**

   c. If $P(n) = \frac{1}{36}$, give a possible value for n. **Sample: 1**

   d. Could $P(n)$ ever be equal to $\frac{1}{10}$? Explain your reasoning.
   No; sample: The denominator must be 36 or a factor of 36; 10 is not a factor of 36.

Name

▶ LESSON MASTER 13-5 B *page 2*

Representations Objective I: Graph probability functions.

5. This fair spinner is divided into 8 congruent parts. The point value of each region is labeled. Let $P(n)$ = the probability of getting n points on a spin.

   a. Find $P(0)$, $P(10)$, $P(20)$, and $P(30)$.
   $P(0) = \frac{1}{8}$, $P(10) = \frac{3}{8}$,
   $P(20) = \frac{3}{8}$, $P(30) = \frac{1}{8}$

   b. At the right, graph $P(n)$.

   P(n)
   0 10 20 30 n

6. A cooler contains 20 cans of soft drinks: 4 lemon-lime (LL), 6 cola (C), and 10 root beer (RB). You reach in and choose a can at random. Let $P(n)$ = the probability that you will choose flavor n.

   a. Find $P(\text{LL})$. $\frac{1}{5}$

   b. At the right, graph the probability function $P(n)$.

   P(n)
   1
   .5
   LL C RB n

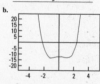

7. A mail carrier delivered four letters. Let $P(n)$ = the probability that exactly n of these letters will be bills.

   P(n)
   .4
   .3
   .2
   .1
   0 1 2 3 4 n

   a. What is the probability that there will be fewer than 3 bills? **0.6**

   b. Find $P(0) + P(1) + P(2) + P(3) + P(4)$. **1**

Name

LESSON MASTER 13-6 B

Questions on SPUR Objectives

Representations Objective J: Graph polynomial functions.

In 1 and 2, an equation is given. a. Complete the table of x- and y-values. b. Plot the points in the table and connect them with a smooth curve. c. Describe the graph. **Sample graphs and descriptions are given.**

1. $y = x^3 + x^2 - 3x - 2$

   a.

x	y
-3	-11
-2	0
-1	-1
0	-2
1	-3
2	4
3	25

   b.

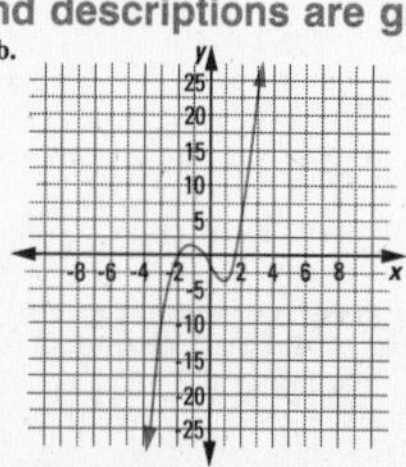

   c. **Graph has at least two curves; y-intercept is -2; x-intercepts are ≈1.6, ≈-.6, and -2.**

2. $y = x^4 - 3x^3 - 6x^2 + 8x$

   a.

x	y
-3	84
-2	0
-1	-10
0	0
1	0
2	-16
3	-30

   b.

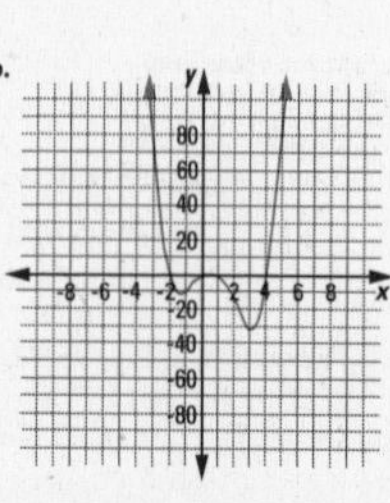

   c. **Graph has at least two curves; y-intercept is 0; x-intercepts are -2, 0, and 1.**

Name

▶ LESSON MASTER 13-6 B *page 2*

3. Consider the polynomial function $f(x) = 3x^4 + 2x^3 - x - 7$.

   a. Give the number of x-intercepts. **2**

   b. Give the number of y-intercepts. **1**

In 4–7, use an automatic grapher. A function is given.
a. Find a window which shows all of the x- and y-intercepts.
b. Draw the graph as it appears on your automatic grapher. **Sample windows are given.**

4. $f(x) = -x^3 + 4x$

   a. $-5 \leq x \leq 5$, $-5 \leq y \leq 5$

   b.

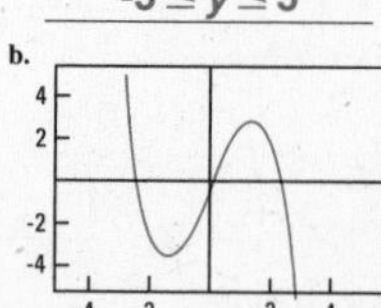

5. $y = x^4 - 2x^2 - 10$

   a.

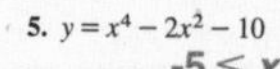

   $-5 \leq x \leq 5$, $-20 \leq y \leq 20$

   b.

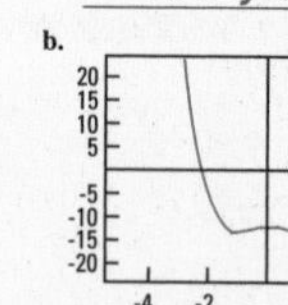

6. $g(x) = 3x^5 - 9x^4 - 8x^3 + 2x^2 + 10x + 30$

   a. $-5 \leq x \leq 5$, $-200 \leq y \leq 200$

   b.

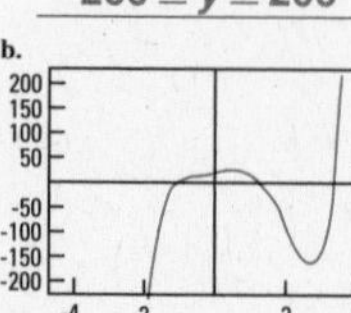

7. $h(x) = .5x^3 + 2x^2 - 5x + 20$

   a.

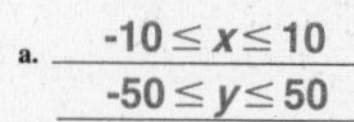

   $-10 \leq x \leq 10$, $-50 \leq y \leq 50$

   b.

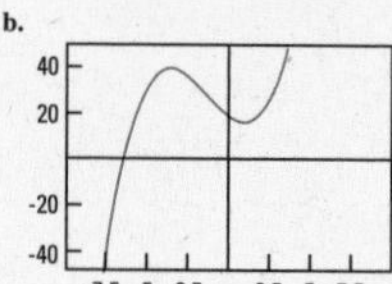

Name

LESSON MASTER 13-7 B Questions on SPUR Objectives

Vocabulary

1. Use right triangle *RST* at the right.
   a. Name the leg adjacent to ∠T. TS
   b. Name the leg opposite ∠T. RS
   c. What ratio equals tan T? RS/TS
   d. Name the leg adjacent to ∠R. RS
   e. Name the leg opposite ∠R. TS
   f. What ratio equals tan R? TS/RS

2. Write a key sequence to find tan 72° on your calculator.
   Sample: 72 (tan)

Skills Objective B: Use the tangent key on a calculator.

In 3–6, round to the nearest hundredth.

3. tan 18° 0.32
4. tan 84° 9.51
5. tan 58° 1.60
6. tan 22.5° 0.41

Uses Objective G: Find lengths of sides or tangents of angles in right triangles using the tangent function.

7. Use right triangle *XYZ* at the right.
   a. Measure ∠Y. m ∠ y = 38°
   b. Measure the legs.
   xy = 3.2 cm ($1\frac{1}{4}$ in.);
   xz = 2.4 cm ($\frac{15}{16}$ in.)
   c. Compute tan Y by dividing the lengths given in Part **b**. Round to the nearest hundredth. 0.75
   d. On your calculator find tan Y to the nearest hundredth. 0.78
   e. How close are the values you found in Parts **c** and **d**? 0.03

Name

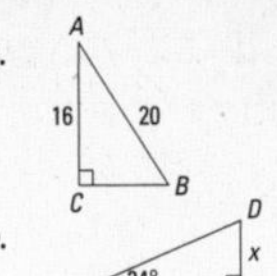

8. Use right triangle *ABC* at the left.
   a. Find the length of $\overline{BC}$. 12
   b. Find the tangent of ∠B. $1.\overline{33}$

9. Use right triangle *DEF* at the left.
   a. Find tan 24° to the nearest hundredth. 0.45
   b. Find *x*. 20.25

In 10 and 11, find the slope of the line.

10.

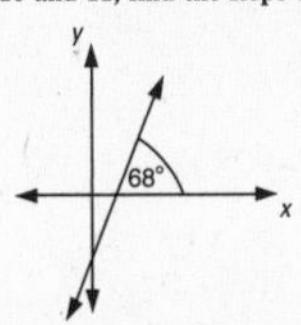

≈2.48

11.

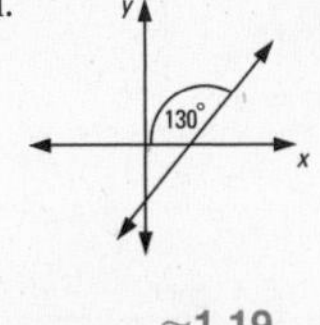

≈1.19

In 12 and 13, find the tangent of the angle formed by the positive ray of the *x*-axis and the line whose equation is given.

12. $y = \frac{3}{4}x - 5$ 0.75
13. $2x - y = 8$ 2

14. When Juan stands 24 feet away from a tower, he has to look up 48° to see the top. His eyes are 5 ft above the ground. How high is the tower? ≈31.65 feet

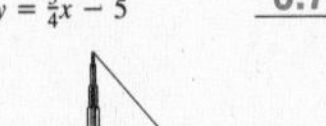

Name

LESSON MASTER 13-8 B Questions on SPUR Objectives

Vocabulary

1. Use right triangle *RST* at the right.
   a. What ratio equals sin T? RS/RT
   b. What ratio equals cos T? ST/RT

Skills Objective B: Use function keys on a calculator.

In 2–9, a. write a key sequence to find each value. b. Write what is shown in the display. Sample key sequences are given.

2. sin 16°
   a. 16 (sin)
   b. 0.2756374
3. cos 8°
   a. 8 (cos)
   b. 0.9902681
4. $(-2.088)^2$
   a. 2.088 (+/−) (x^2)
   b. 4.359744
5. $\sqrt{0.008}$
   a. 0.008 ($\sqrt{x}$)
   b. 0.0894427
6. log(43)
   a. 43 (log)
   b. 1.6334685
7. log (10^6)
   a. 10 (y^x) 6 (=) (log)
   b. 6
8. 8!
   a. 8 (x!)
   b. 40320
9. $\frac{1}{3.44}$
   a. 3.44 ($\frac{1}{x}$)
   b. 0.2906977

Name

In 10–17, give a decimal approximation rounded to the nearest hundredth.

10. cos 33° 0.84
11. sin 15° 0.26
12. log(77,024) 4.89
13. $\frac{1}{.0073}$ 136.99
14. 11! 39,916,800
15. $(62.1)^2$ 3856.41
16. $\sqrt{5008}$ 70.77
17. tan 70° 2.75

18. What happens if you use a function key on your calculator with a value of *x* that is not in the domain of the function?
    An error message appears.

In 19–24, a calculator key with a given function is shown. Give an example of a real number *x* that is *not* in the domain of the function. If all real numbers are in the domain, write *all*. Samples are given for 19–21, 24.

19. (!) 1.5
20. (tan) 90
21. (1/x) 0
22. (x^2) all
23. (sin) all
24. ($\sqrt{\ }$) -3

25. Many calculators have an inverse function key (INV). Try the following.
    a. On your calculator, find sin 30°. 0.5
    b. On your calculator, press .5 (INV) (sin). What does the display show? 30
    c. Study Parts **a** and **b**. For a number *x* in the display, what do you think pressing (INV) (sin) finds?
    Sample: the measure of the angle whose sine is *x*
    d. On your calculator, find log(10,000). 4
    e. On your calculator, press 4 (INV) (log). What does the display show? 10000
    f. Study Parts **d** and **e**. For a number *x* in the display, what do you think pressing (INV) (log) finds?
    Sample: the number whose log is *x*

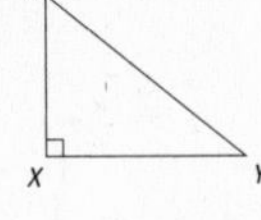